Bill 'Swampy' Marsh is an award-winning writer/performer of stories, songs and plays. He spent most of his youth in rural south-western New South Wales. Bill was forced to give up any idea he had of a 'career' as a cricketer when a stint at agricultural college was curtailed because of illness, and so began his hobby of writing. After he had backpacked through three continents and worked in the wine industry, his writing hobby blossomed into a career.

His first collection of short stories, *Beckom Pop. 64*, was published in 1988, his second, *Old Yanconian Daze*, in 1995 and his third, *Looking for Dad*, in 1998. During 1999, Bill released *Australia*, a CD of his songs and stories. That was followed by *A Drover's Wife* in 2002, *Glory, Glory: A Tribute to the Royal Flying Doctor Service* in 2008 and *Open Roads: The Songs and Stories of Bill 'Swampy' Marsh* in 2017. He has written soundtrack songs and music for the television documentaries *The Last Mail from Birdsville: The Story of Tom Kruse; Source to Sea — The Story of the Murray Riverboats* and the German travel documentaries *Traumzeit auf dem Stuart Highway, Clinic Flights (Tilpa & Marble Bar), Traumzeit in den Kimberleys* and *Einsatz von Port Hedland nach Marble Bar*.

Bill runs writing workshops throughout Australia and is a teacher of short-story writing within the Adelaide Institute of TAFE's Professional Writing Unit. He has won and judged many nationwide short-story and songwriting competitions and short-film awards.

Great Australian Outback Nurses Stories is part of a very successful series of 'Great Australian Stories', including *Great Australian Outback Teaching Stories* (2016), *Great Australian Outback Police Stories* (2015), *Amazing Grace: Stories of Faith and Friendship from Outback Australia* (2014), *The Complete Book of Australian Flying Doctor Stories* and *Great Australian Outback School Stories* (2013), *Great Australian CWA Stories* (2011), *New Great Australian Flying Doctor Stories* and *The ABC Book of Great Aussie Stories for Young People* (2010), *Great Australian Stories: Outback Towns and Pubs* (2009), *More Great Australian Flying Doctor Stories* (2007), *Great Australian Railway Stories* (2005), *Great Australian Droving Stories* (2003), *Great Australian Shearing Stories* (2001) and *Great Australian Flying Doctor Stories* (1999). Bill's biography *Goldie: Adventures in a Vanishing Australia* was published in 2008 and his semi-autobiographical collection *Swampy: Tall Tales and True from Boyhood and Beyond* was published in 2012.

More information about the author can be found at
www.billswampymarsh.com
Facebook: Bill 'Swampy' Marsh

GREAT AUSTRALIAN OUTBACK NURSES STORIES

BILL 'SWAMPY' MARSH

ABC
Books

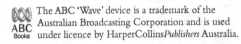 The ABC 'Wave' device is a trademark of the
Australian Broadcasting Corporation and is used
under licence by HarperCollins*Publishers* Australia.

First published in Australia in 2017
by HarperCollins*Publishers* Australia Pty Limited
ABN 36 009 913 517
harpercollins.com.au

HarperCollins*Publishers*
Level 13, 201 Elizabeth Street, Sydney NSW 2000, Australia
Unit D1, 63 Apollo Drive, Rosedale, Auckland 0632, New Zealand
A 53, Sector 57, Noida, UP, India
1 London Bridge Street, London SE1 9GF, United Kingdom
2 Bloor Street East, 20th floor, Toronto, Ontario M4W 1A8, Canada
195 Broadway, New York, NY 10007, USA

National Library of Australia Cataloguing-in-Publication data:

Marsh, Bill, 1950– author.
  Great Australian outback nurses stories / Bill 'Swampy' Marsh.
  ISBN: 978 0 7333 3316 3 (paperback)
  ISBN: 978 1 4607 0212 3 (ebook)
  Rural nurses — Australia — Anecdotes.
  Nurses — Australia — Anecdotes.
  Rural nursing — Australia

Cover design by Hazel Lam, HarperCollins Design Studio
Front cover image: Flynn, John, 1880-1951. Sisters E. Coleman, E. A. Hern and J. Gray at Esperance,
September 1931. nla.obj-142597476. National Library of Australia.
Back cover image by shutterstock.com
Author photo by Lillian Imagines Photography
Typeset in 10/15pt ITC Bookman by Kelli Lonergan
Printed and bound in Australia by McPhersons Printing Group
The papers used by HarperCollins in the manufacture of this book are a natural, recyclable product
made from wood grown in sustainable plantation forests. The fibre source and manufacturing processes
meet recognised international environmental standards, and carry certification.

Dedicated to CareFlight NT, Kakadu National Park's rangers
and the nursing and support staff from Jabiru.
Thanks for saving my life.

Special thanks to senior publisher Brigitta Doyle, and editors Rachel Dennis and Lachlan McLaine, along with the promotions and sales staff at ABC Books–HarperCollins Australia, without whose support these stories may never have seen the light of day; and to my precious support crew of Kath Beauchamp, Craig Langley and Margaret Worth.

Special thanks to Anne-Marie Borchers and CRANA*plus* for all their help and assistance, and to all those wonderful nurses I met along this journey. You are all just so important.

Contents

Contributors

The stories contained in this book are written from interviews recorded by Bill 'Swampy' Marsh. The contributors are:

Steve Anderson

Anne-Marie Borchers

Andy Cameron

Robyn and Keith Carpenter

Barbara Chester

Christopher Cliffe

Anton Colman

Yvette Daley

Dianne Few

Nola Gallacher

Stefan Grabdrath

Richard Hempel

Annette Keenan

Michael Lanagan

Rosemary Lynch

Kerry McKeown

Barb Meredith

Sarah Molloy

Glynis Thorp

Ken and Anne Vicary

Matthew Auld

Annette Brown

Marcel Campbell

Chris Carter

Jane Clemson

Frances and Peter Colahan

Shirley Cornelius

Oliver Delang

Cheryl Fontaine

Glenda Gleeson

Bernadette Greensill

Tayla Howard

Donna Lamb

Marg Loveday

Bill 'Swampy' Marsh

Colin McLennan

Bev Mezzen

Chris Smith

Kaisu Vartto

Margaret Worth

... and many, many more.

Introduction

Great Australian Outback Nurses Stories is perhaps the toughest book I've written in the Great Australian Stories collection. During my travels, I was taken into places that were not pleasant. Unfortunately, a number of those places included remote Indigenous communities. This was an eye-opener that many white Australians either try to ignore or don't get to see. Those who do see it, like the nurses, the doctors, the teachers and the administrators, as well as the many, many Indigenous people themselves, are courageous and caring beyond belief and they manage to carry out their work with a hint of that wonderful sense of Aussie humour.

Despite their efforts, in 2016, a remote-area nurse — Gayle Woodford — was killed in the APY Lands, a ten-year-old girl committed suicide in a remote community out from Derby, WA, and unrest continued in a number of communities where some of these stories are set. In fact, our Aboriginal youth suicide rate remains higher than that of every country in the world bar one — Greenland. And while just three per cent of our population is Indigenous, the prison population is nearly twenty-five per cent Indigenous. Added to that, Indigenous life-expectancy is ten per cent lower than that of our non-Indigenous population. A number of nurses I interviewed described the situation in Indigenous communities as being 'our greatest shame'.

But I have a strong belief that we as Australians, of all colours and creeds, are able, if willing, to overcome whatever difficulties we're faced with and forge a far stronger, healthier and more tolerant society. During my travels I was inspired by an old Indigenous man I met to write the song 'Old Man Australia' …

Chorus — *Oh my heart it belongs to Australia*
Oh my heart it belongs to the land
From the deep blue seas that surround her
To her centre of gibber and sand

Verse 1 — *And I dreamed that we all lived together*
Every child, every woman and man
And we all learned to love one another
Then together we joined in and sang

Chorus — *Oh my heart it belongs to Australia*
Oh my heart it belongs to the land
From the deep blue seas that surround her
To her centre of gibber and sand

Verse II — *When night-time shadows have fallen*
And peace chimes harmony's ring
We'll all raise our voices as one voice
And together we'll join in and sing

Chorus — *Oh my heart it belongs to Australia*
Oh my heart it belongs to the land
From the deep blue seas that surround her
To her centre of gibber and sand

Bridge — *And I feel the homelands a'calling*
The curlew, the gidgee, the bream
Upon the wind the Dreamtime's a'swirling
As the old man he whispers to me

Chorus — *Oh my heart it belongs to Australia*
Oh my heart it belongs to the land
From the deep blue seas that surround her
To her centre of gibber and sand

Andy's Story
G'day Matron

So you want to hear about some of my nursing experiences, do you? Okay, I grew up in New Zealand, at Hawkes Bay. I wasn't the best of students so I left school early. Then one day I was up at the hospital visiting a sick mate and I saw a male nurse bringing around the supper trolley. Around him was a group of gorgeous young nurses and that's when I thought, Gee, I wouldn't mind a job like that, and it had nothing to do with pushing a meal trolley around.

I then sent letters to a few hospitals and one reply came back, asking me to come in for an interview. So I jumped on my motorbike and I went to the hospital and I remember the lady in charge saying, 'Well you don't look like a suitable candidate. But come back tomorrow and I'll give you something to do for the day. If you still want to be a nurse after that, come and see me again.' And I can tell you, she put me in the toughest ward. It was a female medical unit that had all these poor old dears, sitting there, dribbling into their porridge.

Oddly enough, I enjoyed it. So I went back to the lady in charge — 'Yeah I'd love to do this' — and she put me into a three-year training course. That would've been about forty years ago. I was the only male in a full class of females, which raised some eyebrows, but I stuck at it. Then after I graduated I went and worked in intensive care. But I had this thing about being a midwife. Problem being, they kept saying, 'Men can't work in female wards.' And that made me even more determined. So I came over to Melbourne to do my midwifery course and, after passing with flying colours, I worked in the labour wards at the Queen Victoria Medical Centre.

But a few big hospitals later, I thought, No, this's not really for me. I'd like to try bush nursing. By then I'd had done my Bachelor of Nursing, so when I saw an advertisement for the position as director of nursing, on Mornington Island, up in the Gulf of Carpentaria, I put in an application and I got the job. That was in 1992 and the plan was to go there for no longer than a year. But I ended up staying for seven.

Mornington was a lot different than anywhere I'd worked. It had a population of about eleven hundred. At the hospital the ratio of white to the Indigenous employees was about half and half. All the registered nurses — RNs — were white. In those days there were hardly any Aboriginal RNs. If there were, I would've employed them. Still, we had a good set of Aboriginal cleaners, cooks and groundsman and that.

The hospital was an old fibro-asbestos joint, with just ten beds. The nursing staff stayed in little houses next to the hospital. There was no security fencing in those days. In an attempt to entice the nurses to stay longer at Mornington I tried to make their lives as comfortable as possible. I made sure they got all their proper entitlements and I fixed up their accommodation. We had our food supplied and of course there were some nice beaches and the fishing was great and in the end, most of the RNs were staying, on average, for about four years. Oh, that's right, I even organised a vehicle for them. There was one of the nurses and her boyfriend who went camping in the back of her four-wheel drive, down at the low-tide mark near Birri. And, at midnight, when the tide had risen, the boyfriend just happened to get up to go for a pee and there were fish looking at him in the rear-vision mirror. So that was the end of that vehicle.

This was back before they had prohibition at Mornington and a lot of the people blew their welfare cheques on grog. And we got the brunt of it, with abandoned children, the beatings, the fighting;

the lot. It was so bad that the RFDS — the Royal Flying Doctor Service — once had to make three trips within a twenty-four-hour period. The vast majority of the incidents were fuelled by alcohol. There were about twenty suicides a year, and all extremely tragic. I'd often be called out to cut someone down from a tree or the like. Not long after I arrived, I got a call around midnight that there'd been a shooting. When I got down there, two policemen were trying to revive a young man in someone's backyard. It turned out to be an attempted suicide. I said, 'No, it's hopeless. Look, he's put a big hole in his chest.' So we decided to take him back to the mortuary. By then a crowd had gathered around us. I suppose it was just a part of their grieving process, but they were so full of frustration and anger that they attacked us with sticks and rocks as we tried to move him. That was a bit of a nightmare.

But generally, the local folk, the Lardils and Bentincks, were quite lovely. I wouldn't have stayed so long otherwise. We had a great public health system, with chronic disease management — we did the best we could despite the alcohol. We'd often run sessions at the school promoting a healthy lifestyle. People had good access to specialists down in Brisbane, and we had a number of visiting ophthalmologists, ear, nose and throat people, cardiologists, respiratory physicians and so forth, who'd include us in their wider hospitals circuit.

Over time, I gained great respect from the people. In the end, I'd say I knew eight hundred people out of the thousand by their first names. Funny thing though, the locals still called me Matron, irrespective of gender. I'd be walking down the street at night to go fishing or whatever and I'd hear voices coming out from the darkness: 'G'day Matron,' ... 'How's things Matron?'

Anyhow, someone once told me that the best time to leave the party is when you're having the most fun. So after seven years, I moved on. But Mornington wasn't the easiest of places. I heard later that they went through something like five directors of nursing in the next two years.

Against All Odds

I was at the University of Queensland, doing a Master of Tropical Health degree, when I met a female German medical student. We just ran into each other and so yeah, we got married. That was in the late '90s. After my wife graduated, she had to work in a reasonably sized hospital for her internship. So we went to Mackay where she became a resident medical officer at the local hospital. We were there for two years and during that time we had two children. I was thirty-nine, so I was a bit of a late-starter. My wife was ten years younger than me. But she got very homesick and she decided to go back to Germany with our two children. I didn't go, so I was a bit lost then. To that point I'd been in charge of lots of people, which involved all the sorting out of rosters and staffing issues and so on. I didn't want to have to worry about all that sort of overload any more, so when I saw a job going at a sole nursing post, over at Cue, in Western Australia, I thought I'd give it a go. And that's where I went next.

Cue's an old gold-mining place in the mid-west of WA. By the time I got there all the big mines had closed. It was sort of a ghost town really. But it was a lovely place to work. It had great community spirit and I made friends quickly. I lived next door to Kevin, the mayor, and I'd often get invited to council meetings to give my input into various health issues. Then the local policeman would ring me up: 'Hey, we're going out to an abandoned mine for a swim. Want'a come along?' Farm people would invite me out for dinner on the weekends. On Anzac Day, they'd ask me to cook the breakfast for the old diggers and the few ex-Vietnam vets who lived there. Another chap would say,

'How about we go fossicking around an old dump?' and we'd find hundred-year-old pieces of crockery and odds and sods from the old gold-mining days. So I became very involved in people's lives, and in doing so, I'd sort of deal with everything really; from those who were a bit depressed and needed a chat, to people who'd been involved in major car accidents. One particular event stands out. I got a knock on my door at about two in the morning: 'Andrew, come down, there's been an accident.'

I went down. I was just on my own. In places like Cue, there's no big team behind you. Anyhow, there was this poor man. He was a little chap, only about fifty kilos. He'd had a bit to drink and he was walking across the road, in the dead of the night, and he got hit by a car. Just the impact from that broke both his legs. But when he got tossed up into the air, he went straight through the car windscreen. Then, when the driver slammed on his brakes, the chap went flying back out the windscreen. He was in a hell of a bad way. I thought, Surely he's dead?

Anyhow, I did the basic ABC — airway, breathing and circulation — and sure enough he was alive. So a friend came and helped me put him in the back of the car and we drove him to the clinic.

He had almost no blood pressure, and as well as his broken legs, he'd smashed his shoulder and the skin on his head had been ripped off — degloved, as they say — from going through the windscreen twice. I don't know if it was because of the alcohol or what, but he didn't seem to be in too much pain. I had IV drips going in and I'd put a firm sling around his pelvis because it was smashed. I'd straightened his legs out and I got a neighbour to come over and hold his head at a tilt because the blood was pouring out. When I rang the RFDS and told them the story, they couldn't believe he was still alive. I said, 'Well, he is. You'd better come and get him.'

I then had to wait two hours for the plane to come and take him away. And that's the last I thought I'd ever see of him. But no, against all odds, six months later, this chap limped back into the clinic and thanked me for saving his life. I was just stunned as to what a human body could go through and still survive, while at other times, someone could get the slightest knock and they're gone.

Anyhow, while I was at Cue, the Australian Nurse of the Year awards people started sending out flyers to all the hospitals and clinics asking for nominations. I just put the forms in along with all the other waiting-room brochures and didn't think much of it. So I don't know who was behind it — who put in the nomination — but about three months later I got a call saying that I'd been selected to represent Western Australia as their Nurse of the Year. This was in 2004. They flew me over to Melbourne where we had a big cocktail evening and all that. It was a good night. At that stage Tony Abbott was Minister of Health and he gave out the awards. I got mine for being the Western Australian Nurse of the Year. 'Thanks very much,' I said. Then they said, 'Now, for the Australian Nurse of the Year. Stand up, Andrew.' For a second there, I was looking around to see who this other Andrew might be ... but it was me. I was completely blown away.

After leaving Cue I started with the Red Cross as an international humanitarian health delegate. Basically the role involves helping out in war-torn and troubled areas overseas. Nursing-wise I thought I was quite well prepared. I'd dealt with the occasional gunshot patient on Mornington, but definitely nothing like the fifteen who were brought in on the one night at Lopiding Hospital, in Kenya. That was full on. But I enjoyed that sort of work, so I started to do relief work around Queensland in between overseas postings. I've since worked in places like Sudan, as head nurse in a hospital in dusty Juba, which had a staff of around six hundred. I've also been to Afghanistan, where I helped manage the surgical side of the five-hundred-bed Jalalabad Public Health Hospital. I received a personal letter of thanks from the Afghani Minister of Health for that. I've also been to the Republic of Yemen, where I ran primary healthcare programs in the isolated northern mountains, assisting victims of internal conflicts. And then to Iraq, where I was based in Najaf, near Babylon, and led a team of medical and nursing staff in conducting a series of teaching programs.

After Iraq, I went to South Ossetia, a partially recognised state within Georgia, to help improve the skills and conditions of nurses in isolated health posts. That was in 2011, which was when I received the Florence Nightingale Medal — reportedly the highest international distinction a nurse can achieve. Since then I've been back to Afghanistan where I was based in Kandahar and Tarin Kowt, in the Uruzgan Province, to visit prisons and check on the welfare of detainees. I also taught first aid to the troops and negotiated the poliomyelitis immunisers' access into isolated areas. So there's some stories there, because, I mean, none of those were easy postings and some of the situations I got into were pretty hairy.

Jack's Crook

Decades ago I remember flicking through the *Women's Weekly* and reading an article about a couple of nurses who'd worked at the Birdsville clinic, and it got me thinking, Gee I'd like to do that job one day. For ages I'd had this romantic view of Birdsville, and so when I saw the position advertised, I thought, I'll throw my hat in the ring. And they employed me. Now, here I am.

Birdsville's in the central-western corner of Queensland, just twelve kilometres from the South Australian border and right on the edge of the Simpson Desert. It's a place where you have to rely on your own resources and make your own fun. I mean, you wouldn't live here if you wanted to go out for a caffé latte every morning with friends. But for the likes of me, it balances well with my Red Cross work. And I keep busy. We should be a two-nurse hospital, but with having to work nineteen days on and nine off, including manning the after-hours phone, I'm often the only person here. Some people probably couldn't handle it, but I love it. It's a bit like Cue in that there's a great community spirit and the local hospitality is fantastic.

Because of the heat, the population drops down to about sixty in summer. In winter there'd be about a hundred locals. Winter's full-on tourist season. A month ago, when they had the Big Red Bash concert, with Jimmy Barnes, Paul Kelly and Christine Anu, thousands of people turned up and the pub got in a full-time staff of near on forty. It's the same for the Birdsville Races, when we can get up to eight thousand visitors. So that they can get the best camping spots down by the river, some people arrive a month before race weekend. And the town makes it all amenable for them. They lay down hosepipes and tap the water down to the river and put in portable loos. It's all free camping. And of course everyone's got their own particular medical problems. The older ones often forget their tablets and when they come in for more and I ask them what they're on, they'll say, 'A little yellow one and a white one.' So well before the races, we order in a lot of medicines that we don't normally stock, just in case.

During race week the clinic really buzzes. We get in ten extra nurses and during the actual race weekend there's a full-time doctor. We're flat out. We divide the hospital roster into early, late and night shifts. With just two beds, we normally don't keep anyone overnight. We just present the case to the RFDS and let them decide on a plan of action. A lot of the patients we see are dehydrated. We usually only get ten per cent humidity out here and they think that, because they're not sweating, they don't need to drink and suddenly they collapse ... dry as a bone.

Then you have the older ones with heart attacks and strokes. There's a series of protocols we go through with those. We have a machine that we run their blood through to check for various enzymes the heart gives out if it's damaged, and we also do a cardiogram to check for vital signs. In an emergency situation, the RFDS is just two hours away. They come from Charleville or Mount Isa or, if necessary, Port Augusta or Adelaide. Because we're so close to the South Australian border, if we have to go over into SA, technically we should call the South Australian RFDS. They'll usually tell us to take the person to the nearest property that's got an airstrip and they'll pick them up from there.

These days most people carry EPIRBs — Emergency Position-Indicating Radio-beacons — so we can get their coordinates. One time we got a call that a chap had fallen off his motorbike, out in the desert, and had broken his leg. That day I went out with Don Rowlands, a ranger for the Simpson Desert National Park. They call Don 'the walking GPS' because he knows the place like the back of his hand. They'll say, 'I'm by the big gidgee tree, past the billabong, down by the creek, where the pelicans are,' and Don knows exactly where they're talking about. Anyhow, it took us about three hours to drive out in the Toyota V8 Land Cruiser ambulance. When we found the chap, he was in such rough terrain that there was no way a plane could've landed anywhere near us, and it was too far for a helicopter. So we had to bring him back ourselves.

We said, 'It's far too rough to take him out the way we came in. He'll just be in agony.' We had to find a smoother way out. So that's what we did. Don found a little-known way, driving out of the desert and heading south, down a more easy going creek bed, until we reached the Birdsville Track, near Alton Downs. Then we drove back up north to Birdsville. In all, that was a twelve-hour retrieval trip. Along the way I called the RFDS and gave them our estimated time of arrival, and they got to Birdsville half an hour before we did. While they waited, Don's wife, Lyn, opened up the clinic and made them a cup of tea and it all worked out well.

Yes, so, as for my future, I'll be sixty this year. It's been a great career and still is. Hopefully Queensland Health will still allow me to keep my job at Birdsville while I continue to do my international Red Cross work. I mean, they do have a statewide health service to run. So we'll see. Oh, and not to forget, Swampy, did I tell you that they gave me the Order of Australia Medal in 2013? I was pretty stoked about that. It's a great recognition for nurses doing tough work for the vulnerable, in some very difficult places. Since coming to Birdsville I've been to a number of those, including with the Ebola campaign. And I've only just come back from the frontline of the South Sudanese civil war, working with a surgical team. So now I'm back at Birdsville where I'm hoping things will be a bit more sedate.

Then just yesterday, with the horrors of South Sudan still fresh on my mind, a distraught traveller came rushing into the clinic. 'My boy Jack's out in the car. He's real crook. I think he's gonna die.'

'How old is he?'

'About ten.'

'Gee, only ten, ay. Can you bring him into the clinic?'

'No, he's too crook. Quick, I hope yer can save 'im.'

So I grabbed my gear and I rushed outside. When I opened the car door there was Jack — a ten-year-old male Jack Russell. The poor dog was looking such a sad and sorry sight that I attended to him the best I could and off they went. It's coming up to the Birdsville Races and apparently they've camped down by the river somewhere. So that's where I'll be tonight: down at the campsite checking on Jack.

Annette's Story
Everyone's Equal

I grew up on the South Island of New Zealand, in a town called Nelson. That's where I did my basic training. Then later on I went to Massey University, in Palmerston, on the North Island, to upgrade my qualification. The first hospital I worked at was in Auckland, then I went all over New Zealand.

My husband's Maori and once the kids had grown up, we decided to head overseas. First we went to England where I got work through a nursing agency, which allowed me to travel around. My husband started off doing welding, but he hated that so he started security work, which meant he could get time off as well. We were in the UK for about four years. Then in the early 2000s, we decided to come to Australia for a quick visit on our way back to New Zealand; you know, just to have a look around and see some rellies. That was fifteen years ago and we're still here.

The first place we worked was in Kalgoorlie. Kalgoorlie was great, though I didn't get off to the best of starts. First day there I went to have a look around on my bicycle. Being a Sunday there were hardly any cars about. As quiet as. Next thing, the police pull me over. 'You just went through a stop sign. Here's your ticket. Fifty bucks.' Welcome to Kalgoorlie.

Kalgoorlie Hospital's apparently the biggest in outback Australia. It was very busy. The only patients who got flown out to Perth were the real intensive care ones who needed things like heart operations and ventilating. I worked as a nurse in the Emergency Department and they also had a mini ICU — intensive care unit. It was a well-catered hospital and the staff were a great bunch. Many were international. Travellers from all over the world would say, 'Let's go and work in Kalgoorlie for a while.'

It was a very social town. In any other place, if you came off night shift, most things would be shut; it'd be as dead as. But in Kalgoorlie, things were open most of the time. Miners would be knocking off work of a morning and, 'Hey, we're off to the pub.' And it was like, 'Good grief. Okay.'

Kalgoorlie's also got quite a large Aboriginal population. I'd finished work late one evening when the paramedics got a call out to the Boulder Camp. They said, 'We're not sure what's happened but do you want to come along for a ride?'

I'd never been to the Boulder Camp so I said, 'Yeah, okay.'

Anyway, we arrived. There's lots of little campfires but I can't see anyone. Next thing, out of the darkness appears all these Aborigines and they rush to the ambulance calling out how they've got just about every illness under the sun. 'We need to go to the hospital. It's an emergency. We've got asthma. We've got this. We've got that.' Mind you, they looked perfectly well to me. It was so funny. I was killing myself. Anyhow, some of them got in the back of the ambulance and off we go. As it turns out, the hospital's opposite a twenty-four-hour shop in town which sells liquor, cigarettes and food. So when we got there they all jumped out of the ambulance and it was, 'Oh, we're all right now. Feelin'' much better, thanks. See yer later.' And off they went.

And the poor paramedics went, 'Well, at least no one's dead.'

But the Aboriginal people were so friendly. I'd be riding my bicycle home of a morning, after night shift, and there'd be a whole group of them sitting outside the Centrelink office. 'Morning, Sister,' they'd all roar. 'Hello.' I didn't know anyone's name, but they all knew me. I'd see some of them up in Emergency. It was sad in a way because a lot of it was due to alcohol abuse and there were always fights and stuff. But I got on well with them.

As for other experiences: another time we had a couple of the Hay Street ladies in as patients. I don't know if you know or not, but since the old mining days, prostitution has been legal in Kalgoorlie, and Hay Street's the well-known red-light district. These days they pay taxes and everything. But the ladies were telling me how, one night, a drunk bloke turned up at the brothel. They always keep the client's credit card behind the counter, just in case. Anyway, this bloke was so out of it that he almost collapsed as soon as he got inside and before long he was sound asleep, snoring away.

So the ladies tended to him. They gave him a wash, put him on a bed, covered him up and checked on him throughout the night. And they charged him by the hour. So after about twelve hours of being cared for in the brothel, he left well out of pocket, and with nothing to boast about. I said, 'You could've sent him up to the hospital. He would've been looked after for nothing.' And I bet he probably wished that he had come to the hospital, too.

Another thing I liked about Kalgoorlie was — as you may know — there's a lot of money in the town, but you rarely saw it. Like no one's stuck up and showing off. Everyone's equal. It was a real down-to-earth sort of town. It was great in that way.

Then from Kalgoorlie we went to Esperance. That was in about 2006 or '07. Esperance is in the Goldfields health area so it was more or less just a transfer down the road, but nearer a beach where we could fish and swim. And, wow, there was a lot of beach there, and pristine white sand. Though, being right on the Southern Ocean, the water was freezing. People used to say, 'You're not going for a swim are you?' and we'd go, 'Yeah, we're from New Zealand. We're immune to it.'

I enjoyed Esperance too. The hospital was lovely. There were only about fifteen beds all up. They had a maternity unit and a little operating theatre. The doctors were all GPs in town. One of them would be on call each day; otherwise the nurses basically ran the ship. And being so far away from anywhere, you'd sort of think that Esperance would feel remote. But it didn't. There was a picture theatre, a library, supermarkets and some great restaurants. Everything was at your fingertips. You didn't need to be anywhere else. It was like a little oasis.

As for characters: there was Sammy, the monster sea lion. He was quite bossy, actually. He'd hang around the wharf and people would feed him, which was why he was so massive. We took our big bull-mastiff for a walk one day and Sammy went after him. Then there were the sharks. We used to take our dog swimming with us until someone said, 'You'd better watch out. The great whites love eating dogs.'

But again, we just loved Esperance. The only problem being that it was a long way from home, and at that time, my husband's mum wasn't well and my dad wasn't too good either. And to get back to New Zealand was a real trek. First you had to drive the seven hundred and fifty kilometres to Perth, then you had to catch a plane over to New Zealand. In all, it'd take a couple of days. So we thought we'd move over to the eastern side of Australia, closer to home. We started out at Nowra, then we moved up to Sydney. But the city wasn't really our scene and my husband was having to work as security in night clubs, which wasn't all that pleasant.

Time Flies

When I saw the Wilcannia job advertised in a nursing magazine, I thought, I really want to do some more remote nursing like I'd done in Western Australia. But my husband was a bit worried about getting work so I said, 'Let's just give it a go for twelve months and if we don't like it, we can leave.'

'Okay,' he said.

We'd never been to Wilcannia of course, so I looked at a map on the computer and it seemed like Broken Hill was only about ten kilometres up the road. We said, 'Oh good, it'll be just a short drive to Broken Hill, jump on a plane to Sydney, then on to New Zealand.' But I'd forgotten about the distances in Australia, and Broken Hill ended up being a couple of hundred kilometres to the west of Wilcannia and Sydney a thousand k's to the east.

When I told people that I'd got the job, they said, 'Oh don't go there. It's too dangerous. No one even stops in Wilcannia. They drive straight through.'

It was all the usual myths about Wilcannia having a large unruly Aboriginal population and being a socially disadvantaged place. So I then had visions of it being an absolute dump, with rubbish up the streets and all of that. But when we drove into town it was much nicer than I'd been led to believe. There was some grass around the place, there were trees and it's got a lot of history. Being on the Darling River, Wilcannia used to be one of the largest inland ports in Australia. Of course things have changed now: whereas back in its heyday it had about a dozen pubs, now there's only one. And where it once had a population of around fifteen hundred, now there's only about six hundred.

Anyway, that was seven years ago, so time flies. I never dreamed that I'd come way out here, to western New South Wales, and work in a place like Wilcannia. Never. I mean, you couldn't get anywhere more different from where I grew up in New Zealand. Mind you, I'm not saying it's going to be forever, but we're still here, and we're still enjoying it. And it's actually a wonderful town and it is a great hospital. We've got an in-patients and aged care. City doctors visit Wilcannia three times a week and do booked appointments. The rest of the time the patients just come in and see us. We're all in the one building, so we all work together, and of course, we're all looking after the same people; that's the main thing.

In total we've got seven RNs, then there's a hospital assistant, a maintenance person, two cleaners and a cook. About half of those would be locals. The rest are people like me who have come in from outside. Then we take in a new graduate nurse every six months to give them some remote experience. We also get Fifth Year medical students, out on a month's rural placement, before they do their finals. There's a doctor here at the moment who's giving them tutorials. He works for the Aboriginal Health Service, providing primary health care in town and out in the community. By coming out here, the students get the chance to do all the bits and pieces they'd be unlikely to do in a bigger hospital. My thinking is, if they enjoy their time here, somewhere down the track, they might come back out remote, as fully qualified doctors.

The great thing is the staff — if someone's sick, someone's always willing to fill in: 'Yeah, I can do a double shift or twelve-hour shift.' That attitude is more common here than anywhere else I've been. My position is deputy health service manager. I'm currently also acting health service manager. We've lost a couple of managers in the time I've been here. One went to Broken Hill, another one only lasted a couple of months before he burnt himself out. I'd said to him, 'Mate, just a word of advice. I'm not telling you what to do, but you're like a bull at a gate. Just step back a while. Give yourself a chance.' But no, he flung himself into everything: ran around the place, introducing himself to everyone; joining this, that and the other; and taking on lots of extra jobs like the ambulance calls. He exhausted himself, and his wife didn't like it out here. So off he went and it's taken a few months to organise another health service manager, so better luck this time.

But like in any small community, it takes a while to get to know people and for them to get to know you. There's the usual barriers and there's the factions. Right from the start I decided not to take sides and not to have best of friends or favourite families. My husband's the same. Being Maori has helped. The minute they saw he was a brown-skinned person, they said, 'Yeah, he's okay.' And he's found plenty of things to do. He gets a bit of security work and he works out on a property. He's happy. Plus he plays footy, which always helps break the ice. First he played for the local Boomerangs. They went through the season undefeated. That was the proudest moment of his life. It was all he ever talked about — drove me crazy. He stopped playing for a couple of years after that, then a few of his mates asked if he'd join the Broken Hill Saints. But this's his last ever season. He's not going to play after this year, you can bet on it. I've put my foot down.

So everyone knows us now and we're treated well because they realise we're genuine. But like in any of these remote areas, there's the usual logistical difficulties. Just trying to get a light globe for the ambulance is a major undertaking. First you've got to find one, then you've got to get it to Broken Hill; then it's got to get out to Wilcannia. We do have a bus that runs once a day and the oxygen-bottle man comes every couple of days. But if it's extremely urgent, it's into the car and off we go on the four-hundred-kilometres round trip to Broken Hill and back. So it's a challenge and it means a lot of extra staff hours are racked up.

But the ambulance is the bane of my life. Basically the state government gave us an ambulance, plus the gear, and said, 'Here, it's yours. Run it yourself,' which means we've got to have a staff member on permanent call. Another problem is that, with all our triple-0 calls coming in via Western Operations in Dubbo, they don't always pinpoint exact locations. They'll say, 'There's been an accident at a property a hundred k's out. We think it's on the left-hand side of the river but we're not sure.'

And I'm going, God I wish they could give us better directions. So off we go in the middle of the night, with just a general idea of where we're going. It's mainly farm accidents, but there's also heart attacks, motor vehicle and motorcycle crashes, shearing mishaps; anything really. Plane crashes: we recently had one of those. We were told it was seventy k's out on the Broken Hill road somewhere. The ambo and I were heading out, merrily driving along, and I said to him, 'Do you realise we're going to a plane crash out in the middle of God knows where and there's only you and me?' And we went, 'Augh!'

Apparently a property owner had heard a big crash and when he took a look, there's the plane hanging up in a tree. By the time we got there, the pilot was conscious. He wasn't young either; he was an older man. The plane was a write-off but he was all right. He lived. He just had this huge gash up his arm.

Then, just the other week, we had another emergency call: 'There's been a collision between two trucks and they're on fire.'

So it's into the ambulance and off we go. We're thinking the worst: you know, a huge head-on with a massive fire and bodies lying everywhere. When we get there, we discover that a bloke had been carrying hay in a trailer. The hay had caught fire, and luckily, he had the nous to disconnect the trailer. And that was it. No one was hurt. But see, being a triple-0 call, we have to go. We can't say, 'Well are you really sure about what they're saying with regard to the incident?' Still, I guess it's some sort of a relief that, when you do get there, you find out that nothing horrific has happened.

At other times there's a tendency for people to make out that the situation is trivial, when in actual fact it's very serious. In most cases like that it's because they don't want the police involved. If they said, 'There's been a stabbing,' the police would be there in a flash. But if they say, 'Oh so-and-so's cut themselves,' the police are less likely to turn up. Then when we get there, there's been a stabbing and someone's on death's door. But that's life in the bush.

Anton and Annette's Story
Together

Annette — I grew up in Adelaide. I'm a Wildy girl; I went to Wilderness Secondary School. Nursing interested me in as much as it was a job that would enable me to travel, and also, at that time, being trained in a hospital was like an apprenticeship where you got paid while you were learning.

Anton — I was born in London. My father was Indian and my mother was Finnish, so I'm a Finndian. Mum and Dad met in the early '60s when they were working in a homoeopathic hospital near Soho Square. When I was two we moved to Finland. But while Finland was doing okay economically, it was still under the shadow of Russia and so Dad was keen to move on. The choice was either Canada or Australia, and Mum wasn't keen on Canada because the weather would've been the same as Finland — cold — so Australia won out.

I was nine we arrived here and we moved to Elizabeth, in South Australia. When I finished Year 12 I didn't feel ready to go straight on to university. But some of my parents' influence must've rubbed off because I'd always had an inkling to go into some sort of 'human service' type work. So when a job as an orderly came up at Modbury Hospital I jumped at it. And that gave me such a good taste of nursing that I then applied to do my RN's training at the Royal Adelaide Hospital.

Annette — I decided to do my training at the Queen Elizabeth, and because I didn't want to remain living with my parents, I moved into the nurses' quarters there. Quite a few girls did the same so there's some great memories of those days, with lots of bonding and good friendships. It wasn't as strict as in past years. We didn't have curfews or things like that. But the males and females still had to live on separate floors and we weren't allowed male visitors. Though, mind you, a few did manage to sneak in.

Anton — Annette and I had similar pathways before we met. At the Royal Adelaide, the boys and girls were also on separate floors, so we had some good fun.

Annette — With regard to any connection with the outback: as a child I'd done a lot of camping with my parents. In the '70s we'd driven the Birdsville Track. We'd also gone up to Darwin, and oh, after Coober Pedy, the road was just awful. It was dirt and extremely corrugated. Dad had a new Hillman Hunter and by the time we got back home our windscreen had been smashed and the petrol tank was so badly beaten about that it only carried half the amount of fuel. Other times we'd go fishing down to Robe or over to the Eyre or Yorke Peninsula and I think all those experiences are what gave me a taste to explore the more remote areas.

Anton — While I mightn't have had that sort of affinity with the outback, I was certainly someone who had a great sense of adventure. As a child I'd camped at Coober Pedy and had gone opal fossicking. As a teenager I'd go surfing over to places like Streaky Bay and Cactus Beach.

Annette — After I'd done my training I did a staffing year before I took off overseas for twelve months. Up until that stage all my nursing was aimed toward the medical and surgical side of things, which was fine, but I'd also become interested in the mental health area. So when I came back from my travels, I applied to do psych nursing at Hillcrest Hospital.

Anton — Straight after I'd finished my training, I went travelling overseas for a year. Then after I came back, I did my staffing year. And like Annette, during my hospital training, I also became fascinated by the psych side of things.

Annette — Anton and I were in the same student group at Hillcrest. The ratio between males and females would've been about forty per cent male, sixty per cent female. I already had a boyfriend and so Anton was just one of the blokes. He was already going out with someone anyway. But during the course I separated from my boyfriend and Anton separated from his girlfriend and we became friends. At that time we were both living in Prospect — though in different share-houses — and sometimes we'd carpool, or, on our days off, we'd go to the aquatic centre or play squash or whatever. It was purely social.

Then, when we did start our relationship, we didn't tell anyone. That was mainly because a lot of people at the hospital were having affairs and going in and out of relationships and we didn't want to be tarnished with that. That wasn't what we were about, and so, if we'd been out together and someone asked, 'What did you do last night?', I'd say, 'Oh I went out with some of my non-hospital friends,' and Anton would tell the same story.

Then we started going on camping trips together. We really like bush walking. We went to places like Wilpena Pound and over to Yorke Peninsula. But I'd always wanted to go over to Western Australia. Anton had already visited Perth during the America's Cup and had enjoyed it, so, when I mentioned it, he said, 'Yeah, let's go.' So we thought, Stuff it, and, when we'd finished our psych rotation, I basically announced to our friends that Anton and I were running off together. And we did; we put Anton's panel van on the *Indian Pacific* and off we went.

When we got to Perth we got general nursing work at Sir Charles Gairdner Hospital. We lived in the nurses' quarters for a while, and because we weren't married, we were back to living on different floors. Then we got a flat. The good thing with the nursing was that we could organise our shifts to get time off together and we started going to places like Margaret River, Albany, Esperance and Rottnest Island.

Anton — To fit in all our camping gear, we bought a Hilux four-wheel-drive ute. When we decided to move on, we got general nursing work in Carnarvon. Carnarvon's about a thousand kilometres north of Perth. It's a large fishing community and there's also banana plantations and vegetable gardens. It was interesting because I hadn't worked in a place that had such a large Aboriginal population. There were the usual problems with drinking within both the Indigenous and white groups, plus there was some tension between them. But both Annette and I got on well with the Aborigines in particular, and in many ways that's what really kicked off my interest in Aboriginal health.

Annette — In the paediatric ward there was a little Aboriginal boy; he'd been there for ages. He was about three and he had a chronic gastro infection and he was just the sweetest and most lovely human being. Then there was that other man; the Aboriginal man. Who was that, Anton?

Anton — Charlie. That's a sad story. At the hospital, if anyone was drunk or on drugs or whatever, they'd place them under observation in a time-out room, like a padded cell, and you had to open a slot in the door to keep an eye on them. A year or so before we got to Carnarvon, Charlie was coming through the DTs and he'd been put into this observation area overnight. The thing was, no one had checked on him and he had a stroke. So Charlie basically ended up in the little nursing home section, more or less as a vegetable. Yes, Charlie had a bit of a drinking problem. But it's not just the Aboriginals that have a drinking problem; so does a lot of the population.

Annette — On the upside, on our days off we'd go camping to Mount Augustus or we'd go fishing up at Coral Bay, Exmouth and Red Bluff, and just up the coast there was the Blowies. It's like a big blow hole and we'd fish and pick oysters off the rocks. Oh, we just loved Western Australia.

Anton — The thinking was that we'd take a couple of years to work our way around Australia and see where we'd end up.

Whatever will be, will be. So from Carnarvon we spent a bit of time in the Pilbara before going up into the Kimberley. We did some door-knocking for jobs along the way. I can't quite remember what happened but we somehow ended up getting work in Fitzroy Crossing, and we really enjoyed our time there, didn't we?

Annette — Loved it.

Anton — Nursing was a challenge but we had some great times and we met some real characters. The locals took us barramundi fishing. They'd give us mud maps and we'd go camping in places where tourists would never go. Once we went to a large cave where we had to crawl through the various caverns. It was simply amazing.

As far as the characters went, there was Billy. Billy was an old white guy in his eighties. He was a retired station hand, and as with a lot of those old guys, because they'd lived in the bush all their lives, the station people were happy enough for them to see their days out on the property. Billy spent a lot of his time in the pub and one day he turned up at the hospital with an STI — sexually transmitted infection — so he must've still had a bit of a spring in his step.

Another character was Scotty, the cleaner-cum-handyman-cum-hospital-orderly-cum-ambulance-driver. Scotty was Scottish, naturally, and he had such a broad accent that hardly anyone could understand him. He was going out with one of the social workers whom he referred to as 'the Goat', which is an acronym for 'the greatest of all time'. When you'd ask where she was, he'd reply, 'Ah, the Goat's not here.'

Annette — I did a lot of night duty with Scotty, which meant there was just me and him. He was no-nonsense. If anyone knocked on the door in the middle of the night and they looked like trouble, he'd soon defuse things. Then after our shift we'd be off to the Fitzroy Crossing pub. By 8 o'clock in the morning we'd be on our bar stools, having our first drink.

Anton — Another orderly was a young English backpacker. Not being a nurse, he wasn't supposed to stay in the nurses' quarters, but because he didn't have anywhere else to live, apart from his tent, we'd let him sleep in the common room of the quarters. The nurses' quarters consisted of a couple of different buildings. They were basic, but okay. Ours was like a two-roomed transportable with an en suite, and the two other female nurses were in the other building.

Annette — The hospital wasn't huge. It had about ten beds. A lot of the problems involved kids with failure to thrive. There were also the old women and men with their toes missing or leg ulcers or they'd rolled onto a campfire; things like that. And as you may have heard on the news of late, fetal alcohol syndrome was, and still is, quite a big problem, and not only in Fitzroy Crossing.

Anton — With fetal alcohol syndrome it was simply just trying to get the mum back on track with regard to mothering skills and to put into place some sort of plan to try and stop them from bouncing back into the hospital system.

Annette — We'd also get tourists calling in, mostly because they'd run out of their medication or they had a cold.

Anton — I was the senior on night duty one time when a couple of grey nomads came through. The husband arrived at the hospital blue-faced and clutching his chest. By the time we got him onto the brooch he'd had a cardiac arrest. The other nurse on duty had only just become an RN so she wasn't much help. Then, when I went to get the paddles to defib him, the defibrillator wasn't charged up. Anyhow, we did CPR and thankfully we got him back and the following morning the RFDS flew him out to Derby. Apparently he ended up okay, but they're the type of situations that can really give you an adrenalin rush.

Annette — We'd also get the occasional rollovers and we'd get the young backpackers, driving around in their clapped-out old cars, and they'd turn up with severe sunburn, or head or pubic lice. The other thing we did was the ambulance call-outs. We once got a call to an Aboriginal community to see a lady who was in labour. There was just me and the English backpacker who was driving the ambulance. Now I wasn't a midwife — no way — and so, as we were driving out, I was madly reading a textbook, just in case. Anyhow, that one turned out okay as well. She didn't give birth and we got her back to Fitzroy and they flew her to Derby to have the baby.

Anton — Then I had some Finnish relatives coming over to Adelaide for Christmas. By that stage we'd been in Fitzroy Crossing for six months. We were thinking of moving on anyway, so we decided to go back home via the Northern Territory.

Annette — But with having had the midwifery issue with the Aboriginal woman, that started me thinking about doing my 'mid'. So I got in touch with the Queen Victoria Hospital in Adelaide and I was asked to pop in for an interview when we got back.

Without Fail

Anton — With Annette doing her midwifery, I thought, What'll I do? Then I saw an advertisement with Nganampa, the Aboriginal organisation that controls health services throughout the APY — Anangu Pitjantjatjara Yankunytjatjara — Lands in the north-west corner of South Australia. When I saw that the contact person was named Kaisu Vartto, I said, 'Hey, she's also Finnish.' So I met with Kaisu, and even though she was extremely passionate about improving the health of the people on the Lands, I was wavering. It was a big decision as it'd mean that Annette and I would have to maintain our relationship remotely. But then, when Kaisu mentioned that Nganampa were generous in the way of allowances and leave, we decided to give it a go.

So I ended up in Fregon — also known as Kaltjiti — and, while the relationship side of it was hard, I threw myself into this new and exciting experience. There were about four hundred Indigenous people at Fregon and even though it was on Yankunytjatjara land, the majority were Pitjantjatjara. As for the expat community, there were about fifty of us: there were the teachers, the community-advisor-cum-manager, the Arts Centre people and the mechanic–petrol station people; then there were a couple of maintenance people and the family that ran the store.

Fregon healthcare ran on two nurses and a doctor. It was an alcohol-free community, which was its saving grace, because whenever grog got in, we'd end up stitching heads and dodging flying rocks. The health centre itself was very much a place where the women and children went, so we had a male room at the back. When I arrived, we had a high number of STI cases and I thought, Surely I can do something about this? Now, football's very important to the Aboriginal people. They just love their footy and there was a big open area in the community where, of an afternoon, the boys would gather to kick the footy. One day I got an idea. I said to the others in the clinic, 'I'm off to play some football.'

And that became a pattern. Each afternoon I'd go and kick the footy with the boys, and that's how the connection began. This was before television came to Fregon. But seeing how we could play DVDs, I got some city friends to send up footy videos. Then, while I was kicking the footy, I'd put the word out: 'Hey guys, I'm gonna show a footy video in the health centre tonight. Want'a come along?' Twenty or so would turn up, and while we were watching the footy, I'd take them aside, one by one, and we'd discuss any of their health concerns.

As in most remote communities, one of the problems was their access to condoms. The guys weren't keen on carrying them around. So I said there'd be a supply in the power box, at the house I was living in. As the word spread, at about 3 o'clock in the morning, I'd hear the shuffling. Next I'd hear the creaking of the power box being opened, then more shuffling as they grabbed some condoms and took off. And after a short period of time the number of STI presentations had fallen considerably.

Annette — After I'd completed my midwifery I was thinking about having a bit of a holiday. Then one of the nurses at Fregon got the job of teaching Aboriginal health workers over in Ernabella. With her position now vacant, I applied for and got the position.

Anton and I were now back together, but the nursing was sometimes very difficult. But, with the Aboriginal people being so family oriented, we got to know all the grandmas and the granddads, the uncles and the aunties and the brothers and sisters. And culturally, I found it very interesting: just as an example, how the people would demonstrate their unhappiness or resolve an issue with another family. Unlike ourselves, most times it'd be played out in the public forum and there'd be men walking around with spears and stuff, so we'd go and hide until the dispute was over.

Anton — But we were always concerned about getting a knock on the door at two in the morning and finding someone holding a flaccid baby. That'd certainly cause our hearts to skip a beat, because at that age they can deteriorate rapidly. With the worst cases we'd get the RFDS to fly them out or otherwise we'd put IVs into them, to get them going.

Annette — Quite often it was bronchiolitis and they'd present with rapid breathing and a high temperature. I've lost count of the times I set my alarm to get up in the middle of the night to go out into the community and check on someone. Sometimes, because their camps were pretty crappy, it was easier to keep them in the clinic where we could keep a closer eye on them. With their living conditions, there were houses, but lot of the time they preferred to sleep outside in swags. And if someone had died in the house, they wouldn't go back and live in it until it was smoked and the dead person's spirit had gone; so they'd either live with other families or they'd go out bush and camp under tin or tarpaulins.

Anton — And if we had an association with that family, there'd be an obligation to help dig the grave, and after the coffin had gone in, we'd make sure that the concrete got poured for the slab. If it was a child's grave it'd be a pick-and-shovel job and if it was an adult we might get the digger in. But there'd always be the discussion about how the grave was to be dug and in what direction it was to point and where it was to be located in relation to other family members' graves.

Annette — There were also the petrol sniffers. They were usually in their late teens, into their twenties, and although we got on quite well with them, sometimes they could get psychotic and quite euphoric and unpredictable in their behaviour. You'd be walking over to the clinic in the middle of the night and they'd come out of the dark and scare the living daylights out of you.

Then there were the camp dogs, who weren't noted for their friendliness, so we'd have to be cautious with them. Occasionally a vet would come out and give us, like, *The Dummy's Guide to Veterinary Science*, and because there was a camel farm on the community, we'd do the veterinary stuff on camels. We'd also inoculate the mangy dogs and euthanise some of them. There were also lots of donkeys and if a pack of dogs got hold of a donkey, we'd end up having to put that down too. And all the cats lived on the roof, because if they came to ground, the dogs would rip them apart and we'd have to see to them as well.

Anton — We got a few vehicle accidents. One time two cars were on a remote outstation road, and as they come over the crest of a sand hill, they hit head-on. There was multiple trauma with that one, so we had to get the RFDS that night. The first to be flown out was a young kid with a severe head injury. Then they had to come back in the morning and fly a guy out who had a broken femur. There was also the guy with broken limbs and lots of bruising that we had to drive to Alice Springs.

Annette — Earlier on at Fregon, the airstrip didn't have automatic lights, so if we had to transfer someone at night, we'd have to go and light kerosene cans along the runway. Then invariably, just as the plane was about to arrive, a gust of wind would come along and blow the lights out. So the RFDS would be saying, 'How come you don't have the lights on?' and we'd be madly running around lighting them up again.

Communication within the community also had its trials and tribulations. Most people spoke Pitjantjatjara, and English was only their second language. To that end my Pitjantjatjara was very much restricted to phrases like, 'Where does it hurt?', 'Poke your tongue out', 'Lift your leg up' and 'Can I look in your ear?' And even though we had Aboriginal health workers, they were a bit inconsistent about turning up for work. And when they did, they were quite often reluctant to translate or help out because there'd be some sort of conflict of interest family-wise or whatever. Though I must say, with the older people and the little kids they were usually very helpful.

Anton — It's actually a bit of a shame that we didn't learn more of the language.

Annette — And because I was a midwife, I was on call most of the time. But when we could, Anton and I would try and tick off and go camping. Out of respect we'd get verbal permission from the traditional owners to camp on the land. It was their family land and there were some amazing places to go. Then if we had a weekend off, we'd sometimes drive to Uluru and go five-star at Yulara — wine and dine, the whole bit. And now I'm just thinking of some other experiences we had in Fregon. Do you remember that New Year's Eve when somebody had got hold of the car? Was he drunk or just pissed off about something?

Anton — I think it was both. It was New Year's Eve and he took his dad's or his uncle's four-wheel-drive ute and he started doing these huge doughnuts in the middle of the community. It was scary stuff, and because our house was fenced off, just about everyone ended up over at our place.

Annette — There was dust everywhere. Then he finally did one big doughnut too many and he rolled the car right in the middle of the community, and I remember looking at Anton and saying, 'Happy New Year.'

Anton — We were at Fregon for nearly six years, and while we enjoyed it, it wasn't for everyone. Within minutes of meeting a new locum I knew whether they'd stay or not. Some of them would get such a culture shock they'd be out of there at the next opportunity, and there was one young woman who, after she'd arrived, locked herself into her ATCO hut and wouldn't come out.

Annette — One of the reasons why Anton and I stayed there for so long was that we got on well and we could work together. I mean, we did occasionally have our arguments but basically my brief was women's business and Anton's was men's business. And also, after every twelve weeks, we had a week off, and while that was problematic at times, Nganampa usually organised for someone to come in and cover for us.

Anton — After we'd been married for a year and a half, they arranged for a couple to cover for us and we went on a three-month holiday through Europe and Asia. When we came back and Annette was pregnant, our parents were like, 'What? You're really considering taking a baby back to Fregon?'

We said, 'Look, we're not going to do it for much longer, but we're still enjoying it.'

Annette — We also had our second child while we were up there, and I think that's another thing that made it work for us: the fact that we were a couple and we ended up having our children there as well. And being as family oriented as they are, the Aboriginal people saw our children very much as their own. They were even given Aboriginal names — Tjulkina and Merinca.

Anton — But we did probably stay there a bit longer than we originally intended to.

Annette — And in the end, I was feeling a bit lonely. I wasn't working and I was living in Fregon with two little kids.

Anton — We left in the middle of August. It was bitterly cold and everyone came to our farewell barbecue. Even some of the petrol sniffers did a dance for us, and we were given so many paintings and artefacts. People were saying, 'This one's for Tjulkarin. This one's for Merinca. This one's for Anton and this one's for Annette.'

Annette — But we really liked working in Aboriginal health. We felt that we were making a difference, plus we liked the Fregon community and we liked the land and we liked the fact that they spoke their own language and that they maintained a lot of their culture. And also, with it being a dry zone, there weren't all the drinking issues that we'd seen in the Kimberley and Carnarvon. Then when we came back, we lost the peace and quiet. I'd really enjoyed the sense of space and the tranquillity of the bush and the night sky; being able to see all those beautiful stars and the gorgeous sunsets. I really missed all that, definitely.

Anton — It's similar for me. I look back on that part of my life fondly. A lot of our friends thought we were crazy, and at times it was a real challenge. Living in Fregon, you weren't just a nurse, you were a twenty-four-hours-a-day community member. We had some fantastic times with the people and when we'd go camping to places where no other white people had been, it was like, 'Wow, this's just awesome.' We also got to know a bit of their culture through me going off to do men's business and Annette to do women's business. They're the sorts of things that very few non-Aboriginal people get to experience and it was all because they were comfortable with having us around. It was a showing of their appreciation.

Annette — And for some strange reason, whenever any of their special events were going on, the weather always went weird. I'm not spiritual, but there was a lot of spiritual stuff happening out there. Like if someone important in the community died, a wild rainstorm or a huge dust storm or some sort of strange weather pattern would occur. Without fail. It was amazing.

Barbara's Story
The Happiest Days of My Life

My married name is Chester, though, back in the early 1960s, when I was at Birdsville, people knew me as Barbara Struck. I was born in Quorn, South Australia, and I grew up there during the war years. Quorn's a beautiful little town situated in the Flinders Ranges. My mother was a housewife who also did some cooking at the various hotels in town, and my father — well, Dad was a very talented man. Dad worked for the railways in Quorn as a fitter and turner and oh he could turn his hand at anything.

During the war the troop trains would come up to Port Augusta, then go through Horrocks Pass and on to Quorn, along the Pichi Richi Railway line. It was a very busy place. In fact, if you mention Quorn to any of the old soldiers they'd recall how the CWA — Country Women's Association — used to feed them all, over on the oval, as they were passing though on their way up to Alice Springs by rail, then further north by road.

I went to school in Quorn. Then in the late '40s, after I'd done a year or two of high school, I began nursing. How that came about is quite interesting because, believe it or not, my great ambition was to be a pilot. I just had this thing about aeroplanes. I don't know why, but if a plane flew over, I'd get all excited. I'd even go with Dad up to his workshop and make planes. Dad had all the tools, like lathes and everything, all of which he taught me how to use. So I'd draw out the plan of a plane, then I'd get the wood, I'd saw it all up and lathe it into its various bits, then I'd put it together. Oh I just loved aeroplanes. The problem was, nobody could tell me what you had to do to become a pilot. So I came up with the idea of joining TAA — Trans Australia Airlines — as an air hostess. Then, once I'd got into the business, I was sure that someone there would be able to tell me how to become a pilot. When I approached TAA, they said, 'You have to have done eighteen months' nursing training before you can become an air hostess.'

I thought, No worries, and I went over to the Quorn Hospital. But Matron said, 'We don't do nursing training here; you'll have to go to Port Augusta.'

Port Augusta Hospital accepted me as a nursing aid. After I'd done some basic training I came back and worked at Quorn Hospital. But I still had this thing about becoming a pilot, so this time I decided to join the Air Force. I thought my best bet was to get into the traffic section and take it from there. But when they saw what I'd already done, they said, 'No, we'll put you into nursing.'

I was then sent to the Air Force base in Laverton, Victoria, where I continued training to be a nurse. I was only there a short time when I got called in to see the matron and the head doctor. I thought, Gee, I wonder what I've done wrong. Perhaps I'm in some sort of strife. Anyway, I went in and, to cut a long story short, they said, 'You're wasting your time in the Air Force. You've got the makings of a brilliant nurse, and if you stay with us, you'll only end up as a corporal or sergeant.'

I said, 'Well, I really only joined because I wanted to become a pilot.'

I was then told that to become a pilot, I'd have to have such-and-such qualifications — none of which I had — and they suggested that I go and finish my nursing training and become a fully fledged RN instead.

I said, 'But I can't leave the Air Force. I've still got four years to go on my contract.'

Their reply was, 'You're so good that we'll pull out all the stops to get you into nursing.'

And they did. I was accepted at the Salvation Army Bethesda Hospital, in Melbourne. That's where I completed my general training, and where I also did my staffing and midwifery. In all I spent nearly five years at Bethesda, then I did a postgraduate course in Eye, Ear and Nose. That's when I met Brenda Preston. Brenda and I became good friends and along the way we decided we'd like to try remote nursing.

At that time Brenda's brother-in-law was the flying doctor at a mining place called Radium Hill, a couple of hundred miles north of Adelaide. So we thought we'd apply for Radium Hill through the AIM — Australian Inland Mission. Fred McKay had taken over the running of the AIM after John Flynn had died and so a meeting was organised with Fred and his wife, Margaret. Just before the meeting I remember saying to Brenda, 'I hope we don't have to go to Birdsville.' And the first thing they said was, 'We'd like you to go to Birdsville. There's a big drought going on out there. There's hardly any water left in the creek. There's dysentery and we desperately need people. You'll be on a two-year tenure, then we'll send out a couple of other nurses to replace you.'

Brenda and I said, 'Well, I guess we'll go out to Birdsville then.'

That was in 1961 and it took us four days to fly out there. We flew from Melbourne to Sydney, then from Sydney to Windorah. From Windorah we flew to Charleville, and from there out to Birdsville. When we were coming in, I remember the pilot flew us over the town and he said, 'That's your new home down there.' And we thought, My God, how are we going to last two years out here? It was as dry as chips and there were only eight buildings in the place. As it turned out, there were something like eighty people living in Birdsville, and of that eighty, only eight were white. But you know, those ended up being among the happiest days of my life.

The hospital we worked in is still there today, though it's more of a museum now. It was across the road from the Brookie's —

Bill Brook's — at Adria Downs. We'd been told that we'd have to do everything, which we were okay with — apart from having to make our bread, that is, because we hadn't done too well at the bread-making lessons we'd had back in Victoria. Anyway, when we arrived, the best bit of news we received was that fresh bread came in on the fortnightly aeroplane. That was a great relief, though it did get a little stale after a week or so. Another thing we were concerned about was having to milk the goats, but luckily a young Indigenous girl was willing to help us out there.

But we did everything else. We'd take it in turns: while one of us was the main nurse for the week, the other one would take care of all the cooking and the washing and so forth for ourselves, the patients and any visitors we had. Of course we always helped each other out. We were a real team. We did all the suturing, plastering and the cleaning of the wounds, plus everything that came in from when the flying doctor did his clinic. We used to deliver most of the babies. We did the dentistry. We did eyework. In fact, we didn't send very much away at all. Brenda also did some hairdressing. We did a bit of veterinary work as well. Sick goats or horses — people would call us on the flying doctor radio and we'd recommend treatment. One time Brookie's horse almost had its stomach laying out and we sewed it up. And would you believe it, sometime later, when the horse gave birth, Brookie named the foal Brenda.

For electricity we had one of those big generators that you had to crank to get it going. It was just like cranking a car where, once the engine kicked in, you had to get the handle off quick-smart. I remember the handle got stuck one day and it spun round and round till it flew off with a huge crash. Oh, we thought we'd broken the batteries and everything. But no; when we checked, all was still okay. Then for water, a big windmill used to pump our water out of an underground tank.

Of course we had to learn how to use the flying doctor's battery-operated Traeger radio. So we became radio operators as well. Our call sign was 8XR Birdsville. Our radio times were during what's called the 'galah sessions', which were open to everyone. So in the mornings we'd run a clinic and we'd talk to the flying doctor in Charleville. Then we'd call through to all the station properties and they'd let us know if there were any travellers on the road or if they had any problems. Twice daily we'd radio through the weather forecast to Charleville.

We also looked after many of the special visitors who came to Birdsville. At one time, the Governor of Queensland, Sir Henry Abel Smith, and Lady May stayed with us. That was when they came out to give the local policeman, Eric Sammon, his long-service medal. And when the volunteers from the AIM – Australian Inland Mission – came up to help build the two little Old Timers' Cottages, we cooked and looked after them, as we did all the flying doctor people. And when Michael Charlton and his film crew came out to do the Four Corners documentary *Water Is Life* we were interviewed about our work in Birdsville, and he stayed with us and we became quite good friends.

Really, everything that Eric Sammon didn't do, we did, including for the church. Back then the only time a priest was in town was when one of the AIM padres came through and they'd do the christenings and the weddings. And so Brenda and I took it upon ourselves to conduct the Sunday school. There were a couple of Catholic families in town whose children didn't come, but most of the others did, including the Aboriginal children. We'd end up with something like thirty kids, and we'd have them cutting things out and pasting things together. We'd tell them biblical stories. We'd sings songs. And in the evening Brenda and I would run the adults' church service. Then there was the occasional funeral service. Harold 'Pop' Richards' was one I recall. Pop was a very popular man who'd worked on a lot of stations around the area. He died on the side of the road. Just age, I think. I forget the exact story, but his family wanted him buried at Birdsville and they requested that Brenda and I conduct the service. So we were kept busy.

As for other special moments, I remember when one of the station owners rode in on his horse and tied it up at the front gate. As it turned out, he had an infection of some sort and when we told him that he required an injection in his bottom, well, didn't he panic? When we eventually got his pants down around his knees, Brenda held him forward and I injected him from behind. Then — *bang* — down he went on the floor. He'd fainted. This big cowboy, you know, as tough as old boots and he was afraid of injections.

Another great character of the outback was Tom Kruse, the Marree-to-Birdsville mailman. In the '50s they made a documentary about him, *Back of Beyond.* Anyhow, Tom came in one time complaining about his ankles, so we took a look. What had happened was, he never tied up his bootlaces, so when he did his welding, all the sparks used to drop down into his boots and so he had all these big ulcers around his ankles.

We never lacked for entertainment. We'd play billiards over at the hotel. We played tennis. Once a fortnight the flying doctor would bring a film out and we'd have a picture night. Problem being, the acoustics were so bad in the old tin shed that they had to place the projector in the doorway and they'd hang a sheet-like screen out on the road, and we'd sit there watching the film. People would bring a plate to share and afterwards we'd have cups of tea and lots of cake and sandwiches. That little tin shed was also the school. There was no air conditioning, and because the summer heat was so unbearable, they'd start school early in the morning and finish at lunchtime. Later on, when they built the new school and quarters for the teacher, they had a big opening. The Minister of Education came out from Brisbane and the children put on a special performance for him. Quite a few of the station owners flew their light aircraft in for the occasion and tied their planes up at the front of the hotel. For the opening parade, the kids grabbed all their gear and marched from the tin shed across the road to their new school.

But the most exciting time was Christmas. Everyone came into town for a big party. John Martin's, the store in Adelaide, would send up a whole swag of toys, and because Brenda and I knew the ages of all the children, we'd wrap them up, ready to be handed out by Father Christmas. Back then the Flying Doctor Service had a Dove aeroplane which had a little trapdoor in the tip, and the pilot would circle above the town and Father Christmas would wave to us all from out of the trapdoor. When the pilot landed the plane, he'd taxi down to the front of the hospital. We'd then follow Father Christmas inside and he'd hand out the toys to all the children. After that was done, everyone would walk up to the tin shed and we'd have a dance. And some of those men could really dance. Norm Portch, the publican, for instance, was a beautiful dancer. We never had a band or anything. The music came from a tape recorder or the wireless. We'd dance to anything. We'd even dance to the 'Pub with no Beer'.

Brenda and I had such a great time that when our two years were up, we were quite sad about leaving. We didn't really want to go, but that was the rule. Brenda's father, down in Victoria, had even taken her car off the blocks and he'd got it all ready for us. Then, when we got home, we were only there for about a week when we get this call: 'The sisters who replaced you in Birdsville didn't like the place so they caught the next plane out. Could you go back and hold the fort?'

'Oh, yes,' we said. 'We'd love to.'

We drove out to Birdsville this time. We came up through Windorah, calling into a few properties along the way. So we were back, and we were there for a further two years.

Of course, it wasn't all plain sailing and good times. Two major events stick out. The first was an explosion in a shed. That happened on a Sunday. Brenda and I had just finished our chores when three people came running down the pathway with their hands held in the air like you'd do to surrender. It turned out to be Eric Sammon, another fellow called Paddy and a third bloke whose name I've forgotten. And oh, they were in terrible shape. Their clothes were all burnt and hanging off them. Their skin was melting. Serum was running out of them. Paddy was the worst. He'd also lost an ear — it had gone — and Eric's hands were severely burnt.

They'd been working in a shed and they had a little can there — like a Sunshine Milk tin — that had petrol in it. Then one of them went to the door to have a cigarette. It was quite windy and when he went to throw his butt away, the wind blew it back into the shed and it landed in the can of petrol, and up went the shed. It was an extremely urgent situation. We tried to get on to the flying doctor in Charleville, but by the time they'd flown out, it would've been too late, especially for Paddy. I then got an idea. The TAA plane had arrived earlier that afternoon so we approached the pilot. 'We need a plane urgently. Is it possible to use yours to fly these people out?'

He said yes, so, while Brenda stayed behind to hold the fort, I flew to Charleville with the three patients, and thankfully we got them safely to the hospital.

Then later on Fred McKay rang us. 'Who gave you the authority to hire a plane? Are you aware of how much it might cost?'

We said, 'There was nothing else we could do. The flying doctor wouldn't have made it in time and three lives might've been lost.'

Fred thought about it for a second, then he said, 'Excellent. You're both brilliant. If a situation like that arises again, don't hesitate to do the same thing.'

And TAA ended up donating the flight. But poor Paddy stayed in Charleville the longest. Eric and the third bloke came back sooner. Though with Eric, we ended up having to dress his burns every day for the next six months. That's how bad his hands were.

But the most tragic thing to have happened in the four years Brenda and I were in Birdsville would've been the death of the Page family. That was in 1963, around Christmas time. Most of us had been up at a pre-Christmas party at Bedourie, and when we arrived back, we heard that a family had gone missing along the Birdsville Track. I guess the full story won't ever be known but there was the father, Ernie Page, and his wife, Emma, plus their two sons, Douglas, who was twelve, and the younger one, Gordon, who was about ten, and the family dog. I think it was a Labrador. The Pages had migrated from England and Ernie had found work as a mechanic at Marree. From what I can piece together, the Pages were heading north to catch up with their eldest son, Robert, who was working on Clifton Hills Station. They were in a Ford V8 sedan and towing a trailer that had all their gear and supplies in it. Robert was in his late teens, and unbeknown to his parents, he'd headed south, to Marree, to catch up with them for Christmas. Anyway, they coincidentally met somewhere near Cooper Creek and they joined up and headed for Birdsville.

The Birdsville Track was all dirt back in the '60s and there'd been quite a few survey vehicles crisscrossing their way all over the place. Anyhow, Ernie Page must've mistaken a turn and they ended up on a back road.

After we were notified, the search began. It turned into a large news item. Brenda and I were on the flying doctor radio, reporting the unfolding story to Charleville, who in turn sent it all over Australia. Initially Eric Sammon took two black trackers out with him. Then other people joined in. Jack Clancy, from Cameron Downs, had a light aircraft. I think he was the one who spotted the Pages' car. But it wasn't until Eric and the black trackers arrived that they found that Ernie Page and his wife and their two youngest children had died of thirst under a coolabah tree. They then found the bodies of the eldest boy, Robert, and the family dog not far away.

According to what I heard, the Pages had ran out of petrol and water. They'd then left a note on the steering wheel of the car and had walked off in the hopes of finding help. But there was error after error. Apparently, four miles back from where the car was found, they'd driven past some drums of petrol, and they'd ended up not too far from a dam filled with water. With Ernie having bush experience at Maree and with Robert having worked on a property in the area, you would think they surely would've known that you always stay with your vehicle, wouldn't you? But they didn't. And so they ended up dying of thirst two days after they'd left their car. Brenda and I didn't officiate with that funeral. I think Eric and a few of the others took a tractor out and buried them near where they were found, and Eric held a bit of a service.

As for other memories, even these days, there's things that pop into mind. But those people from Birdsville will always be part of me. There was old Brookie. He was an icon out there, as were the Mortons from Pandi Pandi Station. And of course, there was Brookie's son, young David. David's just about everything out in Birdsville these days. He and his wife, Nell, really kicked the place on. There was Eric Sammon and his wife, Joan, and there were the publicans: first the Gaffneys, then there was Norm Portch and his wife, Elva. We also got to know some wonderful Aboriginal people, and of course there was Tim O'Leary, our favourite flying doctor.

I've got a lovely story about Tim. One time the neighbours gave us a budgerigar. Its proper name was 'Pia Pia Cutchertella', which, in the language, meant something like little bird budgerigar. We just called it Pia Pia. We'd have it in a cage, on a bench, and we'd let it out during the day and it'd wander around the hospital and perch itself on any free shoulder it could find. I've even got a photo of Brenda cutting someone's hair with Pia Pia sitting on her shoulder, and when we'd have our sing-songs, it'd come and sit on my shoulder. It just loved a good sing-song.

It was quite intelligent as well. Would you believe it ended up with a vocabulary of nearly forty-eight words? Remember that old slogan 'Aspro will ease it'? We even taught it to say that. In fact, Pia Pia became so well known that both the *Women's Weekly* and *New Idea* wanted to interview it. It got quite out of hand really.

But the most hilarious thing was: Doctor Tim O'Leary was marvellous — one of a kind — so we tried to teach Pia Pia to say, 'Tim's unique'.

The only trouble was that it came out as, 'Tim's a freak'.

So every time Tim flew in to run a medical clinic, Pia Pia would greet him with 'Tim's a freak,' to which Tim would reply, 'I'll kill that bloody bird one of these days.'

Bernadette's Story
Gotta Get Out

My name's Bernadette Greensill. I'm the eldest of five and my mother died when I was very young. Then after my father remarried, things weren't too comfortable at home and so I went to live with my grandmother and uncle in Annerley, a suburb of Brisbane. Over a period of time my siblings also came to live with us and our uncle virtually became the breadwinner for all of us. But I never really knew what I wanted to be and so, after I'd finished my schooling, I got an office job. Then one day I was sitting there and the thought struck me: I don't want to do this for the rest of my life.

But what? So when a friend told me that she was going to study nursing, I said, 'Well, I may as well come with you.'

Grandma was quite old fashioned in many ways. When I told her I was going into nursing, she was horrified. 'Oh,' she said, 'nurses are just jerry carriers,' meaning they only carried around pans for people to urinate in. But I'd made my mind up, so my friend and I went off to Mater Misericordiae Hospital, at Woolloongabba, to do our registered nurse's — RN's — training. And that was nearly sixty years ago.

Training was strict. We lived at the hospital and we worked long, hard hours with very little social life. During our first years we had to be in by 10 p.m., apart from one night a week, and by Fourth Year we could stay out after ten, twice a week. The nuns had their different personalities, but they were good teachers, which is what gave the Mater such a great reputation. I remember one time I was looking for a job and the people said,

'Sorry, there's no vacancies.' Then, as I was walking out the door, one of them asked, 'Where were you trained?'

'The Mater,' I replied.

'Oh,' she said, 'come and sit down.'

After we'd finished our RN's training, five of us Mater girls went down to the Royal Prince Alfred Hospital in Sydney to do midwifery, and oh it was cold. We rented a little house at Stanmore and that summer in Sydney, I can only recall three warm days. I virtually lived, and slept, in my overcoat, beanie and gloves. To make matters worse the pay was so poor that we were always broke. Fortunately the local butcher was in love with me, so I'd be sent off to get the meat. 'Have you got some sausages please?', I'd ask, or 'Have you got some chops?' I never mentioned a quantity. He'd just wrap some up. 'Here yer go,' he'd say. Then the fruiterer was in love with one of the other girls so she'd be sent to get our fruit and veggies. It worked well and after we'd finished our 'mid', we shouted the butcher, the fruiterer and everybody else who'd helped us throughout the year out to the pub.

A nursing friend and I then went to Thursday Island — TI as it's known. We were just following the sun, really. I'd had enough of the Sydney weather and we'd spoken to some girls who'd had a good time up there. With smallpox and TB — tuberculosis — being rampant, we were immunised against those, but no sooner had we arrived than my friend got cowpox and had to return home.

They had a lovely hospital on TI, built right out over the sea. The local ladies would sit on the back stairs and toss in a fishing line. The maternity unit had twenty beds and they were always full. We serviced Weipa, the Torres Strait Islands and Bamaga. If any of the women were premie — premature — or had complications, the RFDS would fly them in. Most were Islanders. The few Aborigines were mainly Weipa people. We had a medical superintendent, two other doctors and about twenty nurses and a small operating theatre that was only used once a week. Other than maternity, I'd work in the general wards. If there was a gastro epidemic in the kids' ward, and we couldn't keep up with the washing, we'd put newspaper on the beds, which would not be acceptable these days. But you just had to make do. There was no morgue so if someone died they were usually buried pretty quick. If they couldn't be buried straight away, we'd put them on a table and fill jam tins with water and place them under the table legs so that the ants couldn't crawl up and get to the body.

The first night I arrived, I met my husband-to-be, Kevin. He had an administrative job in the Department of Aboriginal and Islander Affairs. He'd already been there twelve months. He tells everyone that it was love at first sight, which is absolute crap because he was too drunk to remember. But TI was a very social place. We were always off to parties, and sometimes, when we were off duty, an old guy used to take us in his boat over to nearby Prince of Wales Island where we'd camp and fish, and he'd cook us these beautiful, big curries.

Yes, so Kevin and I were married on TI. He remembers that. Then after two years, he got a promotion to Palm Island, which is off the North Queensland coast from Townsville. I was one of two midwives on the island. In fact, I delivered my first-ever set of twins on Palm. But I did not like the place, not one iota. When we first arrived at Townsville Airport to fly over to Palm, there was a white bloke who was returning to the island after a wild weekend, and oh my God, he stank like a bottle of stale wine. Then when we got into this little old four-seater aeroplane and they handed me a life jacket and said, 'Here, you might need this,' I nearly died. Anyhow, I'm one of those who picks up on a place and the moment we arrived at Palm Airport, I could feel the aggression. So much so that I didn't even want to get out of the plane. Kevin's pulling at me: 'Come on, you've gotta get out,' and I'm like, 'No, no, I don't like it here.'

Palm was a pretty dysfunctional community. Back in the early 1900s, when the original Hull River Mission had been flattened by a cyclone, the mission was transferred over to Palm. After that Palm sort of became the place for any of the Aborigines who'd played up throughout Queensland. One of the beaches was inaccessible, except by sea, so that's where the murderers were sent to live out their days in humpies. Just off Palm was Fantome Island, which had a leprosarium run by Catholic nuns. It was only for Aboriginal and Islander people and they'd occasionally come over to be tested to see if their leprosy was still active. Most of the results were negative, but it was such an idyllic life over on Fantome Island that they didn't want to move anywhere else.

Thursday and Palm islands were worlds apart. Whereas TI had been reasonably peaceful, on Palm, the grog had taken over so there was always brawls and fights. It was awful; just awful. Now I just want to make the point here that I'm not talking about everyone on the island because I'm not, but some of them didn't even look after their kids properly. There were always sick and malnourished children in the hospital. I also worked in the baby clinic and we'd do house visits. One day, one of the mothers wasn't home so I went inside and there's these two little kids, with this dirty black saucepan with dried-up porridge in it, and they're scraping the porridge out of the saucepan and eating it.

Down the road there was a baby in a bassinet with flies crawling all over her, and all over the floor were tins full of worms and excrement. And that's got nothing to do with your being black, white or brindle. I don't care what anyone says: you make choices in life and if you've got a rotten life, for God's sake, why on this earth would you want to pass that rotten life on to your kids? And we were forever chasing people. It was just ... I didn't like it. Kevin even found it tough. He wasn't out in the village like I was but his days were spent arguing about child payments and so forth.

We were there for three years and after we left, I told Kevin that if he ever went back to Palm, I'd leave him. True. There would not even be a discussion about it. But one bright spot was that our first baby, Bridgette, was born while we were there. I didn't work full time then. I just relieved the matron, Ethel Wharton. Ethel was marvellous. We didn't have a resident doctor but Ethel could handle everything. No one got out of line with Ethel, ever.

Three Tribes

From Palm Island, Kevin got an appointment to Kowanyama Community, which is on the Gulf of Carpentaria side of Cape York Peninsula. As I walked off the plane I was greeted by a nurse. 'I haven't had a day off in six weeks,' she said. 'I'm nearly out of my head; can you please help out?' So I did. Bridgette was running around by then so we got an Aboriginal woman, May Smiler, to come and mind her while I was working. May was great. She never had to do housework or anything, just look after Bridgette. At that stage I was pregnant with Kate. Then, when May couldn't come any more, another Aboriginal woman called Francis looked after Bridgette and baby Kate.

Gambling was highly illegal at Kowanyama and part of Kevin's job was Magistrate for Local Gambling. One day forty people were caught gambling, and as the police filed them through the office, Kevin noticed Francis and our two little girls with them. 'Francis,' he said, 'what were you doing gambling with our girls?'

'I wasn't gamblin', Mister Kevin,' she said. 'I was goin' round to see Missus at the hospital 'n I just stopped in to have a look 'n the police came.' I mean, like heck she wasn't. She'd taken our girls out gambling all right. Then she said, ''N if you fine me, you know who'll be payin' the fine. You will, Mister Kevin, 'cause I got no money.' And she was right. Kevin ended up having to pay her fine.

About a thousand people lived in Kowanyama. Anything the hospital couldn't handle, we'd call in the RFDS or Aerial Ambulance. With a car being useless in the wet season, if someone needed to be evacuated, we'd put a mattress on a trailer and hook the trailer up to an old tractor and take them out to the airport like that. But on the whole, during that first year, the Aboriginal people looked after themselves and were clean. Mind you, at times it was a different story with some of the doctors, but I won't go into that. While I was there we got Meals on Wheels going for the oldies. We also started a program where the little kids were given a free lunch, along with vitamin supplements. And still they had runny noses, coughs, colds and sores and we were forever up at the school doing their nits. There was also the usual gastro epidemics and things like that. Tim O'Leary, the RFDS medical super, showed us a fabulous technique to rehydrate babies. He said, 'Pop the needle in two fingers below the umbilical, and depending on the baby's weight, run in a bit of fluid and the baby will rehydrate quickly.' And it worked.

The houses in Kowanyama were quite new. The state government had built them on the old Mitchell River Mission site after a cyclone had flattened the Mitchell River, the Edward River and the Lockhart River missions. In the early days the teachers who came up there to do their bit for the 'poor black people' were from Anglican schools down south, so a lot of the Aborigines had copybook handwriting and they excelled at mathematics. One of those teachers had spent years doing the Aborigines' family trees, which made things much easier when it came to dealing with internal community issues. Kevin's always said that from the day he started working with Aboriginal people, it was always, 'If you're my brother you'll get looked after. But if you're just a neighbour, you can starve.' Everything's family. Particularly in places like Kowanyama where the Edward River, the Mitchell River and the Lockhart River tribes had been lumped in together. They'd never really got along in the first place, and so when it came to things like the community council having to change the makeup of the police force, you could be guaranteed that if the new police force was made up of one particular tribe, their relations never got arrested while all the others did.

We had a very good life at Kowanyama and our kids loved it. Bridgette's a great talker. Each day she'd get a packet of biscuits and some apples and sit outside the store with the old ladies and the kids and they'd all share their food. The thing was, she then wouldn't eat her tea. I once put a sign up in the shop: *Don't feed Bridgette because she's not eating her meals,* and that still didn't stop her. To her, it was a daily ritual. Anyway, one Christmas, Bridgette and I went over to Cairns to do our shopping. We were in this shopping centre, Bridgette's in her stroller, and she's, 'Yap, yap, yap, I want biscuits. I want apples.'

So I bought her a packet of chips. 'Here,' I said, 'eat these.'

Next thing, I looked down and the stroller's empty. She'd disappeared and I couldn't find her anywhere. I was in a terrible state. So I rushed outside, to head up to the police station, and there she was, sitting in the gutter, as content as could be, eating her chips; because that's what you do. That's the ritual. You don't eat your snacks inside. She would've been two. Oh God I nearly died.

I also became a great barra — barramundi — fisherman. Whenever I needed to clear my head, I'd drive down to the juncture of the Alice and Mitchell rivers. I'd put Kate in a bouncer under a quinine tree. Bridgette would walk up and down the bank, trying to fall in, and I'd cast my lure in amongst the mangroves. Sometimes a few of the old ladies would come with us and they'd sit there, singing the fish, or they'd bring all their babies along and we'd all go for a swim. There we'd be, bobbing around in our tyre tubes, having a great time. And oh the mud crabs: when the mud crabs were on, everyone would grab their empty flour drums and we'd go down to the South Mitchell and we'd come home with stacks of mud crabs. And they were beautiful.

Another time, I was down there with the kids and we saw two huge crocs having a big roll, fighting each other. It'd never dawned upon me that the place was full of crocs, and so after that, I made sure someone was always with us.

Something else was the snakes. Just the thought of them makes me feel sick. One day Bridgette was playing outside. Next thing I hear, 'Missus, Missus, snake, snake.' And there's this big king brown out in the yard with Bridgette. Anyhow, that was it. I grabbed a hoe and I put an end to it. I know you're not supposed to, but, during our time there, I dispatched quite a few snakes — 'culling', I called it. While we're on about culling, there were lots of mangy dogs about the place. A man known as Old Whitey would sort them out. You'd hear him at night, sitting on his verandah with his gun, *bang, bang, bang*. And if they got too far out of hand, to attract the stray dogs, he'd put some old meat in a hessian bag and he'd drag it around behind his car and do a little bit of culling along the way.

For the first year, Kowanyama was alcohol free and on the weekends everybody would go out hunting and fishing. But from the day the beer arrived, they didn't go anywhere. They just had to be there to get their beer. The decision had been made along the lines of, 'If the white people are allowed to drink, so should we.' Three hundred people turned up the night they brought in the first load of grog, and they drank eighty cartons of beer. And when the three separate tribes got absolutely off their faces, they just went crazy. The police were bringing us in fingers that'd been bitten off, lips that'd been chewed out; the works. Our hospital manager took a look at one fella who'd stumbled in and said, 'Hey, you can't bring a spear into the hospital,' and when the fella turned around, there was a spear sticking out of his bum.

After the grog arrived, the community started to disintegrate. And with all the stabbings and the shootings, the fights and the trauma, I'd forever be out in the middle of the night, trying to stitch someone up, or I'd be called out at some ungodly hour to deliver a baby in a swag or the police forensics would turn up to investigate a rape or a murder. We also had quite a few bad accidents. One fella had his spine fractured when his stepdaughter whacked him over the head with a radio. Then there were the associated mental health issues. And it wasn't only the men. With a lot of the old ladies, first you'd hear the angry voices, then off would come their dresses and it'd be on. So there was a drama every day, and after a while, a drama every day becomes normal, so you just get on with it.

The Sisters

After three years in Kowanyama, Kevin got a posting to Yarrabah, in Far North Queensland, just outside of Cairns. With Kowanyama being as flat as a table and Yarrabah almost vertical, when we were driving up the mountain to the community, I kept saying to Kevin, 'I'm sick. You're going too fast. Stop.'

But it didn't take long to settle in. We had a nice new house that was perched on the side of a hill, and with having the two girls, I thought, That's it, I'm retiring. I'm never going to work again. But of course, I then found out that they were short-staffed at the clinic, didn't I? So before I knew it I was down there.

Cairns Base Hospital ran Yarrabah. We had two nurses, and a doctor would come over from Gordonvale once a week. It was an old hospital, with just a few beds. We only kept those for the ones who'd soon be back on their feet. The more serious ones were put in an ambulance and sent to Cairns. As well as the usual runny noses and ears, a lot of kids had poor nutrition. With the adults, we'd get the usual call-outs of a night due to the fights. Again, most of it was grog-fuelled. On a Saturday it was unbelievable. They'd set up a bank of six kegs, they'd hit all the taps and they wouldn't turn them off during the four-hour session and they got absolutely rotten.

I had two babies during the years we lived there: Martin and Simon. I never told Cairns Hospital I was pregnant. I just kept ringing up the matron and saying, 'You've got to send someone. I need some help.' But Cairns was short-staffed as well, so after each day's work, I'd drag myself back up the hill, get tea for everyone, then go to bed. I worked right up until a week before I had Simon. By then I could hardly raise a trot, and so during the day, an Aboriginal girl came to look after the kids. And we were always nearby. Kevin and I didn't go to work till 8 a.m., then we were home for lunch and again by five.

By the end I could virtually suture with my eyes closed. I remember one morning, just as we were going to take the kids to the Cairns Show, I popped into the clinic and there's this bloke, holding his ear in his hands.

'What happened?' I asked.

'Someone's tried to cut me ear off with an axe.'

Oh God. So anyway I sewed his ear back onto the side of his head and off he went, and off we went to the Cairns Show.

So there was always something happening. In fact, there was hardly any peace and quiet, and seeing how we lived on the side of the hill, the people-noise would drift up to our house.

Yarrabah was also where we were first introduced to Aboriginal transexuality. Everybody called them 'the sisters'. About six lived in one of the back houses. They never caused any trouble and they weren't ostracised by the community. Normally they wore men's clothes but on Friday afternoons you'd see them in the bar, dressed to the nines, in their beautiful full-length dresses and gloves. One of the guys was known as the African Queen. We called him Lilly. He was a very handsome-looking Islander boy who wanted to be a nurse. 'Please, please Missus,' he'd beg, but he only wanted the job if he could wear a female nurse's uniform. 'No, Lilly,' I'd reply. 'It doesn't work like that.'

Apart from the noise, Yarrabah was a good place to live. Being so close to Cairns, we could take our kids swimming and shopping. Then Kevin got a promotion to Brisbane. Initially we thought it'd be a good move, but it wasn't. In all of the places we'd lived, everything had been family oriented, so we always did everything together; whereas in Brisbane it was, 'Come for dinner, but don't bring the kids. You'll have to get a babysitter.' And that wasn't our style, so we couldn't cope. In fact, we didn't even realise that our nine-year-old son didn't know how to cross a busy intersection until we got to Brisbane.

Under Siege

We'd soon had enough of Brisbane, and so had our kids. So when the Aboriginal housing manager's job and the director of nursing's job simultaneously came up in Normanton, Kevin applied for the manager's job and I went for the director's job, and we both got them. It was funny actually; when Kevin told the staff officer in Brisbane that he wanted to go back up into the Gulf of Carpentaria, he was asked if he needed psychological help.

'Definitely not,' he said. 'In fact, we can't get back there quick enough.'

Normanton suited us to the ground. It was a very family oriented and social place. When we went to the pub on Friday nights, the parents would throw a rug down on the floor for all the kids to play on. But the director of nursing's job was a big one. When we first arrived, they still had the old hospital. We had a doctor, but because they'd change every couple of months, there was no continuity. I was responsible for the healthcare of all the people throughout the area. Then there was my hard-working staff, and it was thanks to them that we initiated a number of programs. We started a women's clinic, including an antenatal program. We got our immunisations up to around ninety-eight per cent. We did a lot of community health stuff like sitting outside shops and testing blood pressures and blood sugars. We ran day care for the oldies, and even though it took me six years, we eventually got the money for Meals on Wheels.

We also worked closely with an organisation called Aboriginal Health who serviced communities throughout the Gulf. I always maintain that I got a lot of help there because Kevin was overseeing both the housing and work-for-the-dole programs in those communities and he was well respected amongst the people. Seeing that I was his wife, they also had respect for me. When they had the big riots over in Doomadgee and the hospital staff walked out, the director-general specifically asked me if I'd go over there and help work things out, which I did. Later on I heard that the Aboriginal Council had told him that I was the only nurse they'd work with. But whenever I went into any of these communities, I always tried to build a strong, professional, trusting relationship with the people. And once you have their trust, they'll open up to you and tell you their secrets. That's how I also gained a good reputation with both Family Services and the police: because the Aboriginal people knew, if they ever rang me about something like child abuse, I'd do my utmost to follow it through to an outcome. There were no worries. No one dobbed me in. No one threatened me.

I've been a trained nurse for almost sixty years now and I've never once gone to work thinking, I don't want to do this. In fact, I've always said how it's been a privilege to be a nurse in areas where there were no counsellors, no psychologists, nothing — just me. Mind you, my family always came first. When I walk back through that door after work, I'm Mum. Yes, I may have missed a few birthdays and at one stage Kevin was threatening to move our kitchen table down to the airport because I was spending more time down there with patients, waiting for the RFDS to arrive, than I was at home. But I'm an organised person. When I'd leave for work, the washing was on the line. Dinner was ready to go in the pressure cooker. Sunday nights I'd iron the kids' school uniforms. So yes, most of my memories from Normanton are good ones, with great friendships. Nola Gallagher was a great friend and support, and her mother was virtually a grandma to my kids. Elsie Royce was her name. She was a lovely lady, and she was the greatest travelling companion you could ever wish for. Elsie always had a port packed and ready to go. I'd say, 'I've got to go to Mount Isa; want'a come for a run?' And into the car she'd get.

But there were a lot of car accidents — mainly young men in rollovers — and in just about every case where someone died, they didn't have a seatbelt on. I was on my way home one time and I called in at the shop. Outside was this brand-new, bright-pink car, with three people in it. One was the dolly-bird wife of a local cattle station owner, then there was a station employee plus a young girl. Anyway, they drove off and I got served. Then just after I got home, the phone rang: 'There's been an accident down the road a bit.'

Anyhow, we drove out in the ambulance, and here's this girl — she's as dead as a doe. Fifteen years old. She was in the front seat with no seatbelt on. The other bloke was all right. He was in the back and he had a seatbelt on, and the dolly-bird wife, I think she survived. It turned out that the girl was the daughter of a good mate of the station boss. She'd just arrived on school holidays from interstate and was off to spend some time with this family. The thing was, the owner had told the other guy that under no circumstances was his dolly-bird wife allowed to drive the car. But for whatever reason, she was. Apparently she went to fiddle with the radio and she rolled it.

But even though we got called out to a lot of unpleasant jobs, we never let a chance pass us by. See, I'm a terrible scone cook, just terrible. This one time there'd been a car accident a couple of hundred k's out the other side of Banrook Station. I don't know how it happened but one person was severely injured and the others were less so and were mainly disorientated and in shock. After I convinced them that they weren't going to die, we put them on intravenous drips, out in the bloody dust, and we got them rehydrated and settled down. Then, with having the severely injured person, I thought, Well it's silly to drive this person all the way back to Normanton. We may as well go back to Banrook, get in touch with the RFDS and meet the plane down at the station's airstrip. So that's what we did. We headed back to Banrook with everyone crammed in the ambulance.

It'd been a long hot day, and after we got there and I'd called the RFDS, I decided to get a drink and something to eat. The station people had had their lunch and there were some scones left over. Just beautiful they were. I asked the cook, 'So what's the recipe?' When we couldn't find any paper to write the recipe on, I went out to the ambulance and said to my offsider, 'You go in now. The cook's got some great scones. She's going to give us the recipe, but I need a bit of paper.' So we fossicked around and we ended up tearing the label off one of the IV flasks to write the recipe down on. In fact, I've still got it here, somewhere. So like I said, even in times of trauma, we never let a chance pass us by.

But gee we had some characters. Take Jacko Wall. There was never a dull moment when he was around. Jacko was a nurse's aide. He'd lived in Normanton for years. He knew everyone and everyone knew him. Anyhow, we used to have a little milk room at the hospital, and whenever a new nurse arrived, Jacko would coax her into the milk room, let go a fart, then run outside and close the door on her.

One of our new nurses, Bev, was a recipient of Jacko's milk room prank. That was when Father John, the Anglican priest, used to come up to the hospital. Father John was a very prim and proper sort of man; really nice. He was single. Bev had no sooner gone into the little milk room than Jacko appeared. He was only there for a moment and didn't say anything and when he left, he pulled the door shut. That's when Bev smelt the fart. Then just as she was about to yank open the door, she shouted out to Jacko, 'You rotten bloody bugger!' When the door flung open there she was standing face-to-face with a rather stunned Father John.

When Jacko first started up at the hospital, he said to me, 'I want to be a nurse.'

I said, 'Look, Jacko, I can put you on as a nurse's aide but you'll need to do some training first.'

'Okay.'

This was during a time when we had a few cases of hepatitis and so we taught him the basics, like how to do urine tests, and I enforced upon him the need for effective infection control and told him that he must always wear gloves. One morning we're having morning tea and in comes Jacko. Back then we used baby-food jars to collect the urine, and Jacko's got this full baby-food jar and he's stirring it up with a stick. I said, 'Get outta here, Jacko. I've told you all about health and hygiene.'

He said, 'What's wrong, lovey?' Then he takes the stick out of the jar and he gives it a big lick.

'Jacko!' we all shouted.

It turned out that he'd added Vegemite into a jar of water.

And he was so good with the old people. Queenie had had a stroke. She was in hospital for about fifteen years before she died and Jacko always made sure she'd had a rinse put through her hair and that her fingernails were done, and he'd do her eyebrows and put on her lippy. And oh, she just loved it.

And he'd say to me, 'I'm sick of walking up and down this corridor. Can I use rollerskates?'

'No, Jacko,' I'd say, 'you cannot use rollerskates; not at all.'

Then one day there comes this screeching noise from down the outpatients. If you can imagine, the corridor was like a big L-shape, and as the screeching got louder, so did the laughter from the patients. We're like, What the hell's going on? Next thing Jacko comes gliding by on rollerskates, with this flowing purple wig on, and he's posing like a ballerina. Oh, he could make even the most sour person smile and feel good about themselves. I mean, where would we be without characters like that in our lives?

Oh, and just a last one about Jacko. I think this was mentioned in your *Outback Towns and Pubs* book. This particular night Bev was rostered on with Jacko. And mind you, there was no beating about the bush with Jacko. Jacko called a spade a spade. Around midnight they heard a call at the front door. When they got there they found a drunken Aboriginal woman, doubled up, apparently in severe pain. As it turned out, Jacko knew her from somewhere. Like I said, Jacko knew everyone. So they helped her into the hospital and up onto an examination table. All the while she's moaning and groaning and going on about how her and her drunken de facto had had this big blue. 'He's gonna get me, good 'n proper,' she's slurring. 'Says he's gonna kill me.'

After doing the usual vital signs and observations, it was still hard to assess the woman's problem, so Bev decided to call the doctor. Mind you, the poor fellow was on call twenty-four hours a day, seven days of the week. If he was lucky he might've got five days off a month, but that's only if a relief doctor could be found and relief doctors were as scarce as hen's teeth. Anyhow, he arrived, tired and strung out. After conducting an initial examination, he decided a more thorough investigation was necessary, which in this case meant giving her a rectal examination. So he said to the woman, 'Excuse me, would you mind turning over on your side so I can examine you more thoroughly?'

Not having a clue as to what he was on about, the woman replied with a drunken, 'Ay?'

'Well,' said the doctor, 'I need you to turn over on your side, please, because I'd like to do a PR examination.'

'A bloody what?'

The doctor then tried to make it clearer. He said, 'Look, I'm afraid I'll have to do a rectal examination to more closely assess your condition.'

The woman was still confused, so she turned to Jacko. 'Hey, Jacko,' she slurred, 'what's this bastard talkin' about?'

As quick as a flash, Jacko replied, 'Don't worry, lovey, he just wants ter stick his finger up yer arse.'

Well, what a miraculous recovery. 'Fuck that,' the woman shouted and she was off that table and down the corridor she ran, screaming how she'd be better off dealing with her de facto's threat of killing her than having some stranger stick his finger up her behind. And that was Jacko. As I said, he called a spade a spade.

As for other memories: we had an old girl there called Granny. Granny was a solitary soul, so for company we bought her a blue budgie. And she just loved that budgie. Granny would sit there with the bird perched on her shoulder, and talk to it, and it'd chirp back at her. Great company they were for each other. The best of friends. The thing was, we had a few resident snakes around the hospital and if Granny's blue budgie wasn't put away in its cage at night, one of these snakes would invariably find its way in through a hole somewhere in the wall and eat it. The problem was, once the snake had swallowed the budgie, it'd be so bloated that it couldn't get back out through the hole. So it'd be stuck in the hospital and I'd have to get someone in to remove it. Now, to save Granny the emotional trauma of losing her best friend, each time a snake had eaten her blue budgie, we'd end up having to race around town to find a like replacement. Then, before Granny noticed that her budgie had gone, we'd put the new one in the cage. Of course it'd take this new budgie a while to settle into its new surroundings, wouldn't it? So it'd just sit there and Granny would say, 'Oh, he's just not himself today. He's not talking.'

And we'd be going, 'It's all right Granny. Don't worry. He'll be fine. He's just having an off day, that's all.'

Another great character was my wardsman, Jack O'Brien. At one time, out of the fourteen beds we had, seven were taken up by mostly Aboriginal oldies. There were various reasons for that, but most of them were malnourished because their families would cash in their pension cheques and spend it on themselves and the oldies would get neglected. Anyhow, we needed to free up some of the beds, so I thought, Let's start day care.

So we started day care three days a week and Jack was just wonderful with them. He'd drive around town and he'd pick them up and he'd bring them to the hospital, where they'd have a shower and a morning tea before they'd have a sing-song or just sit around and talk. After they'd had lunch, they'd have a lie-down and a sleep and later that afternoon, after a cuppa, Jack would take them all home again. And they just loved it. Then sometimes one of the butchers would donate some snags and Jack would take everyone down to the river for a barbecue.

But perhaps the most frightening event that occurred while I was there was this: one night the police rang. 'There's been a shooting out at Inverleigh Station. Can you get the ambulance and the doctor and come out quick?' So I said, 'Righto,' and they told me to meet them about thirty k's out of town, at the Little Bino River crossing.

We're just getting ready and the police ring again. 'No, don't come. We're going to bring in any of the injured.'

'Okay,' I say, 'we'll meet you up at the hospital.'

Then I get another call: 'No, you'd better come.'

So off we go. There's a doctor, Jacko Wall, myself, and Tommy Wall's driving the big old Ford ambulance. Jacko and Tommy were brothers. We get out to the Little Bino. As we drive up, there's a policeman kneeling down with a gun, and he's waving to us. When we go to cross the causeway, he calls out to us, 'Back up! They're over the other side. They've got guns!'

Next comes all this shooting. *Bang. Bang. Bang.* So now we're trying to get down and hide ourselves inside the ambulance. Jacko and the doctor were in the back, squashed down between the two stretchers. I'm in the front, wedged under the dashboard. Tommy Wall's at the wheel of the ambulance. He hasn't moved. Then there's more shooting. *Bang. Bang. Bang.* And the copper calls out, 'Quick! Back up thirty metres!'

By now I've hit the panic button. I said to Tommy, very unladylike, 'Bugger the thirty metres, Tommy, back the fuckin' thing up thirty k's. We're headin' back to town.' And Tommy Wall, as calm as anything, he just put that big old ambulance in reverse. He backed it up thirty metres, then he turned it around and he drove us back to the hospital.

As it turned out, two Murries — Aboriginals — had escaped from jail in the Kimberley region of Western Australia. They'd stolen a car and driven all the way over to the Gulf of Carpentaria and they'd somehow ended up at Inverleigh Station. I'm not sure if they were looking for food or what, but first they went into the men's quarters. Old Seto was there. Seto was from Winton. He was a nice bloke and a good worker, but he was a bit slow, if you get what I mean. So they grabbed Seto and they tied him up to his bed.

When they didn't find what they were looking for there, they then went over to the main house where John Woodburn was. John was caretaker-in-residence for the wet season. Most times, when station people go on holidays, they get somebody in to caretake. That's why he was over there by himself. Anyhow, John was sitting up in bed, nice and quiet, reading a book, when these two Murries walked into his bedroom. John hadn't heard a sound. In fact, the station dogs hadn't even barked. They found out later that the Murries had killed the dogs when they'd first entered the property. Anyhow, the Murries had a rifle and they took a couple of shots at John. One hit him in the neck and the other grazed his cheek and took off one of his fingers. They must've thought they'd killed John, so after they'd collected some supplies, they stole three rifles, dumped their vehicle and took off. When John was sure that the Murries had left, he managed to call the police. That's how we came into the picture, at the Little Bino crossing.

Anyway, the police eventually brought John into us. By now the hospital was crawling with coppers. They must've flown up from Mount Isa, and they were armed to the teeth. They had guns in their holsters, guns in their socks, guns down their boots. Guns everywhere. So we x-rayed John and patched him up the best we could and I called the RFDS to come and get him. In fact, he was very lucky because the bullet in his neck had lodged right next to his spine. I then rang old Seto. He'd somehow untied himself but he was terrified. I said, 'They've gone, Seto. The police are coming out there to get you.' Which they did. By then the RFDS had arrived and they'd flown off with John. So that was that.

It's now about 4 o'clock in the morning and I'm driving home. Nobody knew where these Murries had got to, but they were out there somewhere and I'm scared to my wits. So much so that the two old blokes from next door came over with their rifles and stayed in our house.

A big search was on, and a few days later, with the Murries still being at large, the army was called in. They even got planes and helicopters to join in. But people were too scared to go anywhere. It was like the whole town was under siege. With it being the end of the wet season, there was still a lot of water lying around in the table drains, and so when these Murries heard someone coming, they'd get down in the water and hide there till they'd gone. Even a couple of weeks after the shooting out at Inverleigh, there was still no word nor sighting. Then one day the police were flying around and they saw some wild pigs down one end of a waterhole. Just for fun they decided to take a few pot-shots at the pigs. These two Murries must've thought that the police were shooting at them because they ran out of a nearby water drain and gave themselves up.

So that was that, and for a long time after, if I watched something on TV where guns were fired, it all came back and I had to get up and walk away.

But I tell you, Tommy Wall won me that night. He should've ended up with some sort of bravery medal. He was as calm as anything and there was me, wedged down under the dashboard of the ambulance, calling out to him, 'Bugger the thirty metres, Tommy, back the fuckin' thing up thirty k's. We're headin' back to town.'

Bev's Story
I Lied

I was born when Mum and Dad were at Laura, in Far North Queensland. Dad was a police constable there. From Laura they went out to Pentland, in north-western Queensland. I have an older sister and a younger brother, and when I was about five we moved over to Burketown on the Gulf of Carpentaria. To get there, we first had to catch a train from Pentland to Cloncurry. From Cloncurry we caught another train up to a little place at the end of the line called Dobbin. We then drove the last couple of hundred k's along a dirt track, in one of those old Bedford trucks. Mum and my little brother sat in front with the driver while Dad and us two girls made a hollow up on top of the wagon, in the middle of our goods and chattels, where we could lie down as we bumped and rattled along. That final leg of the trip took three days and two nights. We also had a couple of Aboriginal people travelling with us. I'm not sure now whether they were just getting a lift up to Burketown or if they were part of the police.

I just loved Burketown. We had so much freedom and fun. From there I went to a boarding high school in Charters Towers. When I got to Grade 10, I wanted to leave school. By then Mum and Dad were on Thursday Island. I knew Mum would've been against it. But I also knew how she'd always wanted to be a nurse, so when she asked what I'd do if I left school, I lied and said, 'I want to become a nurse.'

The moment I said that, her face softened. 'Well, okay then,' she said.

The thing was, I'd never been in a hospital and so I had no idea what a nurse did. I started my training in Ayr, which is a small town about fifty miles south of Townsville. But I was too young. I was only sixteen and I got so homesick that I ended up going back to Thursday Island and working in a shop. Then, when I was eighteen, I started my registered nursing course in Townsville. And I just loved it, and I've loved it ever since.

But I was never happy in the city. So after the first year, I transferred back to Ayr, where I completed my training. Ayr was where I first become aware of dementia. Before then I didn't even know such a thing existed. In those days, dementia patients were put in hospitals to just walk around aimlessly. I remember one young woman who was a patient in the hospital; everyone was going, 'She's just being silly. She doesn't want to be at home with her husband and kids, that's all.' And I used to think, Hey, you're being a bit tough there. Another dementia patient had been a classically trained pianist. When I took her over to the nurses' quarters and sat her down at the piano, she just cried and cried. It was so sad. In her haze, I think she remembered how to play, but she couldn't do anything about it.

Ayr was also where I saw my first baby being born. They must've been short-staffed on this day because they said, 'Send someone over to help.' By then I was a second-year nurse so I guess they thought I'd be okay. Now, we must've learnt anatomy and physiology in our training. But the reality of it mustn't have sunk in, because when I saw what was going on, God, I nearly died. And the doctor must've seen how absolutely useless I was going to be, too. 'Get her out of here,' he said.

But we had such great camaraderie in Ayr. We all pitched in to help each other. We became like sisters and later on we were bridesmaids at each other's weddings. And I quite liked the discipline. If you were eating at the table and a registered nurse — a sister, as they were known — walked in, you'd stand until they sat down. It was just a sign of respect. Nowadays, of course, they wouldn't dream of it.

Anyhow, next I went down to Mackay Base Hospital. It was there that I ran into a nurse who'd done her midwifery at the Mater Hospital in Mackay and she said to me, 'Why don't you do your "mid"?'

It might've been because of my previous experience in Ayr that I made the excuse, 'I'm sick of studying. I want to get out into the real world and live.'

But she insisted, so I went to the Mater and met Sister Ephrem who was in charge of the maternity ward, and oh, she was the best thing since sliced bread. Effie was my kind of person. I remember buying a pair of red shoes once and she asked if she could try them on. 'Of course,' I said, and she danced around the ward, swinging her skirts, admiring herself in these red shoes with the high heels. So I did my midwifery at the Mater and in doing so I got over my fear of delivering babies. In fact, I loved it. So much so that I went on to do Maternal and Child Welfare at St Paul's Terrace, in Brisbane.

But oh, I just loved to dance. This was in the real rock 'n' roll days where you went side to side and over their backs. Anyway, while a friend, Kay, and I had been over in New Zealand on a holiday, we'd bought these long rabbit skin coats. One night we turned up at this hotel in Mackay looking like two bunnies and Kay parked behind a big, deep-goldy-maroon-coloured two-door car. It might've been an Impala. Apparently only about five were imported into Australia, so I guess the driver thought he was a bit crash-hot. Anyway, as he got out, he dropped his keys down behind the seats and of course we came to the rescue and I thought, Gee, he's pretty nice.

As it turned out, he wasn't a dancer, which was a shame. But he also wasn't a drinker, nor did he smoke, which was good. He was working for his father who owned a sugar cane farm. We got on quite well. In fact, we were almost on the verge of getting engaged before I had second thoughts and I took off to Bundaberg to work in the Mater Hospital there. But the man was still very keen. He was writing to me and I'd go back to Mackay when I could. But then, after I met up with an old boyfriend, it got to the stage where I thought, What do I do now? Do I go with someone I'm really keen on, who's not going anywhere, or do I go with someone who'd make a good husband and be a good father and provider? Anyhow, I ended up going back to Mackay and the sugarcane farmer and I got married in St Paul's Presbyterian Church: the same church that both my grandparents and my parents had been married in.

By then I was almost thirty-six and when I had my daughter, I went part-time. That worked out well because my mother-in-law had lost her husband a year earlier and she lived next door so, if I had a shift, she was more than willing to babysit. Then when my daughter was two and a half, I ended up having to go down to Brisbane where I had seven abdominal operations over the next three and a half years. With me spending so much time in Brisbane and my husband running the farm up in Mackay, by the time all the operations were over, so was the marriage. It wasn't a nasty separation or anything like that. I didn't feel any anger toward him or anything, and he was never a demanding sort of man. It was just that I couldn't handle what was going on with me and nor could he, and the whole thing just fell apart. So, when I got a nursing job at a boarding college in Brisbane, I said, 'Do you mind if I take our daughter with me?' and he said, 'Okay then, that'd probably be the best thing.'

The college was coeducational. It went from preschool to Grade 12, which meant that my daughter could go there as well. We had two separate sick bays. I was the resident senior sister on the boys' side of the school and I was also in charge of the nurse who ran the girls' side, and we had two relievers. We were well looked after. My daughter and I lived in a little two-bedroom unit with free board and keep.

When we first got there, my daughter was in Grade 2 and she had a wonderful teacher. But in Grade 3, she went from being a really bright student and absolutely loving it, to someone who showed no interest at all. In fact, in one Grade 3 report, her teacher described her as a 'sullen little girl'. Determined as I was that she'd have the best education possible, I didn't think that was good enough. Anyhow, when she'd been born, I'd booked her into Clayfield College to be a boarder, so I went and saw them and they took her in as a weekly border. Her attitude changed almost overnight. She had the most amazing housemistress and before long she was making all these wonderful friends.

But things weren't going well at the college where I was working. In fact, it was very uncomfortable. There seemed to be a real falseness about it. Yes, while some of the masters were fantastic within their Christian beliefs and deeds, I felt that others just pretended. I'd think, It's a pity you don't practise what you preach. To make things worse, I became aware of a paedophile. His position was second to the senior housemaster of one of the boys' dormitories. Now I know that it was rife in a lot of these schools and thank God we're finally talking about it, but at first I was thinking, Gee, I must have a bad mind. Why am I thinking things like this about this man?

I first got suspicious when I just happened to walk into the sick bay and saw the man sitting on the side of one of the boy's beds. By the terrified look on the boy's face it felt like I'd walked in on something. Now, I didn't see the man do anything, and I can't really explain it — perhaps it was to do with the way he withdrew his hand — but I thought, Oh God no. Please don't let it be. At that stage I wasn't sure of any wrongdoing so I didn't tell anyone because I knew that if the word got out and I was wrong, I'd lose my job. But from then on I made it a rule that all the schoolmasters who entered the sick bay had to be accompanied by a nurse.

So that's when I started to keep a closer eye on the man. And it got to the stage where I could pick the kids he was going to work on; the ones he was going to groom. I felt terrible. I thought, That kid's going to be at risk, so I'd try and take them under my wing a bit. Anyhow, it took me three years to be personally convinced of what he was doing. That's when I reported my feelings to the senior housemaster. But nothing happened. It was never mentioned again. It was all hushed up. So then I went to see the principal, and his response was, 'What's your proof? You just can't go around saying things like this.'

I said, 'But I have to. They're somebody's kids.' I said, 'Look, if I'm wrong I'll regret it until the end of my days, but I'm almost a hundred per cent certain.'

I also knew that some of the parents had their suspicions because they'd asked if I thought there was something odd about the man; the way he didn't seem to have a social life of his own and how he always took the kids out on camps. I said, 'I honestly don't know, but I've already reported my feelings. If you're so concerned, go to the senior housemaster or the principal.' But I don't think they ever did. I think they were too frightened that their child would never get to be head boarder boy or school captain. Anyway, I just wouldn't speak to the man. I'd have nothing to do with him. If he came into the sick bay I'd say, 'What do you want?' And if he had no specific reason, I'd say, 'Do you mind leaving?'

After I'd reported him, I sort of wanted to stay on at the college, just to be sure they got him. And it took years before it came to a head. By that stage everyone was aware of my concerns and I was virtually ostracised within the college. Then he must've tried it on with a boy who'd run over to the girls' side of the college and told his sister. Next thing, she came across screaming hysterically at the master on duty. That's how it all blew up, and you know, not one person apologised for giving me such a hard time over it all. But that didn't matter. What mattered was that they got him and I'd just love to tell you his name, but I'm afraid there might be legal ramifications. He was a great big fellow who'd apparently been a Commonwealth Games shot-putter or something. He went to jail for about three months and was barred from working anywhere near a school. When he was released, his first job was at a gymnasium, right beside one of the top Brisbane boys' colleges. So, so much for that.

Where I Belong

During the time I was dealing with all the horrible business at the college I really wanted to take a break and clear my head. That's when I remembered just how much I loved growing up in Burketown. So when I saw an advertisement where they were looking for nurses at another town up in the Gulf of Carpentaria, over the Christmas holidays, I rang the nursing director. She said, 'Send me your résumé,' which I did, and that was it. For the next ten years, every Christmas school holidays, I'd head up to the Gulf.

I didn't take my daughter the first year. I dropped her off at her father's place in Mackay on the way through. But after that I started taking her. She was going on eight. With everything that was going on at the college, I just couldn't wait to get out of the place. I'd be leaving Brisbane like a dog with its ears flapping in the breeze. That's how I felt. It used to take me two days and nights to get there. First I'd drive to Blackall, then on to either Cloncurry or Julia Creek and up. Julia Creek was faster but it was just a one-lane bitumen road.

Lots of funny little things would happen along the way: at the Burke and Wills Three Ways Roadhouse there was a beer-drinking camel. It didn't like soft drink, only canned beer. So people would buy it a can of beer and it'd take the can in its big lips, tip its head back, guzzle down the lot then spit out the can. And when we'd be driving up there, it was always as dry as chips. One time my daughter and I were playing 'I spy' and she said, 'I spy with my little eye something beginning with N.'

I said, 'Inside or outside?'

She said, 'Both.'

After about fifty k's I said, 'Okay, I give in.'

She said, 'N for nothing.' I always thought that was a good one: 'N for nothing.' Trust kids.

Then by the time we'd be heading back to Brisbane, the wet season would've started and the grass was over head-high.

My daughter also loved it up there. She couldn't ride her bicycle in Brisbane, so we took it up and left it at the doctor's, where it'd be safe. Then, when we went up the following Christmas, her bike would be waiting and away she'd go with all her friends. But other than having a much-needed break from the college, while I was up at the Gulf, with all the various remote-living allowances and so forth, I could make quite a lot of money over the six to eight weeks.

But oh, I had such wonderful times. Would you like to hear a few memories from my time up in the Gulf? I've called this one 'Welcoming the New District Manager'. Anyhow, the new district manager was arriving from Mount Isa to meet us and check out his area. The hospital was, as always, spotless and well run, but the matron and staff were still quite anxious about the visit as the previous feller had been a bit of an arsehole. Oh, can I say that? Though, mind you, some of these district managers were like that. So it was with great anticipation that we waited to meet this new bloke.

Seeing how he was arriving around lunchtime, the kitchen staff had prepared a special finger-food luncheon. In those days we used to have morning and afternoon teas, and I can tell you, the kitchen staff really knew how to put on a spread. Anyhow, the new district manager duly arrived, and after the preliminary greetings and a chat with the matron, he was ushered into the old unused theatre, which was the tearoom for the day. Along with the extra-special finger food, piping hot tea was served from a large tea pot and a second pot contained hot water for the instant coffee. Most of us drank tea in those days.

Anyway, the luncheon feast got underway, and as the district manager continued to meet-and-greet, he sipped from his cup of tea. 'And what a beautiful spread,' he said, which made us warm to the man, as I believe he had likewise. Then, with a contented lick of the remaining lamington crumbs off his fingers, he went back for his second cup of tea. When he tipped up the teapot — *plop* — out fell a well-steamed gecko. As he looked down at it and it looked, steamy-eyed, back up at him, a deathly silence descended on the room. It was only broken when he said with a grin, 'Well, perhaps I'll have an instant coffee instead.'

So that was the new district manager, and now I've got to tell you how us nurses got the reputation of being shit stirrers. At one time there was no sewerage laid on up at the hospital. We just had the septic system. I think that's because the hospital was so far out of town. Anyhow, beside the nurses' quarters, there was this huge septic tank and during the wet season it used to fill up, leaving nowhere for the toilet waste to go. I mean, the liquid would flow over the top, but the solids would either just sit there or come back up through the toilets. During the week the wardsman would sort it out, but on the weekends it was left to us nurses. So we'd don the rubber gloves and outside we'd go. There used to be this big long stick there, and after we'd taken off the lid, we'd have to flick the solids up and out, over the wall of the septic tank.

At that time, Bob Walker was the mayor. Bob was the first Aboriginal mayor in Queensland as well as being a health worker at the local community health centre. And Bob was determined to get sewerage at the hospital. To that end, he got up at one meeting and announced, 'It's about time Queensland Health did something about it because everyone's now describing our nurses as being the biggest shit stirrers in the state.' And so the hospital got its sewerage system.

Another story's called 'Wallaby Stew'. One time I was running late for a home visit. When I knocked on the front door, there was no answer. Upon hearing activity coming from the backyard, I decided to go around there and announce myself. When I arrived, there was a whole group of Aboriginal people sitting around a big fire. I was greeted by my client and someone kindly placed down an old upside-down milk crate for me to sit on. Now, on top of the fire, awkwardly balanced, was a big copper boiler into which my host was throwing some veggies. That was okay, but what really got me was that the whole back leg of a kangaroo had been stuffed, hip first, into the pot. To make matters worse, the skin had been pulled back along its leg and was left hanging over the side of the boiler, down into the fire. As I gagged at the sight, sound and smell, my host said, 'Do yer want'a stay fer dinner?'

For a moment my mind was blank. Then I blurted, 'Oh, how generous of you, but unfortunately I have a previous dinner engagement.'

'Well, perhaps next time?' she said.

'Yes, that'd be lovely,' I replied, and I was out of there in a flash.

Now this story is a bit of a strange one, but it's true. On many occasions, particularly in hospitals, I've had odd sensations where I either hear or see things that other people can't or don't. The staff, particularly the Aboriginal staff, just used to say, 'It's because you're very spiritual.'

Mind you, sometimes I thought, Gee I wish I wasn't. Anyhow, the workload on night duty, up in the Gulf, was either a feast or a famine. This particular night there were no inpatients, but we did have a man's body in the morgue down at the far end, past the men's ward. Now, one of our duties was to check that all the fridges in the hospital were working. That included a visit to the morgue a couple of times per shift; that's if it was occupied, of course. Around midnight the nurse and I headed down the corridor, which led to the morgue, to do a fridge check. As we passed the men's ward, I distinctly heard a man's voice saying, 'I'm cold. I'm cold.'

At that point I stopped. I thought I must've been imagining things but as we walked on, I heard the same voice saying, 'I'm cold. I'm cold.'

This time I asked the nurse if she'd heard something. 'Yes,' she said.

We were pretty shaken up, so just to make certain that someone wasn't playing silly buggers, we did a thorough search, but we found nothing and no one. As it turned out, the dead man in the morgue had suffered from a serious illness and had spent quite some time as one of our patients. Towards his end he'd told his family how the nursing staff had looked after him so well that when he died, he'd look after us. In an interesting twist, the nurse I was on duty with that night recalled how the man had always complained about the air conditioning being turned up so high and that he was forever saying, 'I'm cold. I'm cold.'

Another story along those lines happened when I was on night duty with an Aboriginal nurse named Elsie. Elsie was a lovely lady and a really good nurse. We were having a cup of tea in the tearoom at about 5.30 a.m. when, right out of the blue, Elsie looked up and said, 'My mother's just died.'

I asked, 'How could you possibly know that?'

She then started to cry. 'Mum's just walked past the outside window.'

That would've been impossible because there were tanks and palm trees right up to the window. Half an hour later a telephone call came through to say that Elsie's mother had died. She'd passed away at 5.30 a.m. I've got no explanation for this, except that it happened.

We had another patient; her name was Ella. Ella was a part-Torres Strait Islander who had emphysema and asthma. Before each Christmas, I'd sell raffle tickets down at the shop, and out of the proceeds, I'd buy our clients a Christmas present. Then at the Christmas party, I'd dress up in the Santa Claus costume and give them the whole show. Mind you, I was very thin back then and they had to stuff me with pillows so that I could fit into the suit. I remember once being midway through a hearty 'Ho, ho, ho' when the safety pins gave way and I lost my duds in front of everyone. Anyhow, I'd get each of the clients to come and sit on my knee and tell me — Santa — what they wanted for Christmas, then I'd give them what I'd bought anyway. One year Ella had sat on my knee and said, 'You know, Santa, I've never ever had a doll in my whole life.'

In my best deep voice I asked her, 'Well, what sort of doll would you like, Ella?'

She said, 'I'd love a Barbie doll.'

Next Christmas that's what Santa gave Ella: a Barbie Doll. And when she took off the wrapping and saw what it was, she held it tight to herself and she rushed out onto the verandah and she cried and she cried. Nobody could console her. I thought, Oh no, I've really upset her. But she loved that doll, she really did. She wouldn't let it out of her sight. Then during the following year, she passed away. She would've only been in her fifties. She was a tiny little frail thing. But I did give her her wish.

At these Christmas parties we'd light up a Christmas tree in our multipurpose room, and we'd bring in all sorts of different food and put on a feast. With having so many Indigenous clients, we'd sing a few Island songs and carols. Having lived up on Thursday Island, I knew some of the real dinky-di Island songs. One in particular, which everyone loved to sing, was about a boat named the *Black Swan*. This Christmas we decided to sing the *Black Swan* song especially in honour of Ella. Gee, I'm even getting goosebumps just thinking about it. It was so beautiful because, when I started to sing, a great big boom of voices joined in, and as they did — without a word of lie — the lights on the Christmas tree started to flicker on and off. And when we finished singing the song, they stopped. I said to my administration officer, 'Did you notice the Christmas lights flickering?'

'Yes,' she said. 'Ella was here.'

So how do you explain things like that?

Then this last one's called 'Who's Stupid?' Now you sometimes wonder if an Aboriginal client sees you as someone who genuinely likes them and cares for their health and wellbeing, or as simply a paternalistic white woman who's there to tell them what to do. So it's hard to know just what they think of you. And I do love these people. For about two years, the health worker and I had been making home visits to an Aboriginal lady with diabetes. Her name was Betty. We'd go daily, Monday to Friday, and try to encourage her to give herself insulin injections.

The thing was, Betty had very little self-confidence and she was terrified of needles. Still, we kept up these daily visits and we were sort of making some progress. Anyhow, Betty's Aboriginal partner, Hector, would always joke about her situation. He'd say, 'She'll never learn. She's too stupid.' Mind you, he didn't say it in a mean way. It was just to tease her. In fact Hector was a really nice bloke. He was not a big drinker, except in occasional bursts, he always held down a job, and he provided well for his family.

One day when I arrived for our insulin injections tutoring session, Betty met me at the gate. She invited me inside and said that she had something funny to tell me. Apparently, earlier that morning, Hector had taken his troopie — Toyota four-wheel-drive troop carrier — about three k's out, to tend to his horses. Mid-morning he'd arrived back home for breakfast. After he'd eaten his breakfast, he told Betty that he was going back out to the horses again. Minutes later he walked back inside. 'Do yer know where me troopie is?' he said. 'It's not outside.'

'It's still out there with your horses,' she replied. 'You walked home.'

'Oh, did I?' Hector said.

'So now who's stupid?' Betty remarked. They had a bit of a laugh about that. But from then on, Hector never once mentioned how 'stupid' she was.

Some years later, when I was visiting the Gulf, I popped into the aged persons' hostel to see someone I knew. As I walked in, this voice called out, 'Hey, Bev, what you doin' 'ere?'

It was Betty. She looked a lot older and frailer, so I went over and kissed her on the cheek and we sat and talked. She told me that Hector had died about eight years before. I said that I was sorry to hear that. When she mentioned that she still couldn't give herself insulin injections, we recalled the above story about who's stupid. In doing so we shared another laugh. Then, as serious as you like, Betty said, 'You know Bev, when my old man died, I didn't worry 'bout no one else. I just stayed to myself.' And she began to cry. 'I really miss my old man, I do, Bev. I really miss my old man.'

I mean, just how lucky am I, and just what a huge privilege it's been, to get to know some of these people.

Bill's Story
Kakadu Rescue

<u>Bill 'Swampy' Marsh</u> — <u>writer</u> — Back in 2013, a mate and I performed on the *Ghan* as part of Great Southern Rail's Anzac celebrations. In payment, I received a free Gold pass for two plus my vehicle. In early June of that year, my partner, Margaret, and I took the *Ghan* up to Darwin. At that time I was working on the book *Amazing Grace: Stories of Faith and Friendship from Outback Australia.* After we'd crammed in a few days of interviews in and around Darwin, we headed out to Jabiru where I met up with a priest from Frontier Services and his wife.

Two days later, Margaret and I decided to have a look around Kakadu National Park. A couple of years earlier, on the same deal with Great Southern Rail, we'd been out to a place called Gunlom Falls. Gunlom's at the southern end of the park and it's one of the most beautiful spots in Australia. A huge escarpment leads up to three interconnected ponds, and from the bottom-most of those ponds, you get one of the most amazing views. So we decided we had to go back to Gunlom for a second look.

On this day we made a picnic lunch, grabbed our swimmers and we drove down the Kakadu Highway, toward Pine Creek, then turned off onto the dirt road leading into the falls. When we got there, I parked near the campground area and we set off up the steep escarpment. It's a rugged track of something like two hundred metres, twisting and weaving its way around rocks, trees and shrubbery. You have to be careful. When we eventually got to the falls, we bypassed the bottom-most pond and went right to the top. After we'd had our lunch at the top, we started to make our way down to the bottom-most pond. There people were swimming, having a good time. It was a perfect day.

Margaret already had her swimming gear on under her clothing, so when we got to the spot, she got into the pond. I didn't have my togs on yet, so I had to go a bit to the side, out of view, to undress. If you can imagine, the pond is sort of like a dam in as much as the water's held back by a rocky wall. With it being just the start of the dry season, some water was still flowing over the rocky wall, falling three or four metres onto a small flatish ledge of rock before it disappeared the couple of hundred metres over the escarpment, down into a larger waterhole below.

After I'd got into my togs, I noticed that Margaret was out in the middle of the pond, floating on her back. To get closer to her I started to step my way, carefully, along the top of the rocky wall. I noticed that the rock where the water was still flowing over was sort of darkish in colour. It wasn't mossy or anything, so I thought it looked safe enough. But when I took another step, my feet went from under me. There was nothing I could do. I fell headfirst down onto the flatish ledge.

I'm not sure what happened next but I remember lying there with blood swirling about me. My body was numb, yet I was aching all over. When I tried to get up, my wrists wouldn't hold me. Then there were two young men standing over me. Their names turned out to be Stefan and Oliver. They were speaking to me, but due to their thick German accents, I couldn't understand what they were saying.

Margaret — artist and partner — I remember it being a beautiful day, and you were keen to get to Gunlom Falls early so we could get a swim in. After I made a picnic lunch, we drove down the blacktop to the turn-off. It was just after the wet season and they hadn't yet completed clearing the dirt road into the falls.

So we bumped our way along this very rough section until we arrived at a pleasant, wide-open picnic area at the base of the falls. Looking up at the escarpment, I recalled just what a tough climb it'd been the last time we'd been there. After our picnic lunch we set off. I was very conscious of how steep that climb was, and my capacity to manage it. I think I might've even said that this was the last time I'd attempt to climb up to the ponds. Still, I knew that if I took it nice and steady, I could get there, which we eventually did.

We didn't go to the main pond first. Instead, we climbed further on, past the two higher ponds, right to the top. After a brief rest we then made our way back down to the main pond. Some people were already swimming and some were just sitting around on the rocks. As I'd already put my bathing suit on, I decided to go in first. It was quite rugged around the pond. I couldn't just walk in, so I found a spot where I could cautiously slide in off the rock wall that held the pond water back. I swam out to the middle of the pond. I then turned over on my back, spread myself out like a star, looked up into the blue of the sky, and thought, This is a bit of heaven.

By then you were ready to get into the water. For some reason you didn't try and get in the way I did. You started to walk over to the other side, across the rock-face wall. When I'd got in the water, I'd noticed that parts of the rock wall, where water was still flowing over, were a different colour. It looked like it had traction, but that obviously wasn't the case, because when you stepped on it, you must've lost control.

I didn't see what actually happened. I was still floating on my back. But you must've called out to me because I have this permanently indelible memory of seeing you disappearing headfirst over the outer edge of the rock wall. In that nanosecond, I tried to recall whether there was a ledge before the top of the falls or not. The dread was that you'd gone right over the top and had fallen the couple of hundred metres to the bottom. When I swam over to where you'd slipped, I heard foreign voices, and I could hear you saying, 'Oh no. Oh no. Oh no.'

At hearing your voice I felt an immediate sense of release. So I started to climb over the rock wall. Just like you, I didn't pick that it was slimy. It didn't glisten, so I slipped exactly as you did. The only difference being, I was on my bottom and I slid down feet-first, following the contours of the falling water. When I landed I somehow hit my head. There were two men in their late twenties helping you. They turned to me in shock and asked in a German accent, 'Are you all right?'

'I think so,' I said. 'I haven't broken anything.'

The two Germans, Stefan and Oliver, had a first-aid kit and they were wrapping your forehead, where you were bleeding, with bandages. I think they also knew you'd hurt your wrists, because that's how you'd tried to brace your fall. I think their plan was to then carry you out of there, over to a safer spot. When they couldn't lift you, one of them went for help. That's when Ken and maybe a couple of others came down, and together they helped get you off the rock ledge, around the top, and over to a sandy bit under a tree. By then people were testing their mobiles. When no one could get a signal, a fit, young lad said, 'I'll go to the bottom. There's a phone down there. I'll call the ranger,' and off he scampered. That's the last I saw of him. He didn't come back. I can only guess that, after he'd made the call, he knew that he'd set the rescue in train.

By then a few other people had gathered around you, all willing to help. Other than Ken, there weren't too many older than us. Ken was there with his wife, and I think they had two young teenagers with them. They were from Queensland and Ken looked like he was experienced in dealing with most circumstances that might arise.

Ken — the traveller — Every year Anne and I take off in our caravan for three or four months. This time we started out by ourselves, but then we flew home and grabbed our two teenage grandsons and brought them up to Kakadu for a couple of weeks. None of us had been to Kakadu before, so, as you do, we went to the information centre to check out all the places we should see.

That day we went to Gunlom Falls. We'd not long got there. The boys were mucking around in the pools. Anne was taking photos. I was just sorting out our backpacks and getting a drink when I saw a fellow go over and speak to Anne. She, in turn, pointed him over to me. When he came over, because of his German accent, I couldn't really understand what he was saying. But I certainly knew that something was very wrong and he wanted me to follow him. By that time our two grandsons were over on top of the rock wall, looking down onto the rocky ledge. When I tried to get across, it was so slippery that I had to get down on all fours so that I didn't go arse over. My grandsons didn't have shoes on so I gave them the short shift: 'You boys scram out of there.'

When the German fellow and I got down onto the rocky ledge, his mate was already there with you and I think Margaret might've been there as well. You had your back against the rock wall and the water was falling down over you. You must've received a fair conk on the head because the water was fairly bloodied. You were looking like a stunned mullet and when I spoke to you, you were quite incoherent. The thing was, we weren't sure what to do. I was at a bit of a loss myself, I suppose. But I was very aware that you were badly hurt and that you needed to be moved to safer ground. The problem was, you couldn't walk, and because the rocks were so slippery, it was going to be a real struggle to get you out of there without hurting ourselves, and you even more. To make things even more of a concern, Margaret said, 'He's got a heart condition.'

Anyhow, we somehow managed to get you over onto a sort of more level area, on a sandy bit under a tree, where the

German fellers bandaged up your head. By then you'd sort of given us an indication that your injuries were more to do with your wrists and ribs. You couldn't really lie down, so to give you something to sit and lean your back on, I went and pulled a stump out of the ground. That wasn't too successful because when you tried to sit, it still had bits of branch sticking out. But you were in heaps of pain. Other than a deep cut above your eye and your damaged wrists, my assessment was that, because you had a lot of difficulty breathing, you'd most probably broken some ribs and perhaps punctured a lung. It was obvious that there was no way we were going to get you down off the escarpment. What we needed was someone to run down to the picnic area and get help. Our two grandsons were keen to go but then another young feller said, 'I'll go,' and he was off like a bullet.

So we hung in there with you. I don't know how long it took until the ranger and his mates arrived, but it seemed like an eternity. By then everyone was concerned that we were going to run out of light. There were a few fit, young fellers about and so I said to the ranger, 'Is there any chance of carrying him out before it gets dark?'

I remember him looking me up and down and saying, 'If we have to, I think we'll be able to get by without the help of an older person like yourself.'

That was a pretty fair comment, and so seeing that you were in pretty good hands, Anne and I decided to grab the boys and leave. When we got down to the bottom of the falls, a group of park-ranger-looking people were standing in a group. One big feller seemed to have some sort of authority, and when I went over to speak to him, he said, 'We're just trying to sort out a helicopter to bring a nurse down from Jabiru.'

I'd say that the helicopter pilot was probably the same bloke who did the joy flights. Anyhow, yeah mate, that's about all I can remember. We left pretty soon after that. But you were in a pretty bad way. I was just hoping that they could get you out of there before it got dark. If not, God knows what would've happened.

<u>Steve — senior park ranger</u> — Kakadu National Park's around twenty thousand square kilometres and it's broken up into five districts. I was stationed in the most southern part in what's called the Mary River District, which is on Jawoyn traditional land. On that particular day we had some people out from Canberra, doing an occupational health and safety inspection of the Mary River office and the workshop. We were partway through the inspection when I got the call from our headquarters at Jabiru: 'There's an emergency at Gunlom Falls. Someone's fallen and injured themselves at the top rock pool and they need medical assistance.'

I had a new boss — an operations manager — there that day and he said, 'Well, we'd better get going.'

From the ranger station down the bitumen to the Gunlom turn-off is thirty-nine k's, then the campground's about three k's of dirt road further in. So we got down there. My new boss came with me and some other rangers came along as well. By the time we got up to the top of the falls, a few people were already helping you. You'd apparently fallen three or so metres from the top of the rock bar that held the pond water back, down onto the ledge. We then helped get you to a sandy area, under some shade. You were obviously in great pain and needed help as soon as possible.

It would've taken far too long to get an ambulance out to you and it would've been a hell of a struggle to get you down off the escarpment. So after we contacted Jabiru Hospital, we got in touch with a small R44 Robinson helicopter operation who, in emergency situations like yours, would fly a medical person down to the scene of an accident so that a first assessment can be done. Once we got that underway, we then had to try to find a flat enough place for the chopper to land. As it happened, the pilot knew the area well, and after he landed on top of the escarpment, he and the nurse walked the three hundred metres or so downstream to get to you.

The nurse that day was an Englishman named Stuart. He was the one who assessed you. I also remember there were a couple of young German guys and an older fellow there with you. My job was to support the rescue process by liaising with everyone involved and to keep the people back from where you were. Anyhow, after Stuart assessed your medical condition and had stabilised you, he said, 'Things look serious. We're going to have to get Bill out of here before dark.'

The helicopter was far too small for an operation like that so they called up the district medical officer on a satellite phone. After Stuart explained your condition, the decision was made to get you out of there in the CareFlight helicopter. Once they were contacted, we then had to wait. Stuart did a great job. Even though you were in a fair bit of pain, you were well looked after. But by now the whole operation had turned into a bit of a tourist spectacle, and because it was going to be such a big chopper and the downdraft would've been so forceful, I told the visitors, 'Look, you don't have to leave, but we want you all to move up to the second pool.'

When I look back at it now, the place ended up looking like a Roman amphitheatre. There was you and Margaret and the other helpers, plus Stuart, down on the flat — centrestage — and looking down upon you all from the rocky surrounds were rows of onlookers. And when the CareFlight helicopter came in and hovered above the falls, and the wind from the downdraft started blowing waves through the water, they were absolutely awestruck. If that wasn't dramatic enough, Matt, the nurse, then appeared from out of the helicopter and was lowered down onto the rocky ledge, followed by the lifting stretcher.

The chopper now had to find somewhere to land to save fuel. We had a helipad down at the campgrounds, so the pilot went down there while Matt and Stuart worked on you and started to prepare for the evacuation. Once that was done, we helped ease you onto the stretcher, where we tied you down, ready to be taken out. I then got in radio contact with one of the park staff, down at the campground, and he passed on the message that all was ready. By now it was coming on dark. With the small R44 Robinson helicopter from Jabiru not being able to fly at night, Stuart had to quickly pack up his gear and walk back up to the helicopter at the top of the escarpment.

After the Robinson had left, the CareFlight helicopter came back and you were air-lifted into that and off you went. Our job was pretty well done then. But I must compliment my new operations manager. At no stage did he try to exert his authority by barging in and trying to take over. He said to me, 'Look, Steve, this's your turf. You know what you're doing. Just go for it and I won't interfere.' And I've got to hand it to him for doing that. Then the last thing I did was to help get Margaret back to Jabiru. By now it was dark and the last thing we needed was to have to attend to another accident. So I got someone to go back with her in your car, just to make sure she got there nice and safe. And that was about it.

Matthew — registered CareFlight nurse — Ironically I'd just finished my advanced winch training for helicopter rescue operations in Darwin the day before, on the 19th June. Winching was a quite new thing back then as civilian helicopters with winch capability had only recently been deployed in the Territory, plus it's usually pretty flat country and so it's generally easy to find a place to land anyway. But I seem to have this uncanny knack of, once having learnt a new skill, tending to use it very soon afterwards. So when I rocked into work on 20th June, I said to the pilot and air-crewman, 'I reckon we'll be doing a winch job today,' to which they laughed and replied, 'You're dreamin'.'

The day started out normally. We had a crew briefing, then I checked my big red medical bag, which contained all the necessary drugs and equipment such as the monitors, the ventilators and all that kind of thing. While I was doing that, the pilot and air-crewman undertook the daily safety checks of the aircraft. The helicopter we had back then was a medium-sized twin-engine MBB/Kawasaki BK117. It's a great helicopter but a bit on the small side for the vastness of the NT. After our checks, we were just about to take a break when the emergency call came in. That was at 1445 hours. We were notified by our coordination unit that someone — i.e. you — had taken a fall at Gunlom Waterfall in Kakadu National Park. Initially the information was a bit sketchy so we didn't know if you were at the top or the bottom of the falls.

Our logistics people then got in communication with the rangers and found out that you were at the top of the waterfall and that it might be a winch rescue. So we then configured the helicopter for a winch rescue, and at 1530 hours, we headed off on the two-hundred-kilometre direct flight from Darwin down to Gunlom Falls. Along with me and the pilot, JB, we had a helicopter crewie named Dan. He's the person who operates the winch and helps with navigation, radio communications and the safety checks. Anyhow, while we were in the air, we received information that the accident had occurred to a middle-aged man and his injuries were significant enough to prevent him from being taken down the steep track to the campground at the bottom of the escarpment. You were apparently in a lot of pain and you weren't mobile at that point in time.

We arrived overhead at 1645 hours. The pilot and the crewie undertook a reccy and worked out exactly where you were. We then looked for a safe place to winch me down; preferably where it was kind of flat and away from the cliff edge. Once that was established I was winched down in my harness, along with my big red medical bag. Following my safe landing they sent down the stretcher. To save fuel, the pilot then went and landed down on the campground. I knew it'd take me at least forty minutes to do a clinical assessment and then to set up the stretcher and get you safely packaged, so I radioed the pilot and told him to start up the helicopter at 1740 hours to come and retrieve us. Because I was going to be busy, I asked the head ranger, Steve, to be my timekeeper. I said, 'We really have to winch Bill out before dark, so tell me when every ten minutes has passed.'

Stuart, the nurse from Jabiru, had already put in an IV cannula and he gave me a handover. I then did my own quick assessment — a primary survey. As well as a large cut above your eye, you had a broken wrist. At a later stage, I think they discovered that you'd broken your other wrist as well. Anyhow, seeing that you were in a lot of pain we gave you some morphine. But my bigger worry was that you also had a pneumothorax on your left side, which can be quite life threatening, especially after trauma or an accident. Basically, a pneumothorax is when air gets into the pleural space, which then causes the pressure to build up in the cavity between the lung and the chest wall. When that happens, the lung may well collapse, causing breathing difficulty, and it can progress to a tension pneumothorax, which can kill you very quickly.

When I looked for significant signs and symptoms of a pneumothorax, you had quite a few: you were breathing quickly; you had a very fast heart rate; your chest looked like it was splinting; you had decreased air entry and probably a collapsed lung and, because your lung wasn't working properly, the oxygen levels in your blood were quite low. The emergency treatment with a tension pneumothorax is to decompress the chest with a procedure called a needle thoracotomy, which is me sticking a big needle through your chest, into the lung space, to relieve the pressure by allowing the air to escape. In this case I decided against doing such a radical procedure as that and to just monitor you and make sure you didn't get any worse.

After my assessment I unpacked the stretcher, and because it comes down in pieces, I put it all together. By that stage you were standing, but you couldn't really move, so we placed the stretcher behind you and eased you down into it. To help with your breathing I then sat the back of the stretcher up at forty-five degrees. Once that was done I put you in a special sleeping bag type thing to protect you from all the dust and the dirt. You were then strapped in and I gave you some more morphine through the IV cannula to help with the pain, and administered oxygen to help your breathing.

I was ready a bit before the allotted forty minutes, and with a satellite phone being quite problematic in situations like that, Steve contacted a fellow ranger, who was down at the campground, to ask him to inform the pilot that we were ready. We now moved you from the sandy bit, under the tree, and took you over to the top of the swimming area and put you down on a flat bit of rock on the ledge.

Because the light was fading fast, Stuart had to leave at that stage. So he went off and when our helicopter came back, I went through all my safety checks, via my radio, with the crewie. You probably don't remember but I also gave you a safety briefing and I put goggles and hearing protection on you. After they lowered the hook down, I went through another set of checks before I gave them the okay to winch you up. While you were being winched up, I was on the ground holding onto a stabilising rope — a tag line — that was connected to the stretcher. If we both would've gone up together, with the downwash from the helicopter, we would've got into a horrible spin. Once you were safely in the helicopter, the crewie sent the cable back down, which I hooked onto my full-body harness and up I went.

We departed Gunlom at 1745 hours and flew to Jabiru to refuel. When we arrived at Jabiru we had to take you out of the helicopter for safety precautions. I mean, if there'd somehow been a fire, and you were still in the helicopter, your day would've gone from bad to worse. So we put you down on that tarmac. I remember being relieved when you started complaining about the mosquitoes and how the sleeping bag was making you hot. Though I couldn't do much about the mosquitoes, I did unzip the bag to give you some relief. Once we'd refuelled, we loaded you back in the helicopter and we headed straight to Darwin Hospital.

On the way I kept checking your condition. I also gave you some more morphine, just to keep you comfy and to help you to forget about things. Mind you, I was still concerned about the pneumothorax you'd suffered. That was still clinically significant and the rescue treatment for a deteriorating patient in the back of the helicopter, with a condition like that, is quite dramatic. So I was happy that you didn't deteriorate in-flight and we landed you on the helipad at Darwin Hospital at 2030 hours. You were then taken by ambulance straight into the trauma room in the resus area, and after I gave them a handover, they got to work on you. I don't know if you actually remember or not, but I came to see you the next day. You were still in a bit of pain, and as I suspected, they'd put a drain-tube in your chest.

Margaret — artist and partner — In many ways, Stuart, the nurse from Jabiru Hospital, has been left out of this story. And that's what so often happens in history. Even though we tried to contact him and we sent him a book and a card of thanks, we've yet to receive a reply. He, like Stefan and Oliver and the helicopter pilot and the second CareFlight nurse — the crewie — was a major player in your accident. Stuart did his part superbly and yet he's not going to feature as a voice, so I'd like to speak on his behalf.

From what I can piece together, the Jabiru Hospital happened to be holding a class that day when someone came in and said, 'We need a nurse for a helicopter pick-up. It's an emergency.' And this young English fellow, Stuart, who'd no doubt come to

Australia to broaden his experience, put up his hand and said, 'I'll go.' So out of the class he went, to meet up with the pilot of the helicopter.

Even for an experienced pilot, Gunlom Falls would've been a challenge. There were lots of trees, rocks and the huge escarpment drop with plenty of wind turbulence, so when the helicopter arrived, they couldn't find a spot to land close by the scene. In the end they landed further up the top of the escarpment. Stuart then had to strap a huge medical backpack on his back and make his way over and around rocks, trees and boulders, down to get to you. When he arrived, he was absolutely exhausted and took a moment to collect himself. He then settled in, right beside you, and he started the job of applying all the necessary first aid: sorting out the bandages and getting the IV drip in and checking you for further damage. To his mind, you were his charge and he was determined to make sure you got the best possible attention he could offer. He then stayed with you right through the whole event and was of valuable assistance to Matt after he arrived in the CareFlight helicopter.

Once you were securely tied into the cocoon-like stretcher, Stuart, along with four or five others, helped lift you across that horrendous rocky climb, back onto that dangerous ledge, in preparation for you to be winched up. By that time, things were becoming quite tense, with the wind coming up and the light dropping. So it was a brilliant piece of flying from the CareFlight pilot to keep the helicopter steady while you were winched up to the crewie. Then, when Matt went up, I knew you were going to be safe. And that's when Stuart packed up his gear and made his way back up to the top, to be helicoptered back to Jabiru before it got dark. As I said, that's the last time we saw him. But he, along with Stefan and Oliver, plus the helicopter pilot and the crewie, who also haven't been able to be interviewed, were the unsung heroes of that day. I've got the highest regard for Stuart. I've got the highest regard for them all.

As I later wrote in the *NT News'* letter of the day — published on July 4th, 2013 — under the title, 'Humble heroes saved the day': *Ordinary people did something very extraordinary at Gunlom Falls in Kakadu late last month. Representing four NT organisations, Steve, the NT National Parks senior ranger, from Mary River, Stuart, the Jabiru Hospital nurse, Matt, the CareFlight attendant and his pilot, and doctors at the Royal Darwin Hospital, together with Stefan and Oliver (two overseas visitors), and Ken, who was visiting from the Gold Coast, all coordinated brilliantly to rescue a person from a life-threatening accident.*

The rescue was caring, professional and committed beyond what any job specifications could require. It was undertaken and carried out with generous, humanitarian spirit. Those of us involved are filled with admiration for the NT way of doing a wilderness rescue. The family and friends of the person rescued extend their heartfelt thanks.

It was just one person. A very small part of Australia was given the benefit of major resources and so much good will towards survival. It's a very humbling experience. And an inspiring one. It fosters a lifetime commitment to contribute back in some way. The person involved, this time, is a writer of Australian outback stories. I can see, coming in future, a collection on the every-day-any-day rescue heroes. Thank you to the individual heroes and to the organisations that were represented. — Margaret Worth, SA.

Chazza's Story
Wherever I Go

Okay, so I was born in Longreach. My mother and father worked on, and managed, station properties around that area till I was twelve. Then they bought a property down between Maryborough and Gympie, which they later extended. So it was like two separate cattle stations that we ran together.

We were a family of girls, and that was all right. Dad coped. In fact, it worked out well because us girls loved horses and working with the cattle. I didn't like school that much. It wasn't till later, when I started courses that I was interested in, that I began to enjoy learning. It's even the same now. I'm still doing nursing courses mostly online. In fact, just the other night, I was looking at doing one and it cost two and a half thousand dollars and I thought, Oh my Lord.

My interest in nursing started when I was in Julia Creek. I was married by then, kind of. Well, I sort of run away from home with a man who was a lot older than me. He was a kangaroo shooter from Richmond. But we didn't elope. How it happened was, my parents were very strict — more so Mum. I suppose you could even describe her as being quite a cruel woman in many ways, whereas Dad was a bit more of a softie. Running away was really Dad's suggestion. 'And don't tell her,' he said, referring to my mother. So it was more or less, 'Get out of here while the going's good.' That's pretty much how I ended up in Julia Creek.

My 'husband' and I used to do a lot of pig hunting and if one of the dogs got gored or injured I'd ring the vet — veterinarian — over at Cloncurry and he'd tell me what to do. So I learnt to give local anaesthetics and do suturing; things like that. That's how I got to be known as 'the pig-dog doctor'. Then anyone who had an injured or crook dog, they'd bring them to me. From there I started treating all the other types of animals – apart from snakes, that is. You won't get me anywhere near a snake. They can all die as far as I'm concerned. But with the horses there was a lot of barbed wire cuts; colic was another common one.

So when Julia Creek was struggling to get qualified ambulance people, I signed up to do the training course. I went to Townsville a few times for driver training and also to learn what to do in certain medical and accident situations. Anyhow, I reached all my skill levels first go and became an ambo — ambulance officer — and I ended up spending so much time up at the hospital that the director of nursing put me on the books as an AIN — Assistant in Nursing — so that I'd get paid for it. Then I thought, Well, if I'm going to do this, I may as well do it properly. So I did, and because I got recognised prior learning — RPL — through my ambulance course, I only had to do twelve months' study, instead of the usual eighteen. It was the same when I went on to do my registered nursing certificate; I got RPLs from both the ambulance and enrolled nursing courses I'd done.

Ambulance work in Julia Creek was mainly to do with farm and vehicle accidents. We also had the usual sick-type people and those who'd had heart attacks and what-have-you. The toughest accident I had to attend to was when my daughter rolled the car. That was about five kilometres out of town. At first I didn't know it was her. I'd just got home from doing ambo work at a football match. I was about to take my uniform off when I got the call that there was an accident out on the Punchbowl–Julia Creek Road. I knew my daughter and two granddaughters had gone out that way so my first thought was, Oh fuck, I hope it's not them. It must've been still niggling at me as we were going out because I remember saying to the ambo bloke I was with, 'Gee, I hope it's not my family.'

'Oh,' he said, 'in this line of work you should never jump to conclusions.'

Anyhow, as soon as I saw the car I said, 'It's them.'

'You'll be useless now,' he said. 'I'll take over and look after it.'

But, as soon as we got there, he totally lost it. He just walked away from the accident. Deserted the ship, and he didn't even know anyone involved. He was only there on relief from Townsville.

But it was a real mess. They were coming in from Punchbowl, late in the afternoon. It was a dirt road and my daughter thought she'd taken all the corners she needed to take, so she gunned the car. But there was one corner left and when she hit it, she overcorrected and over they went. There were seven in the car, when there should've only been five. Some had seatbelts on, some didn't. My daughter was in shock, as you would be. She was pretty much okay apart from having been bumped around on the head. Another feller had an arm in the thorax happening, and the others were like walking wounded.

Luckily my youngest granddaughter had been in a car seat, and after the car had come to a halt, one of the fellers had put her out on the flat. She was also pretty much okay, other than also having been bumped around on her head. But the eldest granddaughter — the three-year-old — she wasn't wearing a seatbelt, so she'd been thrown out of the car as it rolled. She was critical. She was lying there unconscious, and from what I could see, she had a fractured femur and was suffering severe head injuries.

With this other ambo bloke having gone walkabout, I was left to deal with it the best I could. So when the police got there, I said to the sergeant, 'Look, punch him in the head or something. Make him wake up to himself 'cause I need help, and I need it now.'

So the sergeant went over and — *bang* — he punched him. But it still didn't help, because when I called out to him, 'Can you please come and take care of my little granddaughter? I just need to distance myself a little bit from the situation,' his reply was, 'No. I don't do things like that.'

There was a big report about it afterwards and he ended up getting chucked out; so yeah. But I somehow managed. Really, I think his shitty attitude was what probably kept me going through it all. Actually I was feeling quite okay. It might've been the adrenalin or the training, I don't know, but we got my granddaughter into town and we got her on a plane to Townsville. It was only later on that I found out they'd had to resuscitate her a couple of times before they got her to Townsville Hospital.

The father — my son-in-law — wasn't involved in the accident. He wasn't in the car. He was in a buggy following along behind and he was an emotional wreck. He also had a fear of flying and they had to sedate him to get him on the plane to go with his wife and daughter to Townsville because he'd had a panic attack.

My husband and I drove down to Townsville early the next morning. It's like a seven-hour run from Julia Creek. When we got there I walked into the hospital and found my son-in-law. He just kept shaking his head and saying, 'No. No. No. No one's going to hurt my little baby.'

I said, 'All right, where's the doctor?' So I barged straight in to see the doctor. As soon as he told me what the go was, I grabbed the operation consent form and I went back out and I said to my son-in-law, 'Right, here, just sign the bloody paper.'

So he signed the paper. And just as well he did too, because when they operated, they discovered that the only thing that was slowing some of the bone fragments from getting into her brain was that she had a clot between the brain and the fractured skull. So she was very lucky. It was a hell of an experience, I tell you. I was doing well up till then, but the moment I knew she was going to be all right, that's when I fell to pieces. Thankfully the Queensland Ambulance Service had support people to help me through it.

And yeah, that was that. Then I'm not sure if it was the trauma of it all or what, but my daughter never handled it real well. When the little one came home from hospital in a head guard and a body cast, my daughter couldn't bear looking at her. So seeing that my granddaughter needed constant care I took over and looked after her. In the end I had her up and walking and she was learning to run in the cast. Kids are very resilient.

But their relationship didn't last. My son-in-law and my daughter split up a couple of years later. By then there was another couple of kids and my daughter took off and carried on with another bloke. The last little boy was only about four months old at that time. My daughter originally took him with her but she found that she couldn't work because she had the baby. So she brought him back home and left him with my son-in-law and the other three kids. Of course, he then found that he couldn't manage to work and look after the kids as well. That's when he and I started sharing the kids. He lived in one street and I lived in the other, so we worked it that when I was at work, he looked after the kids, and when he was at work, I'd have the kids.

Anyhow, that accident would've definitely been the most difficult one I've had to face. And even though I've been nursing for fifteen years now, I'm still on the books as a casual ambo driver. But I've also done nursing in other places. I've spent some time in Alice Springs and a couple of weeks in Tennant Creek. Alice Springs was when I was finishing my RN's training. To help the situation at home, my two eldest granddaughters came over with me and my husband only joined me after he'd been in an accident. So he ended up being the babysitter.

I quite enjoyed the work I was doing in Alice Springs. It wasn't general nursing as such. I was more involved in doing policy work with the Elders, from the various Aboriginal communities. The thing was, the people who went out to visit these communities needed to know what they could do and couldn't do. There were a lot of complex cultural sensitivities involved. For instance, you shouldn't look an older Aboriginal man in the face. And with the women, you had to be aware of their family structure and how you approached certain subjects. After that contract finished, I thought I'd like to work some more in Alice Springs. And I did, but only for a short while. The hospital was very security conscious. The grounds where I was staying had all these six-foot-high fences around them, and in the end, I couldn't stand living in the enclosed areas. It was like being a prisoner and I thought, No, this's not for me.

So I settled in back at Julia Creek Hospital, and oh, I've got some fond memories from there. We had a bloke come in one evening; he said, 'Can I get a wheelchair? I've got me mate in the back of the ute.'

We said, 'What's happened?'

He said, 'I think he's broken his leg. But it's all okay. I've got him on a brand-new mattress. It hasn't even been used before. It's still got the plastic on it, so there won't be any germs on it.'

'Okay.' So we go out and there's this poor bloke lying in the back of a Toyota tray-back ute, with a bone sticking out of his leg. He's in agony, but the driver's still harping on about how he'd been real careful to put the bloke on this brand-new mattress, that still has the plastic on it, so there won't be any germs on it. It was all about the germs, even more so than his poor mate. But the thing was, he'd just driven a hundred and twenty k's, over an extremely rough dirt road, with this fellow, who had a compound fracture of the leg, bouncing around in the back, on this brand-new mattress, that still had the plastic on it. And he'd done the journey in an hour. Anyway, we ended up flying the poor bloke out to Townsville and things turned out okay.

Another time this bloke comes running into emergency. 'I've just shot me best mate in the leg. Can I bring him in?'

'Okay,' we say, and we're thinking, God, this's going to be terrible. Then when the bloke comes back in, there he is carrying this huge dog. So my previous pig-dog doctor skills came in handy on that occasion, and now it's happily ever after. The bloke's back with his best mate, his dog — the one he'd somehow shot in the leg. Oh we've had some doozies, I can tell you.

Another one that really sticks out is the lady who came in: 'I think I'm going into labour. I think my waters broke.'

That was obvious. 'Yes, love, your waters broke.'

The thing was, I'd never delivered a baby, so I said to my offsider, 'Quick, go and call the doctor.'

But before he could, the lady called out, 'I think it's coming.' So there's this big panic. My offsider and I, we grabbed the lady and we took her into a ward. And it was a breech birth. As I said, I'd never delivered a baby before, let alone a breech birth, so I asked my offsider. 'When's the doctor coming?'

'I've been too busy with you,' he said. 'I haven't had the time to call him.'

There was a midwife somewhere around the place so I sent him off to find her. So there I am, trying to help this lady with the breech birth. Anyhow, it took an eternity for the midwife to arrive. Just as she did, there was a little bubby poking its head out. And it'd started breathing. Gee I was relieved.

Yes, so that was Julia Creek and now here I am up at Normanton. Whereas Julia Creek was a designated ten-bed hospital, Normanton's a sixteen-bed hospital. How I got here was that when my husband retired from roo shooting, there was nothing for him to do in Julia Creek. In fact, one of the doctors said that I'd spoilt him too much; that I should make him do stuff for himself. I mean, at home he wouldn't even walk out of the house to turn the sprinkler on. That's how bad he was. The only thing he liked doing was fishing, so I said, 'See yer later,' and, to help the situation at home, the two school-aged grandkids came with me. They were the ones from the car accident. So then, me and the girls, we're just settling in when, lo and behold, who should blow into town with his boat in tow: my husband.

So he then settled in with us. And he started having a great old time taking the nurses out fishing in his boat. I thought, Oh well, if this's what's going to keep him active, I might as well move up here permanently. Which I did. I bought a place. Everything was going well. Me and my husband and the two grandkids were nice and settled when, lo and behold, who should blow into town: the estranged son-in-law along with the other two grandkids.

It just seems like wherever I move, they all pretty much pack up and follow me. I can't get rid of them. But that's okay. That's the way I like it.

Chris' Story
Love Is ...

I grew up in a pretty scummy part of Adelaide. I was one of five boys and we had a sister. We're basically a family of nurses. My mother was a nurse, as is my sister, me and one of my brothers. That said, nursing wasn't in my plans. I was waiting to get into university when the opportunity for nursing came up and I thought it'd be a great way to meet girls. So I decided to give it a go for a couple of years and here I am, thirty-five years later, married with two adult children and still nursing.

My wife and I got married when we were twenty-one. A few years later, a job came up as a flight nurse in Broken Hill so we moved up there. That was back in the '70s when they had those logo things like 'Love is ... something-or-other'. You know, 'Love is ... not having to say you're sorry' and all that type of stuff. Well, there was a saying around my workplace that went, 'Love is ... not pressing charges', and that came out of an incident where there'd been a domestic dispute at a town about a couple of hundred kilometres east of Broken Hill.

This bloke and his de facto wife had come home after a session on the grog, they'd had a blue, and amongst the turmoil, she'd grabbed a large kitchen knife and knifed him in the chest. Down he went like a sack of potatoes with the knife sticking out of him and blood gushing everywhere. When the woman saw what she'd done, she panicked, rang the ambulance, and before they arrived with the police in tow, she took off out bush. As you might imagine, it was quite a mess and the victim wasn't too well. That's when we got the call to fly out and pick the bloke up and bring him back to Broken Hill Hospital.

By the time we arrived, the ambulance had brought the bloke out to the airport, ready to be loaded straight onto the plane. A couple of the local coppers were there as well, just in case. At that point the bloke still had the kitchen knife embedded in his chest and he was still conscious. Then, as they started to wheel him out to the plane, his de facto appeared out of nowhere. When she'd seen the plane come in, she realised what was going on and so she'd rushed out to the airport. But just as she started to run out to the plane, she was nabbed by the police officers. Now if you can imagine the scene, there we are, loading this critically injured bloke onto the plane and about a hundred yards away, there's this woman being restrained by the coppers. And with the tears flowing down her face, she starts sobbing out at the top of her voice, 'I'm sorry, darlin'. I didn't mean ter do it!'

And this bloke, there he is with the knife sticking out of his chest and he struggles to raise himself from the gurney and he calls back at the woman, 'That's all right, sweetheart. I forgive yer!'

Then she replies, 'I love yer, darlin', honest I do!'

'I love yer too, sweetheart,' the bloke calls out. 'And don't worry about a thing. I'm not pressin' charges!'

News Flash

After working in Broken Hill for thirteen years my wife and I wanted to live closer to water and there's not a lot of water around Broken Hill. But we've always loved the Murray River so I applied for and got a job running a hospital in the Riverland. And that was okay, but I was only there for about fifteen months and I started to miss the outback. So I then got a fly-in fly-out nursing position up in the far north-east of South Australia, at the Moomba oil and gas fields. So now I've got the best of both worlds. We live on a little five-acre block on the Murray River, near a place called Winkie, and I work two weeks on, two weeks off, in the outback. There's been a lot of nasty accidents up there, but here's one with a lighter side.

This was back in the early 1990s. I hadn't been at Moomba all that long and it was one of those rare times when Lake Eyre was flooded. When that happens it's an amazing sight, with all the wildlife, and so a lot of tourists go out there and have a look. To get the best view, they go on charter flights out from places like William Creek, Port Augusta and Leigh Creek. Now, when Lake Eyre's in flood, in most places it's only about two foot deep and on a really calm day, when you look down from above, it's like a mirror. And that causes an optical illusion where you could be flying at a hundred feet and it looks like you're at thirty thousand feet. The other thing that's unusual about Lake Eyre is that it's below sea level. So when you're flying over it, the aeroplane's altimeter might tell the pilot that they're at true ground level when in actual fact they're not. Add to that the optical illusion effect and you'll understand why there's been a few accidents out on the lake.

This particular time there was a charter flight full of oldies — snowbirds — and of course they all wanted to have a real good, close look. Now, for whatever reason, the pilot mustn't have been paying too much attention as to how low the plane was flying and the plane came down, right into the middle of Lake Eyre. Fortunately no one was hurt, apart from the pilot's ego being bruised. Anyway, the plane sort of skimmed along the water then — *chung* — it ground to a halt. As soon as that happened, the plane's emergency global positioning alert system went off and we were asked to go out on a search-and-rescue mission.

So we jumped in the helicopter and headed out to Lake Eyre. As I said, nobody was hurt, but with it being such a cruel winter's day, by the time the snowbirds had clambered out of the aircraft they were cold, wet and miserable. Then one bright spark came up with an idea. To help increase their chances of being found he suggested that they strip off their wet clothes and place them down on the wing of the plane in such a way that they wrote the word 'HELP'. What's more it'd help dry their clothes.

So we tracked them via their emergency alarm until we saw this little dot in the middle of the lake. As we came in closer, the helicopter pilot said, 'I can't land in water but I'll just fly over to reassure them that we know where they are. Then we'll head to the nearest station property and sort things out from there.'

'Righto. No worries.'

So the pilot flew down and hovered over these snowbirds so they'd know they'd been found. But then, as we pulled away, the helicopter created such a huge updraft that it lifted all their clothes up in the air and scattered them back into the water. So now their almost-dried clothes were all wet again, which they weren't too happy about. And so a few of them started shaking their fists at us.

Anyhow, we contacted the people at Muloorina Station, which was the nearest property to where the snowbirds were, and when we arrived they had some flat-bottom boats ready for us. So we got some four-wheel drives, loaded them up with the flat-bottom boats and we drove down as close to the ditched aeroplane as we could. We then put the flat-bottom boats in the water and sort of walked them out to the aeroplane and we began to bring these cold, wet and miserable snowbirds back to shore. From there we took them back to Muloorina Station where they were to stay the night until a couple of light planes could be organised to come and pick them up.

But the odd thing about it was, almost as soon as we started to bring them into Muloorina, two small aeroplanes landed. One was the RFDS plane from Port Augusta, who'd been asked to come up just in case we needed backup, and right behind that was the Channel 9 news plane from Adelaide. Now, how on earth they found out about the accident so fast, I would not have a clue. Anyway, it was quite funny, because here we are, out on an outback station; it'd been a tough day, so everyone's a bit rough around the gills and looking tardy, and then this lady from the Channel 9 news crew steps out of their plane, looking like she'd just walked right out of a fashion magazine. And when she started running around, wanting to interview everybody, we were like, 'Look, excuse me, can't you see that we're a bit busy trying to coordinate a rescue here?'

But all turned out well. When she'd got her story she relaxed and she and her film crew started helping us out. And after we'd rescued the last of the snowbirds, the people from Muloorina provided us all with a barbecue then we all bunked down in the shearers' quarters together. So as good a night as possible was had by all.

Next to Buckley's

When I look back over my thirty years of nursing, the greatest change to working remote has been the huge advance in communications. When I first started, there was no internet or mobile phones. In fact, the flashest piece of technology we had was a fax machine. People were just stunned as to how you could write something down on a piece of paper, put it through a fax machine and it'd come out the other end, thousands of miles away, as an exact copy. And nowadays a fax machine is obsolete. The only time you're likely to see one is in a museum.

Anyhow, this incident also happened at Moomba. Usually, throughout that north-eastern area, it's as dry and desolate as you could possibly imagine. But for some reason, again there'd been a lot of rain and it'd caused extensive flooding. Anyhow, there was this bloke who'd always dreamed of trekking from Innamincka north-west through the Sturt Stony Desert and up to Birdsville, which is just over the border into Queensland. He was a very experienced bushman. He'd done all his research. He had all the maps and backpacks, and to help carry his supplies, he'd made a special cart that he could harness himself into.

All was set. Then, at the last minute he decided to take a younger mate of his along, an Englishman, who was a very inexperienced bushman. But that was okay because this was in the middle of winter, and even though it gets bitterly cold at night, the days would be comfortable for travelling. So these two set off from Innamincka and they'd been walking for a couple of days. Now, in those regions, when you get big rains, a lot of water comes down all the little creeks and anabranches and it overflows across the floodplains, so there's surface water spreading out everywhere. Naturally, because this water's such a rare occurrence, it doesn't appear on a map. Anyhow, they came to this big spread of surface water. They then had to make a decision: Do we take a couple of extra days and go around it or do we try and walk across?

As a trial, they walked out a couple of hundred yards, and because it was only a foot or so deep, they decided to walk across. To save their supplies from getting wet they took as much as they could out of the cart and added it to their personal load. After they'd reached the other side they were going to load the cart up again and continue the journey. So off they go, walking through the surface water. But there must've been a washaway that wasn't marked on the map because suddenly they went from knee deep to well over head deep. And as loaded as they were, they sank like stones.

Somehow the inexperienced Englishman managed to scramble to safety. But when he looked around, the experienced bushman wasn't there. It was only sometime later that he found him, face down, still harnessed to the cart, and unfortunately he'd drowned. The Englishman's first thought was to get his mate back onto dry land. So he unstrapped all of the dead fellow's gear, cart and all. Then to lighten his own load, he left all his gear beside the cart and he started dragging his dead mate back through this stretch of surface water. Eventually he made it to higher ground, but when he went back to get his gear, he couldn't find where he'd left it.

So there he was, out in the middle of nowhere with his dead mate, with nothing but the clothes he was wearing, which was a pair of shorts and a T-shirt. That's all. He'd even taken his shoes off. Now he's thinking, How do I get myself out of this mess? I've never been in the outback before. I don't even know where I am. More than likely I'll die, because while there's plenty of water around the place, I've got nothing to eat. Then he remembered that two days previously they'd crossed something that resembled a graded track. He thought, If I can get back to the track, I might be able to find someone.

So he left his dead mate under a tree and he started backtracking. For two days he stumbled through the bush until he eventually came across a dirt track. But unbeknown to the Englishman, this track was never meant for vehicles; it was what's known as a 'shot line'. Now, with oil and gas exploration, they just sort of bulldoze these tracks through the desert, in a grid-like fashion, so that, when they fly over them, they act as survey points. That's all they are – survey points. But not knowing that, the Englishman sat beside the track, hoping that a car might appear and he'd be saved. When no cars came along he decided that it'd be better if he kept moving. He was then faced with another problem: Do I turn right and walk and see what I can find, or do I turn left?

What you've got to realise at this point is that this Englishman's away out in the Sturt Stony Desert and the nearest town, Innamincka, is a hundred k's away. But he decides, for whatever reason, to turn left and walk down the track a bit and see how he goes. So that's what he did and about a mile or so further on he walks over a small sandy rise and there, sitting out in the middle of all this vast nowhere, is a wrecked telephone booth.

Now, about fifteen years before this, there'd been a little camp there that the grader drivers had used when they were marking out the shot lines. You know, there might've been four or five guys, living there in caravans for a week or so before they moved on. And back then they never had radios for communication. All they had was one of those old wind-up telephones, which they'd stick a makeshift telephone box around and then they'd run maybe twenty or thirty miles of above-ground telephone cable over the desert until it met up with another of their telephone cables, and they'd just splice into that. Then when they abandoned the camp, they'd pick up the telephone box, wind the cable up and move on to the next site and set up camp again. But for some inexplicable reason, the grader drivers had abandoned the lot.

When the Englishman saw this telephone box, it's like an apparition. The problem being, it'd been exposed to the elements for so long that the doors were hanging off, there were no windows, and the old Bakelite receiver was all cracked. So the Englishman gets into this telephone box, picks up the receiver and he starts winding the handle. And all of a sudden, out of the deadness comes this voice. 'Hello Santos, Moomba Comms. Can I help you?'

After the Englishman had told his tale of woe to the communications guy at Moomba, the comms guy said, 'Look, we didn't even know that this telephone line existed, so do you have any idea where you are?'

'No,' said the Englishman. 'Two days into our walk from Innamincka to Birdsville my mate drowned and I backtracked for a couple of days until I came across this track and I turned left and over the rise there was this telephone box.'

The comms guy said, 'Tell you what: stay on the line, I'll get a couple of old blokes who were out on the surveying camps years ago. Perhaps they can give us a rough idea as to where you might be.'

Anyway, these couple of old crusty blokes came in. When they were told the story they didn't hold out too much hope of locating him. But still, they blew the dust off their old survey maps and laid them out on the table. 'Gawd, it could be this camp.' 'No, it couldn't be that one, but this other camp could be the one.' And between them they sort of figured out, 'Well, he might be somewhere in this area; then again he could be somewhere else. But if we were going to have a guess, there's as good a place as any to start looking.'

That's when I was called. 'Look,' they said, 'we've got a guy. He's out there somewhere in an old telephone box. He's on the line and we want you to go out with the helicopter pilot to try and find him.'

So we got the helicopter pilot in and these crusty old miners suggested that we do a grid search, starting from the point where they thought the Englishman might possibly be. Now, in fact, this lost Englishman could've been at any one of a hundred and fifty possible old camp sites throughout that area. Anyway, we got into the chopper and off we went. An hour or so later, this Englishman was still on the phone to Moomba Comms. Next minute he looked out of the telephone box and there's this chopper coming towards him, so he starts waving and going on. Then, when the pilot brought the chopper in to land, he switched off the engine and he walked over to the Englishman. 'Excuse me,' he said, 'are you the guy who phoned for a taxi?'

And this English guy couldn't believe it. Neither could we. All the cards had fallen his way. Like, it was tragic that his mate had died, but he said, 'I've never believed in God but gees, I do now.'

Anyway, before we went back to try and find his mate's body, first of all we flew the Englishman back to Moomba where I checked him over. While his feet were badly blistered and he had a bit of sunburn, amazingly, he wasn't too bad other than, of course, with having not eaten for a couple of days, he was extremely hungry. So after I'd finished a basic heath check, I threw him a pair of overalls and said, 'Put these on and we'll go and get you something to eat.'

Now the Moomba mess hall is this great big dining room. It can cater for up to four hundred workers and the food's phenomenal. You can get just about anything. It's like a huge buffet at a hotel. So we go into this mess hall and this Englishman, like an hour and a half earlier he thought he was going to die from starvation and now he walks into this food fest. In an instant he'd grabbed a plate and he'd piled it high with three huge T-bone steaks. And I've never seen anyone wolf down three T-bone steaks so quick. Just as he'd finished he turned to me and said, 'Oh, cripes, I've just forgotten. I'm a vegetarian. I haven't eaten meat in ten years.' Then he said, 'But I tell you what, that was the best meal I've ever had in my entire life.'

Christopher's Story
September '93

I'm the current chief executive officer of CRANA*plus*, the peak professional body for the remote and isolated health workforce throughout Australia. I grew up near Kapunda, South Australia. Mum and Dad had some land and ran sheep, then cattle at one point, and they did some cropping. It was a great place to live, with a lot of space where I could run around barefooted. I went to Kapunda Primary School, then on to Kapunda High School. The actual high school building was Sir Sidney Kidman's — the Cattle King's — old homestead which he donated in perpetuity. So it was pretty cool having such a history behind it. In actual fact, at CRANA*plus* we do all this workforce data analysis and it shows that most of the people who end up in rural and remote health come from a rural or remote upbringing. I guess I just followed that line.

But at that time, even though I felt destined to work somewhere in the healthcare area, I don't actually recall what sparked the idea of nursing. I guess I was just lucky to have fallen into a career that I love. When I left school, I did a really diverse and intensive three-year nursing course at university, which prepared me well. Then my last placement before graduating was at Angaston Hospital, in the Barossa Valley. They had a well-skilled group of sisters and nurses — and they were still called sisters back then — who I absolutely looked up to. There I was, their first university-trained and their first male nurse, and they were keen to teach me all they knew. In those days they wore white dresses and red cardigans, while I had to wear white pants and a white top. After I'd graduated, I continued on at Angaston, still in my white pants and white top. I remember one of the older sisters named Margaret. She was this big, intimidating German woman. Being very much her junior, I was terrified of getting anything wrong. One day at handover, she looked me up and down. 'Christopher,' she said, 'I think it's time you got yourself a red cardigan.' And that was it. I felt as though I'd made it. I was over the moon, and it had nothing to do with the university degree. It was all about Sister Margaret deciding that I was good enough to fit in.

Angaston was a busy hospital. It had about forty beds. There were two general areas, a labour ward and a maternity area. Most of the time a midwife was on duty. If not, we'd call one in. Then we had two largish private general practices who'd send their doctors up if there was an emergency. The emergency department dealt with some terrible vehicle accidents, mainly from along the Sturt Highway. I was a volunteer ambulance officer and we attended a few real nasty ones on Sedan Hill, with rollovers and that. Often they were young males going too fast and losing control. Another unsettling one was where both the parents and one of their children were killed and a second child was trapped in the car.

From Angaston I went to Coober Pedy as a second-year nurse, on a three-month locum. I remember loading up my little red Pulsar and heading off. Coober Pedy's a very isolated place. In many ways it's like the Wild West. It's about eight hundred and fifty k's north of Adelaide and I'd never been so far from home. After I got to Port Augusta, I just kept driving and driving and driving. Glendambo's about the nearest place north of Port Augusta and that's at least three hundred k's. There's nothing at Glendambo; just a petrol stop. Then it was another two hundred and fifty k's further on to Coober Pedy.

There were about forty-six different nationalities in Coober Pedy, which made it quite chaotic at times. It was a smaller hospital than Angaston, with about ten beds. It was fairly new and quite an unusually shaped building, almost on the top of a hill and sort of rounded. You could just about walk up one side of the hospital, over the top and down the other. A registered nurse and one enrolled nurse were on duty at all times. The main focus was on the emergency area. With this being my first remote locum, it got quite confronting. At times I was wondering, What on earth am I doing here? There were the local Aboriginal people who I got to know well. Then at different times of the year, we'd have the people coming down from the Pitlands — Pitjantjatjara Lands — and they were quite different. When alcohol got involved there was a lot of social unrest and the level of inter-Indigenous conflict would get nasty. It was all to do with family, which was too complicated for an outsider like me to fully understand. But it was almost like warring factions. I'm sure the police had a much better insight. We just sort of saw the carnage of it.

Yes, so I was meant to be there for three months and after a year I went to the director of nursing and said, 'Do you realise that my three-month contract expired like about nine months ago?'

She said, 'Well, you didn't say anything so I just assumed you wanted to stay.'

In the end I stayed three years. I even bought my first house there, a comfortable four-bedroom dugout. And I got to love Coober Pedy. It's a very active place. People were quite engaged and there was an intense friendship group within the chalkies — schoolteachers — the coppers and the nurses. So much so that you'd only have to cook at home once a week. It was a true outback experience and I got to do stuff I'd never get to do anywhere else. Even though the town's dusty and most things are underground, you didn't have to go far to find beautiful waterholes. Then there's the Breakaways and Dalhousie Springs where we'd go and camp out in swags, under the stars.

Again I was with the volunteer ambulance. The worst trauma I attended was in September '93. I'd been on night shift. It was early afternoon and I'd just woken up. I was still in my pyjamas when the phone rang. 'Oh,' they said, 'we've heard there's been a minibus rollover about seventy k's out on the William Creek Road. We don't know if anyone's injured. Are you okay to go?'

'Yeah, no worries.'

It was around 4 or 5 o'clock in the afternoon when me and another nurse hooked up with our female volunteer ambulance driver. Actually, it was her first day on the job. With it being such a long way out, they'd decided to send two ambulances, just in case. We were in the old sedan. Ahead of us was the big four-wheel drive, with two volunteer ambulance officers in it. It was a pretty rugged road — all dirt and corrugations — and it was cold and blowy.

Anyway, we were driving along and the other nurse and I were just nattering away. About thirty k's out of town, the ambulance in front of us got a flat tyre so we stopped and asked, 'Do you want us to give you a hand?'

'No,' they said, 'we'll be there soon. You just go on and assess the situation.'

So we tootled on for a while longer — chatting away — and just as we came around this big sweeping bend, there, about a kilometre in front of us, was one of the most harrowing scenes I'd ever seen. Spread across the road was this twisted, deformed tourist bus with a big trailer, and there were people and bodies everywhere. The poor ambulance driver stopped at the shock of it. She just sat there, shaking at the wheel, and we're like, 'You have to drive closer.'

When the people saw the ambulance, they started to run down the road toward us. It turned out to be a group of about forty-five fifteen- and sixteen-year-old kids from a college in Melbourne who were on an outback trip. The bus had hit a large bulldust-covered pot hole. It'd then rolled and slid along the road, smashing all the windows down one side, before it'd rolled onto its roof, then back onto its side. Some of the kids had been thrown from the bus when it rolled and it'd fallen back on top of them as it kept sliding.

One girl was killed outright. The bus driver had been ejected out the front window. From memory, he'd broken his back. Ten kids were critical, with injuries like degloved legs, which means all the tissue had been ripped off. One girl was unconscious, with head injuries; another girl's arm had been amputated. There was a number of broken arms and legs, and a few of the kids were still trapped inside the bus. They were okay, though extremely disoriented and frightened. The kids who weren't badly injured were trying to assist those that were, as were the two or three schoolteachers. They were okay, though one had a smashed nose and her face was a mass of blood. She looked terrible, but she kept on helping.

By this stage it was getting on dark and there we were, amid this horrific scene, seventy k's from the nearest help. I'm not sure how long it was before the other ambulance arrived; probably another ten or so minutes. The thing was, we had to get the message back to the hospital that this was far worse than just a minibus rollover with no specific injuries. Thankfully a few cockies had heard about the accident and they'd positioned their vehicles about fifteen or so k's apart, along the road back toward Coober Pedy, so that we could relay the message to the hospital that they now had to prepare for this massive unfolding emergency. With the hospital only having one doctor, a visiting ear, nose and throat surgeon and five or six nurses to call on, when the message reached them, they were like, 'Oh my God.'

On that night, a lot of police and teachers were at a party in town so someone from the hospital ran down there, turned the music off and announced, 'There's a big emergency. We need all the help we can get.' When the extent of the accident was explained, people started ripping out the back seats of their four-wheel drives to accommodate as many people as possible and heading out to the accident, accompanied by somebody who was able to care for the injured during the hour-long trip back to the hospital.

I was one of the first to head back to town. I was in the four-wheel-drive ambulance with the two most critically injured girls: the one with the head injuries and a degloved leg, and the one who'd had her arm amputated. By then the police and a few of the teachers were arriving on the scene. But all the supplies were depleted. I had no more IV fluids, no drugs, nothing, so I just sat in the back of the ambulance comforting these girls the best I could. An Aboriginal police aide, Jack Crombie, was driving the ambulance. Jack's a beautiful old man, a real gentleman and a total diplomat. The thing was, Jack was a very cautious driver. It was like *Driving Miss Daisy*, which was kind of good, but it was also going to take us at least two hours to get back. So I'm going, 'Jack, can we go a bit faster?' and he's like, 'But it's a bad road. It's dirt.' And I'm saying, 'Yeah I know that, but we've got to get these girls back as quick as we can or they may die.'

So Jack kindly picked up the pace a bit. By this time the town had woken to the news and a massive response was underway. The logistics were huge. The RFDS were flying in from Alice Springs, Broken Hill, Port Augusta and Adelaide and their people needed to be picked up from the airport and taken out to the accident scene or to the hospital. Stores had opened to provide us with eskies and ice. So when we reached town, people were walking across the main street everywhere. I said to Jack, 'You really should put the emergency ambulance lights and sirens on to warn people to get out of the way.'

When Jack couldn't find the switch, I leaned through from the back and turned it on and so we headed down the main street with the sirens and lights full on. Good. So now I'm preparing the girls for our arrival. Jack then drives into the emergency entrance, where everyone's waiting. But poor old Jack's now stuck in the ambulance bay, trying to find the switch to turn the sirens and lights off. Everything's still going full blast and the sound's resonating through the entire hospital building. When the back door of the ambulance opened, I was greeted by a group of drained-white faces.

Anyhow, Jack finally found the switch and we got through it. But it was a miracle that nobody else died in the accident, and it was an amazing community effort. In all it took about thirteen hours to evacuate people from the scene and those that needed further treatment were flown out to larger city hospitals.

Under a Tree

From Coober Pedy, I had a year off. When I say 'off', what happened was, I'd applied to work overseas with Red Cross and had to wait a year while they went through all the processing stuff. So I went to Oenpelli, which is in west Arnhem Land, in the Northern Territory. Working in the NT isn't like working anywhere else. It's a bizarre place but it seems to function. It was a true remote nursing experience. There was no hospital, just a clinic. We had four nurses: one was the manager, then there were us three nurses. We also had two Aboriginal health workers. Being the only bloke, I took on a bit of men's health. Generally speaking, I'd go into the waiting room and the receptionist would tell me if someone preferred to see a male nurse or not, and I'd take it from there. Health issues included the usual rashes and coughs, and there were a lot of sick babies with chest infections and the like.

Babies are usually quite resilient but when they get sick, they get sick very quickly. Next thing they're nearly dead. The problem was trying to capture them before they dropped, and unfortunately, in a lot of remote communities, you don't have that opportunity. You only see them when they're really sick, and it's not easy to get fluid into a really sick baby. If you put a nasal gastric tube down, they'll often just vomit up the fluid, so, in those days, we put intravenous lines in. And that's not easy in an adult, let alone in a tiny baby who's as flat as a tack.

Oenpelli was a beautiful community, apart from when the tavern was open and the people drank too much. But an incident that really sticks out was when we got a call from one of the outer camps: 'A lady's got a stomach ache. Can you come out?'

The woman wasn't known to the community. Her group could've been from elsewhere in Arnhem Land and they were passing through, which was why she was in one of the outer camps. Anyway, we went out to pick her up. When I got there, the lady's under a tree and there's a baby halfway out. Around her were some concerned older women. If the baby had been alive, the older women would've delivered it, as they had done for hundreds of years. But it was dead. So here I am, a bloke, arriving on a scene of what normally would be women's business and I'm up the proverbial creek.

Luckily we had HF radios and I rang Rhonda, a midwife at Oenpelli. So Rhonda comes out, she just waltzes in and clears a bit of sand next to this lady. Then she just plopped down and she's like, 'Calm down. How's it going?', and she helped make sure that the placenta was delivered okay. There was no drama. No stress. It was very respectful, and it was respectful of the older ladies too. Finally it was agreed that the lady should come into the clinic for a cup of tea, which was how we got her and the deceased baby back to Oenpelli. And that's how you learn, by watching these amazing nurses do their craft. And watching Rhonda in action was fantastic. She must surely be one of the gurus of remote nursing.

But that attitude of 'Oh, someone's got a stomach ache' was quite typical up there. If it was major drama, people would be cool, calm and collected. I once got the call, 'Two boys were runnin' 'round the yard 'n they banged into each other.'

I said, 'Well, they can come up to the clinic.'

They said, 'No, they can't come up to the clinic.'

I thought, Okay, I'll drive down to where they are. When I got there, it was quite a major trauma. They boys weren't just 'running around in the yard', as I'd been told; they were driving cars and they'd collided head-on.

Other times, people would come in all hysterical: 'There's an old lady! She's not breathing!'

'Where is she?'

'Oh, she's standin' right behind you.'

So it was very difficult to gauge the degree of an event, especially when you're new to working remote or cross-culturally, and so mistakes can easily be made. Though the first rule of thumb is that you always go out for children, no matter what. Just from a telephone conversation, you don't know how far they've gone. Even if you've already seen the kid twice you might think, 'Nah, they'll be okay,' and of course they're not.

So Oenpelli proved to be a great experience. I was there during the transition of the health service being handed over to the community to control. I then went to Amata, which is about fifteen hundred k's north-west of Adelaide, in the Anangu Pitjantjatjara Yankunytjatjara Lands. It was similar remote nursing to Oenpelli, though, being away out in the desert, over near the Western Australian border and just south of the Northern Territory border, they were different people and the community was quite traditional. Mind you, there was nothing wrong with the Aboriginal bush telegraph. I was only there for twenty minutes and everybody knew who I was and why I was there and what I'd done and hadn't done previously.

That was probably about '95, and like everywhere, most people were beautiful. They kept to themselves and only came in if they needed help. But petrol sniffing was a big issue. Sometimes it was unsafe to go out at night. There was one particular group of young sniffers who'd go troppo and lose their minds and attack other people. Another time they tried to burn the clinic down.

I lived in a pretty basic sort of house. The fence had been ripped down. You could lock the front door but the lock on the back door had either been ripped off or kicked in. Again I was an ambulance volunteer. Normally, if you were on call, people would see where the ambulance was parked and come and knock on the door. Anyhow, I was sitting in the lounge one night and this old man just appeared in the kitchen. No knock or anything. Scared the shit out of me, it did. As it turned out, it was a night of men's business out in a camp and one of the young boys had been injured during his initiation. When they'd heard there was a male nurse in town, this man had come in to see if I could help. Due to tradition, the lad couldn't be seen during the day so I convinced the man to bring the boy into the clinic under the cover of darkness and I promised that no women would see him while he was there.

I can't tell you what the actual injury was. It's very secretive and they don't like you talking about it. All I can say is that it was of an interventional kind and the boy needed to be evacuated to Alice Springs. But because Amata didn't have a night airstrip, we not only had to keep him in a back room at the clinic, out of sight of any females, while we waited for the RFDS to arrive; there also had to be a male pilot and male nurse on the aircraft. But in typical community fashion, everybody soon knew that something was going on and they remained respectful of the rules. In fact, a lot of people just disappeared out of the town, so it was nice to see that level of cultural integrity still thriving.

Earthquake

After my so-called year 'off', I worked for the Red Cross in places like the Sudan, Georgia, Armenia, Azerbaijan, Afghanistan, Sri Lanka, Papua New Guinea and most recently in Haiti after the earthquake. There's two different parts of the Red Cross. There's the International Committee of the Red Cross, which is the mob that created the Geneva Conventions. They have a legal responsibility and their job is to maintain those. Then you have the International Federation of the Red Cross, who prepare for and respond to countries during times of disaster. I worked for the latter. I'm not quite sure what motivated me to do it — certainly not the money — but my accumulated nursing skills, particularly my remote experience, suited perfectly. Analysis shows that the best people for that type of overseas work are those who've had experience in resource-poor environments where they've had to be innovative and have a high level of skills.

Another advantage is, by not being involved in the particular conflict or disaster, we're neutral from the politics. But you do wear out pretty quick because you're there at a critical time to meet people's very basic needs. We work on the premise that if you give a man a fish, he'll eat today. But if you teach a man to fish, he can feed his family forever. It's the same with healthcare. If you go in and treat people, yes, they may get better, but when you leave, there's no follow-on. So a lot of the time we're showing, teaching and building relationships with the local doctors and nurses. Even then it's quite a balancing act. Organisations like the Red Cross need to be invited into a country and then tread gently-gently. I mean, we'd be pretty pissed off if say, the Americans just barged into our hospitals and said, 'This is how you should do it. That's how you should do it,' wouldn't we?

Take the Haiti earthquake for example. We were invited in there. I was back in Australia when the earthquake happened in January 2010. The disaster hadn't yet reached the mainstream news when the Red Cross got in touch. 'We need somebody who can go and go quickly.'

I was up to date with my vaccinations and my medicals and stuff so I thought, Well, okay, I've never been to that part of the world before. Next thing I'm on my way to San Francisco, then Miami, then to the Dominican Republic. By then I was well out of the news cycle and unaware of the gravity of the situation. Two countries share the one island: the Dominican Republic and Haiti. When I got to the Dominican Republic, I met up with a Japanese Red Cross unit. They all spoke English. There were two surgeons, a medical director, two nurses, someone else, and I was the public health person. We were told that we couldn't get into Haiti by sea, because the ports were destroyed, nor by air, because the runway was destroyed. So we jumped in a car and we set off over the mountains. As this was a country not to get lost in, our driver was a local. And each step of the way, we came upon more and more destruction.

Eventually we came to Port-au-Prince, which was in a bit of a basin, and I just couldn't believe my eyes. It was annihilated. I'd done a few first-response disasters before, like the Aitape tsunami in PNG and the Bali bombings, but this was, by far, the biggest and worst. The smell was gross. Bodies were lying out in the streets. The estimate was a hundred and fifty thousand deaths. Millions had been displaced. There was no water. Most of the residences had been destroyed. All the big infrastructure had come down. The hospitals had been destroyed. The schools had been destroyed. The prison had been destroyed and thousands of prisoners were running wild around the city. People thought they were going to die, and they were probably right. They had very little to lose, so there was a lot of criminality. We felt particularly insecure because a) we had water, and they didn't; b) we had food, and they didn't; and c) we had a vehicle, and they didn't.

So we made our way to this compound that the Red Cross had set up in conjunction with the UN — United Nations. They'd moved some rubble out of the way and set up the compound in the clearing. Having come self-contained, we set up our emergency response unit. That can be done quickly, with minimal infrastructure. We then started treating the wounded and every day we'd open the gates and people would just flood in. But, of course, treating the injured is just one miniscule part of disaster response. There's infrastructure. There's security. The US military had just started setting up tents for all the displaced people and children and all these sort of shanty towns were springing up almost overnight. But because the earth tremors were still occurring, it was impossible for us to get into some of them. Oh, it was a complete catastrophe.

Now I do bless the Japanese, but they do come from a very traditional medical model and hospital environment. They don't have remote areas. But with having worked in remote Aboriginal communities, I'd seen some of these diseases related to poverty. Like they couldn't work out what the rashes were, and I'm going, 'Guys, it's scabies.'

Still, it was an impossible situation. We could've handed out antibiotics all day long, but we were never going to lessen the death toll. Near us, one big camp must've held at least sixty thousand people. It was a massive sea of tents, and it only had one toilet. So really, our time may've been better spent digging holes for people to shit in. It would've likely saved many, many more lives. But for international donors and the like, putting their money into digging toilets wasn't as sexy as setting up a little hospital, so we just did the best we could.

So that was Haiti, and now back to Australia. To cut a long story short, when I'd been in the Territory, CRANA stood for the Council for Remote Area Nurses of Australia. They were low key, with just a few staff and a couple of hundred members. They put out a small magazine. They ran a dozen excellent courses around the country and they had a fun conference. So I attended one of their conferences. I knew a lot of the people. I went to some of the educational sessions. The party afterwards was fabulous and so I wasn't feeling the best at the AGM the next day. When they were looking around for a new board member, someone piped up and said, 'Oh, Chris'll do it.'

And I'm like, 'Oh yeah, whatever.'

So I got elected and I got active. A year later, when the president of the board stepped down, I put my hand up and said, 'If I get elected president, let's change things.'

Now, traditionally, remote area nurses have been the backbone of healthcare, over ninety-five per cent of the continent, for probably two hundred years. Up till twenty years ago, if you were a nurse who went bush, you had to be one of the old triple-certificated nursing sisters with probably ten years' experience. These days it's a totally different environment. I recently did a stint up in the Torres Strait, on Coconut Island. There's two hundred people on this very small island and just the one nurse. Now, that one nurse is never going to be able to provide a full medical service. If a patient wants to go to Thursday Island to receive treatment in the hospital there, that's fine. But not everybody wants that. Some people want to stay put. So the job of the nurse on Coconut Island is to get that person referred and to organise whatever services are needed, if not by a personal visit, then at least by telephone or Skype.

So when I got the job as president, I said, 'We can't afford to be a cottage industry any more. We're going to build the organisation and move it forward.' And we did. First we changed our constitution to include everyone in the remote and isolated health workforce, thus the CRANA*plus*. That entails looking after the workers' welfare and providing courses in preparation and resilience-building to ensure people have the adequate skills to work within resource-poor environments. Before that program started, catastrophic burnout of staff was much more common. We still have a high turnover of staff out remote, but at least people often come back now. The other thing to note is, because they're usually working in stressful environments, with little structure around them, we run a 24/7 counselling service via phone or Skype called the Bush Support Services. It's free, it's confidential, and it helps prevent people from burning out. And that includes health workers on ships at sea or down in Antarctica or out on mine sites or flight nurses who do aviation retrievals.

Two years ago I stood down as president. The organisation was robust. It was running well. A year later the CEO retired. Seeing how I knew the organisation inside out, I thought, I'll give it a go. I've been CEO for just over a year now and I'm loving it. I get to do lots of exciting things, as well as live in beautiful Cairns, and have a voice at both state and federal government level. What a life, ay?

Colin's Story
Born and Bred

Believe it or not, I was born right here in this very hospital at Wilcannia. In fact, I was named after the two doctors that worked here at that time. One was named Colin and the other one was Gregory. Coming from a family of eleven kids, I don't know if my mother just run out of names or not, and so when she had me and in walked these two doctors, that was it: Colin Gregory.

My mother was a local and my father was from Burra, in South Australia. He and his brother followed the railway line up here, making water storage dams for the steam trains. That was back when tank sinking was done by horse teams. Dad had a good reputation for it too. I've got a photo where he had forty-one horses working for him. That's from when he sank the biggest tank in South Australia: Oodla Wirra I think it was. It's just a little train stop up along the railway line. It was back in the Depression and it was a pretty good job, money-wise. But it's unreal the way he fluked it. He finished the Oodla Wirra tank one day and it rained the next, so it filled up overnight.

I went to the local public school but I didn't have a real good education. It's a long while ago, those days. Back then, once you got past primary school you went on to correspondence, so you never had a teacher with you. They were in Sydney. But we had a fair few primary school kids — both white and dark — and a fair few teachers. The schoolroom was in an old sandstone building and when there was too many kids for that, they used a tin shed. It'd be a hundred and bloody twenty-five in the shade and you're supposed to be concentrating on your schoolwork;

like hell. But lot of them kids I went to school with have died off now, especially the dark boys — a lot of them died young.

There was also a Catholic school. A lot of the property owners' kids used to come in and board there. The nuns ran it. This was back when the Catholics and the non-Catholics didn't get on too well so we'd have a go at them through the fence, and they couldn't get back at us because they weren't allowed outside the fence. But when we played sport against them, they used to make up for it.

After I left school I worked at the big store down the street for about five years. When I finished there I got on the public works and ended up restoring the police station. But the old supervisor at the hospital was always on to me: 'I'll get you a job. I'll get you a job.' Then one day he come to see me and said, 'There's a job there if you want it. I won't even advertise.' So I kind of said yes and I've been here forty years now.

When I started, there was thirty-six beds and twelve baby cots. It was full-on in them days. I was on the maintenance staff, as a general handyman, and I also worked the boiler. The boiler ran the hot-water service and everything for the hospital. I'd stoke it up at half past six of a morning and knock off at half past twelve, then I'd come back at four and close it down at six. Of a wintertime I'd often come in to work and there'd be dark boys sitting round in front of the boiler, trying to keep warm. 'Thanks for waking us up,' they'd say and away they go. They were no trouble.

There was six of us maintenance staff back then, and now I'm it. So they've cut it back a fair bit. These days they've got a refrigeration mechanic, a plumber, an electrician and all that who come out through the bush areas every month. They tell me I'm not allowed to touch any of the stuff the tradies do. 'Don't touch the air conditioner,' they say. Then, when the pump on the air conditioner breaks down, it's, 'Oh, we won't be out for another couple of weeks; can you fix it?' So I do.

Ten years after I started, I began on the ambulance. That's been a bit of fun. Like twenty or so years ago Wilcannia was a pretty wild town. We'd get called out to someone who had a broken leg, and while we're trying to deal with that, we'd get another call: 'There's been a stabbing.' So off we'd go and leave them. I mean, they weren't going to go too far with a broken leg, ay? But I remember the time a bloke and his wife had a big fight and she stabbed him. When we got there they were still carrying on so I got the knife off them, and when I got back to work, I threw it in the boiler. Only afterwards I thought, Gee, if that bugger dies, I've burnt the evidence.

Other times we'd get called to someone who's supposed to have a real bad back. When you'd get there they'd say, 'Won't be a tick,' and you'd see them walk out the backyard carrying a big bag of dog biscuits, off to feed the dogs before they came to the ambulance. Most cases like that, they just wanted a night in hospital. You'd have nurses, new from the city, who'd feel sorry for them, so they'd take them in for a night or two to get some tucker into them. Then on pay day, off they'd go, and they'd be back a couple days later, wanting to come in again. That used to happen a lot. Sometimes you'd even see them out the front, sticking a finger down their throat to make themselves sick. When a nurse walked outside she'd see them spewing, and she might give them a bed for a couple of nights.

That doesn't happen these days, of course. Nowadays it's all done by the law. And anyway, the hospital's also a bit of a retirement place now, so we haven't got the spare beds. There's about six or seven old people in here at present. One bloke's from out of town and he doesn't want to go back home. He likes it too much here. And one old lady was an ex-nursing sister who'd worked here years ago and she wanted to come back to town. They started out feeding her through a drip-type setup; now she's come good and she's feeding herself. We also had three old retired blokes; one was ex-navy and the others was ex-army.

They all had Gophers carts, and right on the dot of half past three, they'd get in their Gophers and away they'd go, racing each other down to the club to have a few beers. Then, after they'd had their little session, it'd be back into their Gophers and they'd race each other back to the hospital, just in time for tea.

As far as the other beds go, you get the usual medical problems. They're pretty easy to handle. If you've been around for a while you know which patient to watch. I'm sort of like a security guard to the nurses as well. If anyone comes in looking like trouble, I'll get called to the sisters' station and I'll just stand in the doorway so they can see me. But a lot of it's to do with alcohol and drugs. You get the ones who've got the DTs — delirium tremens. They get to be a bit of a problem. Then you get some of these new nurses who think they know everything, and you'd tell them to be careful because this particular patient punches out.

'Don't worry,' they'll say. 'I can handle myself.'

Next thing, *bang!* They get hit.

But the DTs can really get to some of the patients. Like years ago, a lot of them in the horrors, they'd take off on you and you'd end up having to chase them around the block. Or some of them, they'd grab onto you and they wouldn't let go. One night a bloke was playing up and when the police come to get him, he shot out the back door with the coppers after him. This was when they were building the new part of the hospital and they had a big wire fence around the back part. Anyhow, it was dark, and this fella, he runs straight into the wire fence — *bang* — down he goes, flat on his backside. Then — *bang, bang, bang* — so did the coppers. There was bodies lying about everywhere. It was like the Keystone Cops. Gee, I had a good laugh.

But oh, some of them get it real bad. Another time we had to take a fella to Broken Hill Hospital, which is a couple of hundred k's up the road a bit. He'd been playing up something terrible and so there was a police officer, a nursing sister, the ambulance driver and me. And no way was the police officer going to sit in the back with me and the patient. In the front he jumps and I'm in the back with this fella and he's kicking out and he's shouting and he's throwing his arms all around the place and I'm struggling like hell, trying to hold him down. Anyhow, we'd organised for a changeover; that's when the police from the other town meet us halfway and take over the patient. Well, I'm pretty buggered by the time we get to this changeover spot, out on the road, so I get out of the back of the ambulance to have a rest; next thing, the police are all over me. They think I'm the one who's got the DTs. And there's the patient still sitting up in the back of the ambulance.

There was another bloke in the horrors. This was back when we had the big river floods and the water got right up to the back of the hospital. Anyhow, he was in his bed, in his pyjamas, and, all of a sudden, he got it into his head that someone was chasing him. So he shot out of his bed and he took off out the back of the hospital. He dived into the river, in full flood, and he swam all the way down to the bridge. When he got to the bridge, he climbed up and he ran across to the other side; then he jumps back into the river and he swims across to the caravan park. After he got to the caravan park, he ran straight across the road and into the police station: 'Someone's chasing me! Someone's chasing me!'

I tell you, we've had blokes who've been on the grog and they've come in here for a couple of days to dry out and next thing they're knocking the bloody metho off the cleaner's trolley. That's why they took the metho off the cleaner's trolley. True; one bloke downed so much that he fell over and split his head open. Another time there was a knife on the meal trolley and a bloke in the horrors grabbed the knife and he starts chasing people around the place. Oh, you used to see it all around here. There was this dark boy; he'd been in jail in Broken Hill. Anyway, he gets out; he's got no money, so he can't work out how to get back home. He's wandering up the street when he sees this ambulance parked out the front of a house. It's still got its motor running so he jumps in and he takes off for home, with all the flashing lights and sirens blaring. And he made it. He got here. But he didn't last long. He soon ended up back in jail again.

A lot of the trouble comes from out at the mission. What happened was, when we had the big flood in '76 they moved them out the east side to higher ground, and put them up in army tents. When the flood went down, a lot of them didn't want to come back, so the government built them houses. But they have their little 'bugger-ups' amongst themselves every now and then. If they're in the horrors, we sometimes have to tackle them to the ground so we can get a needle into them, to calm them down. The police and that always wear work boots when they go out there, especially at night. See, there's no lights and there's broken bottles and that type of thing lying around, so you don't know what you're stepping on. It can get pretty rough. I've taken doctors and nurses out there and they're scared stiff that they're going to be attacked or something. But I always tell them, 'They'll make a lot of noise and they'll swear and go on, but if they know you're out there to help them, they'll respect you. They'll look after you.' And they do.

Then you get these young fellas — real good kids — who self-harm or hang themselves. That sort of knocks you around a bit, because, being such a small town, you know their family and all of their relatives.

Two years ago I reckon it was, we went out on a call. No sooner we arrived than a young fella comes running out: 'Someone's been stabbed!'

But by the time we got to him, the fella had bled out. They were a real good family too, but he'd got into a fight and he was stabbed in the heart and the blood just got pumped out of him. The thing was, the nursing sister I was with knew him really well. She'd had a lot to do with him and his family. They had a handicapped kid and she'd sometimes help take the kid over to a town that had a special school. Another time she'd organised for

Angel Flight to take the kid to Sydney for some sort of treatment or other. But this fella, he was a real big bloke and his wife was a tiny little thing and so yeah, he used to carry the handicapped kid around everywhere. After he got murdered, his wife had to do it all herself and like the kid was nearly as big as her. Anyhow, gee it knocked the nurse around. It really knocked her around, it did.

But you also get your laughs. See, the Aborigines are very suspicious people and one time there was six beds in the ward, all occupied by dark boys. And just before one of them left the hospital he said to one fella, 'See that bed you're lyin' in, someone from Wanaaring recently died in that bed.' Then he pointed to a bed that one of the other fellas was in. ''N just the other week, a bloke from White Cliffs died in that very same bed that you're in.' And he went around the ward, telling each of them how someone had recently died in the bed they were in. In the end he said, 'Well, I'm goin' now, boys. See yer later,' and, within five minutes, all the other fellas were lining up at the office to sign themselves out. There was no way they were going to stay in a bed that someone had died in. They were out of there.

Another time this dark fella was giving an old white pensioner a real hard time and the pensioner said, 'When I die, you bastard, I'm gonna come back 'n haunt you.' Anyhow, the night after the pensioner died, this young fella — the one who was giving him a hard time — he lined up to sign himself out.

'What's the matter?' the nurse asked.

'That old man,' he said, 'he's haunting me. He come back in the middle of the night 'n was tryin' to pull the blankets off me.'

So a lot of them stories are from back in the old days when it was a pretty big town. We had the old DMR — Department of Main Roads — service depot here then. That's when they was tarring the main roads, so they had a lot of vehicles. But when the DMR closed up, near on thirty families left town and once thirty families leave any small town, that's about the end of it. These days about fifty support agencies have come to help with employment for the locals. But there's no work. Like, years ago when the government work-for-the-dole scheme was on, it bettered the town and it gave people something to do. You'd see the difference in them. People was happy. The council put in new footpaths and curbing and guttering; all that type of stuff. There was so many jobs going that they might sack you one day and then they'd take you back the next: 'Here, you're re-employed.'

So she's a pretty quiet sort of place these days. But that's okay with me and I love it up at the hospital. I just like helping the old people and the ones who are in different situations because they really appreciate what you do for them. And I like it here in Wilcannia. When I was younger I was offered jobs in other places but I just wasn't interested in moving. I was happy here. My wife's the same. She come up from Adelaide and she likes it here. She says she won't move. She started out working at the service station, then she went into an office and now she's just finished with TAFE — Technical and Further Education. She worked with TAFE for twenty-five years, then one day they discovered that her position was supposed to be for an Aboriginal person, and she wasn't. So they put her off just last Christmas.

But she'll walk down the street and she'll see a young dark kid with a baby in a pram and she'll always want to have a nurse of the baby and a bit of a chat to see how they're going. That's how you gain respect. You get to know everyone, and if you look after them, they'll look after you. We never lock our house and we've never had any trouble. Wilcannia's that sort of place. People rubbish the place, but most of them have never even been out here to find out. We had this nurse that pulled up down the road, at Cobar, and she was told to top her car up with petrol because it's too dangerous to stop in a town like this.

She said, 'Well, I've worked out there for the last six months and I haven't seen anything too dangerous.' She said, 'Perhaps you should go over and have a look.'

'Oh yeah,' they said. 'Perhaps I might.'

Dianne's Story
On the Inside

Even though my older sister did her training at Royal Townsville Hospital, in Queensland, and my mother worked there as a domestic, I had no inclination toward nursing. Instead, I followed in my father's footsteps and became a soldier, as did my twin brother. That was in 1983 and I went to the Women's Royal Australian Army Corps School at Mosman, in Sydney. We were the second last intake there. After that the women who enlisted started in Kapooka. I went on to be a trainee cartographer at the army base in Bonegilla, on the Victorian–New South Wales border, then I transferred across to the signal corps, at Watsonia, in Melbourne.

My husband, Peter, was also in the army. As with most relationships in the military, it's difficult for both partners to be posted to the same place at the same time. I first met Peter at his farewell from Cabarlah in Queensland. The day I marched into the barracks was the day before he was heading off on a posting. We got on well for the two hours we spoke and we met up again six months later when I went to Melbourne for a course. I was just about to head off to Canberra on a posting and so we got engaged pretty much straight away, and soon after we got married. For our wedding, Peter flew from Melbourne to Canberra and from Canberra we drove up to Townsville, which was where my parents were living at that time. After a night in the new casino up there, our honeymoon was spent driving around Far North Queensland for four weeks before heading back to Melbourne, where I dropped Peter off. Then I drove back to Canberra, where I stayed until I was also transferred back to Melbourne six months later.

When Peter later moved over to the air force, we realised that if I stayed in the army we'd never get posted together. So I also applied for the air force. After seven years in the army, I finished up at midnight on the Sunday and enlisted in the air force at 9 o'clock the following morning. A couple of years later we had our first child, a son, while we were over in Perth, and when he was six weeks old, we moved to Canberra. Eleven months later, when our daughter was born, I got in touch with the air force and said, 'Look, I think I might get out now.'

By that stage my parents were living in Adelaide and when a few years later my mother was given just a couple of months to live, Peter got a compassionate posting here. Anyhow, one day I heard on the radio that they were taking nursing students at UniSA, so I applied. I suppose my thinking was that, wherever Peter was sent, there'd always be a medical centre nearby. Being in my early thirties, I was one of the older students. It was quite tough at times, especially with an ill mother, Peter being away so often, plus there was the kids' schooling. But I guess if you want something enough, you'll work hard for it to happen. And when I'd finally completed the three-year course, the kids were so proud. They were eight and nine at that time and they'd always been very quiet children, but when I had my degree conferred, all I could hear was my son calling out, 'Good on you, Mum!'

My first position was at Ashford Hospital. I started out in emergency, which I absolutely loved. Then I went to the maternity ward, and I don't know if it was because I was older or if it was because I'd already had children, but it just wasn't for me. So I went over to the high dependency and intensive care units at the Memorial Hospital which was more of a fit. Then one day when we were moving a patient, she grabbed onto me and she basically ripped my shoulder: ligament damage, bursitis and all that sort of thing. So that was that. I wasn't able to lift people any more. I didn't wanting to be on worker's compensation, so when a male nursing friend said, 'How about you come and work at Holden's? You won't have to lift people,' I thought I'd give that a go.

I did the afternoon shift, five days a week. Basically you had to be there just in case something happened, and you'd be surprised how often things did happen. Injuries varied. There were return-to-work assessments, treatments, continuing care and things like that. We also had some silly people doing silly things, like driving too fast and T-boning each other. The thing was, with those European cars being left-hand drive, we had to explain to the hospital why their injuries were on the opposite side of their bodies than what they would've been in a right-hand-drive vehicle. Still, it was lots of fun. That was back in Holden's heyday and I only left because the group of doctors I worked for had been asked to tender for their own positions, and they weren't successful. I wasn't happy with that, so when the other company took over, I only stayed on for a little while. Then, when the same male nursing friend said, 'Hey, I'm now doing casual work at the prisons. How about you come here?' I thought I'd give that a go.

The person who interviewed me was Raylee Kinnear. Raylee was director of nursing for the South Australian Prison Health Service and she was the most amazingly wonderful woman. Raylee was responsible for around a hundred and fifty nurses, plus all the doctors, dentists, occupational therapists and psychologists, plus all the medical services and health provisions for every patient, in every prison and remand centre throughout the entire state — and her office was virtually a cupboard under the stairs in the main building at the old Glenside Hospital. And she had to do it on a shoestring budget. Raylee was just great. I went to the interview hoping for a part-time casual position and I walked out with a full-time job at Adelaide Remand Centre.

I started out as a nurse-on-site and a year later I became nurse manager, in charge of the daily running of the remand centre. Part of my responsibilities included the prison opioid substitution program. That's where medications like naloxone and methadone were given to prisoners to help treat their drug addiction. The problem was, many of them would try to sell or trade the drugs with other prisoners. For example, naloxone's a tablet that's placed on the tongue and they're supposed to swallow it. But they were forever trying to hide it under their tongue or in a tooth cavity so that they could sell it on. Same with methadone. Methadone came in a pre-bottled dose to be taken with water. The thing was, they'd then go back to their room and regurgitate it through a sock or something, to take out any lumpy bits, and sell it on.

Oh God yes, the easiest thing to get in a prison is drugs. The other day I heard that they had drones dropping drugs over the prison walls. They'd also try and smuggle them in in babies' nappies or through kissing their girlfriends. Then sometimes their mates would load up tennis balls full of drugs, and while the prison officers were busy sorting out a concocted riot at one end of the prison, their mates would be hurling the tennis balls over the wall down the other end. So there were huge issues with drugs, and you also had to be careful not to fall for some of their stories or get too familiar with them. The thing is, you have to realise that prison's not some sort of game, because while we get to go home, they don't. Prison's their life and there's no respite from the intensity of it. And so, if any of us are favouring one prisoner over any of the others, there can be dire consequences. It's what's called 'splitting'.

Most times it's prisoner against prisoner, and under the dictates of prison justice, they'll never tell anyone what actually happened. It's just amazing how many times a badly injured prisoner has been brought to the infirmary and they'll tell you they've slipped over in the shower or they've fallen and hit their head on a hand basin, even if you can see the footprints all over them. But the group that's most prone to prison justice is the protectee prisoners. They're the paedophiles, the rapists, the informants or those who have harmed a child or the elderly. They have to be under full-time protection from the mainstream prisoners, because prison justice decrees that if a prisoner comes across a protectee, they're to inflict maximum injury upon them. To that end we even had to set aside a separate day for the protectees to be escorted to the medical centre.

If trouble occurs, there's different alert codes. Code Yellow means 'officer requires assistance'. When that happens, there's an instant lockdown and the other officers run to their mate's aid. The medical staff then wait for a Code Black, which is a 'medical emergency'. A Code Black means that somebody's been hurt or they've been smashed up or they're hanging. A Code Blue is when we attend. All prison officers are trained in first aid, which is good, because I've had them doing CPR while I'm busy getting lines in or getting the oxygen on or attending to injuries. And I can tell you I've seen some really nasty things: deaths, hangings, attempted murders, lots and lots of assaults and hundreds of slash-ups. Slash-ups are often caused by patients with mental health issues who find that self-harming makes them feel emotionally better. It's a release, as are the attempted hangings.

Yes, so working in the prison system was a very interesting experience. Though in saying that, I've never felt safer as a nurse than I was in the prison environment. That's because, for your own protection, a prison officer is with you at all times. It's all out in the open. They've got your back and you've got theirs. So if someone on the medical staff gets hurt, the attending prison officer will get blacklisted, and I guess that could also be described as yet another form of prison justice.

In Detention

I left the prison system and took leave without pay to get a feel for working in the detention field. That's how I ended up at the Inverbrackie Immigration Detention Centre. The centre opened at the end of 2010. It was only ten minutes from home. There was a huge stink over its location in the Adelaide Hills. To begin with, a lot of Hills people thought that their property values and so forth would diminish. Then in the end, nobody wanted it to close down because of the economic benefits it'd brought to the area. I was a clinical team leader there, and as I was to discover, nursing in any detention centre's probably the hardest gig you'll ever have. From the moment you arrive at work to the minute you leave, it's an emotional drain; it's extremely traumatic and some of their stories were very challenging. Too challenging for some. We had one young female doctor of Iranian background who was in great demand, but it proved to be all too much for her, so she didn't last. Everyone pleaded for her to stay, but she couldn't. And that's just one case of burnout. There were numerous others.

Most of the 'detainees' were flown from Christmas Island to Adelaide Airport, then bussed up to Inverbrackie, where we'd be on hand, along with the interpreters and other staff, to do initial checks to see that they were okay. Over the next few days we'd conduct further medical assessments. The people came from all over: we had Afghans, Tamils, Kurds, Iranians and Iraqis, plus a few families from Pakistan and Syria. To that end we not only had to deal with a lot of different cultural backgrounds but we also had to be wary that certain religious groups couldn't mix with other religious groups. Then there were the different expectations of what would happen to them once they got here. Most of the child-bearing-aged females were desperate to become pregnant because they were under the mistaken belief that if their baby was born in Australia, they'd gain automatic citizenship. And that is not how it worked. Language issues were another huge problem, and while our interpreters were fantastic, they also didn't last too long. Again, a case of burnout.

However, the worst thing I found was that my personal security wasn't what it could've been, and everybody should feel safe in their place of work. While the security people did a great job, there was a deep unsettledness about the place. It was as if things could blow up at any given minute. As well as that, we had to cope with a lot of political issues. Anyhow, I stuck it out until I was asked to go to Christmas Island. Why I agreed to go, I don't know. With Christmas Island being the detainees' first point of contact, it was obviously going to be much 'heavier' than Inverbrackie. In fact, there always seemed to be the potential for a riot. But no sooner had I returned from Christmas Island than I was asked to come back to Adelaide as there were issues back there as well. Not long after that I got a call from head office in Sydney: 'We want you to project-manage the new detention centre at Pontville. It'll only be for a few weeks.'

I'd never project-managed, but with it only being for a few weeks, I thought it'd be an interesting challenge. 'Okay,' I said. 'When would you like me to start?'

'In the morning.'

I said, 'Pardon? What morning?'

They said, 'Tomorrow morning. You'll need a good GPS, or you'll never find the place, and, because of the weather, you'd better take a pair of knee-high gumboots and a raincoat.'

So I did all that. Most of our setup team stayed in Hobart, in a lovely place called the Old Wool Store, and we had hire cars. Michael, our health manager, was a hell of a nice guy and we worked well together. Pontville's about fifty kilometres out of Hobart. It's right next to the town of Brighton, and because no one else had been cleared to enter the detention centre site, we had to begin interviewing for staff at the local bakery. The detention centre itself was being built on Crown Land, on an old army firing range. By the time we arrived many of the buildings were already in place and it was just a case of us checking that they were suitable for our medical staff and to house all the medical equipment and supplies. In the end there were five or six buildings and we employed a group of about thirty mental health nurses, general nursing staff and administration. And they were great.

Just like Inverbrackie, the detainees were flown in from Christmas Island, and, due to time differences, sometimes we'd have to be out at Pontville at one in the morning to check everyone. But unlike Inverbrackie, Pontville was a four-hundred single-men's detention centre, and being an all-male setup, it had its own particular issues. Other than the usual medical conditions, we had to deal with a lot of psychological mental health issues. Again there was that huge emotional drain within a very unsettling atmosphere. And it was cold. I froze.

As I said, I was originally told that I'd only be there for a few weeks and it ended up being more like three months. Anyhow, when it came time to leave, Michael, my health manager, had to write an appraisal on me. When I went to pick it up he said, 'I've just put three letters on it.'

I said, 'Yeah, what's that?'

He goes, 'FSH.'

I said, 'What does that mean?'

'Fuckin' shit hot.'

Out Bush

Nurses keep in touch. The network's alive and well. I'd email someone to see how they were going and they'd email back, telling me what they were doing. Anyhow, this girl I'd met through the detention centre system got in touch. 'Hey, why don't you come and work up on the Queensland gas pipeline?'

It sounded like a good idea, so I contacted the company involved and I flew up to Brisbane for an interview. I thought I was going for a position out on Curtis Island but the woman said, 'No, you can't have Curtis Island because you need to have one year's experience in the construction field for that.'

I said, 'Well, unfortunately I don't have any construction field experience at all. But I'm more than willing to learn.'

She then had a bit of a think. 'Oh,' she said, 'we've also got a job just out from Miles. It's a greenfield, meaning it's a start-up site. Oh, but you have to have three years' experience for that one.'

I said, 'Well, if I haven't got one year's construction field experience then I obviously haven't got three years' experience, have I?'

After the interview I phoned my husband, Peter, and said, 'Well, that was a wasted trip.'

When I got back to Adelaide, the woman who'd interviewed me rang, wanting to know what I was planning to do next. This was on the Wednesday. I said, 'I've just been asked to go back to Christmas Island on Saturday, but I really don't want to go because Christmas Island's a real burden.'

'Okay,' she said. And that was that. Then on the Thursday afternoon she rings again. 'We'd like to offer you a position.'

I said, 'Fantastic. I've never been to Curtis Island.'

'No,' she said, 'we're sending you out to Miles.'

I said, 'But I thought I needed three years' construction field experience?'

'No,' she said, 'you'll be fine.'

I was employed by a private health company, who were under contract to the gas pipeline contractor. It was the start of one of the biggest shale gas jobs in the country. They were building a 540-kilometre-long, 42-inch-diameter pipeline from just outside of Miles, through to Gladstone, then over to the concentrating plant on Curtis Island. My back-to-back nurse and I were contracted to do two weeks on and two weeks off, fly-in fly-out swings — work rotations — and we each had a paramedic with us.

Everything was supposed to be in place by the time I got there. But it wasn't. I didn't even have a clinic, and all the medical equipment was still locked up in shipping containers. So I started off in a filthy crib room that wasn't just filthy with mud and dirt, but the tables and walls were covered with stick magazines and pornography. When my back-to-back arrived, she only lasted three days. 'These are disgraceful working conditions,' she yelled. 'I'm out of here.' So I ended up doing two straight swings while they sorted out a replacement, which meant two months of being stuck in the filthy crib room without a clinic.

Our accommodation was dongas. As is usual, the medical ones were the closest to the still empty clinic-donga, and with the pipeline being under construction we were to move camp every few months. I was just lucky that me and my paramedic, Joe, got on so well, because it really wasn't an environment for women. The male-to-female ratio would've been around two hundred to one, and the males were initially very cautious of us nurses.

Early one morning I was in the shower when someone started banging on my donga door. 'Come quick! Someone's sick in the dining room.'

It turned out to be a young man having multiple seizures. Thankfully the workers had had first-aid training and they'd moved the tables and chairs and they'd got him in the recovery position. Anyway, we got the young man over to the clinic and he was evacuated out to Miles by ambulance and an hour and a half later he was being flown out to hospital. After that event I remember sitting on the floor of my empty clinic and saying, 'Right, I don't care what happens. I'm not leaving this place until I've got a fully functioning clinic.'

I must've put my case extremely well to the health and safety manager because within twenty-four hours I had a clinic. I had the power on. I had hot water and the shipping container had been emptied and everything was set up, including radio communications. Then because the work on the pipeline could stretch over a hundred and twenty kilometres at any given time, we set up a map with everyone's GPS coordinates on it, just in case of an emergency.

The following swing, my boss came out from Brisbane to do our first three-month appraisal. She was the one who'd interviewed me, and as she got out of the car, she slammed her hand in the car door, giving herself a huge blood blister under that nail. Straight away I put a hole through the nail to relieve the pressure and fix it. After that she thought I was okay, and more importantly, she loved the job we'd done on the clinic. That was the beginnings of me being accepted on the job, and from then on, whenever I came back from a swing, the guys would greet me with, 'Great to see yer! We weren't sure you'd come back.'

Throughout the two and a half years of the project we lost four people — though none were directly work-related. All were good friends and each loss had a profound effect on me and the crews. But the most common work-related accidents were eye injuries cause by welding. Even though they wore all sorts of protection they'd still get weld burns or flash burns or welds in their eyes. So I got to be very good at picking foreign bodies off an eyeball. We also had a nasty accident where a guy lost a limb while he was trying to pull a branch out from a mobile trench digger. That had a huge impact on me as my son, who by now was also working on the project, had been doing the exact same job for the previous five months, until he'd decided it was too unsafe. So there I was, organising immediate support, chopper evacuation and all that that entails — all from a distance — while feeling relieved that it wasn't my son, yet, at the same time, feeling immense guilt as it was another mother's son.

Then there were the ones who'd be walking through the tall grass, on uneven ground, and they'd stumble and break their ankles. Other than that there were the usual cuts and grazes and sicknesses like gastro. Though men being men, they'd rarely let on what their ailment was. And they certainly weren't going to take the time to visit a doctor on their days off. So to remain on top of things, one of the things I did was I had a blender and I made smoothies and milkshakes, and on hot days, if a guy came in, I'd say, 'Want a drink?'

'Yeah, thanks,' and I'd make them a drink with lots of ice and milk and a bit of topping from the kitchen. And you could almost see them cooling down. Then while they were relaxed, I'd take their blood pressure and do basic obs — observations — and check on their medications and so forth. Then it'd be, 'By the way I'm feeling a bit crook in the guts', or 'Can you take a look at this or that?'

There were also mental health issues. The pipeline was hard for a lot of the guys. While they were paid well, they had absolutely no life. Their swing was twenty-eight days on, nine days off. But when one and a half of those days off was taken up with travel, in reality they were only home for seven days. So a lot of relationships suffered. In cases like that I had to be their friend, their mother, their aunt, their sister, their sounding board or whatever. Many were the times they'd come in for a smoothie and they'd flop down and start to vent their problems; you know, 'The bloody wife!' or 'The bloody partner!' or 'Bloody kids!' or 'I don't know if I can do this crap any more,' and I'd just sit and listen.

And it worked out well. In fact, I really enjoyed the camaraderie of that job. And I missed it for a long time after my contract had ended with the completion of the pipeline. And that's something I'm also proud of. I was there for two and a half years, from the very start of the project, to the very finish.

Down the Mines

After doing a specialised training course that allowed me to work in mining, I started to get some more fly-in fly-out contracts. As yet I've only worked underground, in various copper, gold, lead and silver mines in Queensland. And to date the furthest I've been down is nine hundred and fifty metres.

The medical clinic's usually the donga type, up top, on the surface, where the other offices and things are. When you first arrive on site you're supposed to be given a day or two's orientation. I say 'supposed to' because, with some of these medical companies being such tight-arses, I've rarely had that and I've never had the required orientation underground. So my first underground retrieval was quite an experience. It was dark. It was hot. And the deeper I went, the hotter and stickier and steamier it got.

As it turned out, although the guy was pretty badly banged up, I knew he wasn't going to die. We evacuated him to hospital where he spent some time in intensive care, then he was okay. So far, most of the retrievals I've been involved in have been when someone's been hurt and they're not stable enough to get to the surface under their own steam. As part of the emergency response team, an incident like that could happen any time of the day or night, and if it's serious you can request and expect a chopper to be waiting by the time you get back up top.

Again, injuries vary. They can be anything from deaths, due to rock falls or heart attacks, to minor abrasions and bruises. A few years before I started at one particular mine, they'd had a bad rock fall and a few limbs had been torn off. That may sound a bit callous but the thing is, as a nurse, you can't allow your immediate emotions to take over. It's all about focusing on the job at hand, and even though you sometimes wonder if you could've done better, you've got to realise that you can only do what you can at any given time, under the given circumstances. And sometimes you get lorded for it and sometimes you get criticised. Just as an example: a big job on any mining or construction site is being the qualified drug and alcohol tester. Even then, there's drugs that don't immediately get detected. That's because there's a particular detox treatment that the guys can put themselves through. I've seen it. It isn't well known, so I won't say what it is, but you can buy it online and it's guaranteed to pass any drug test. In the mining and construction industries the guys usually get notified on the afternoon before they're required to present for a drug test. That usually gives them enough time to detox and so they'll come up negative.

I remember only having just arrived on one particular mining site and we had an injured guy who was presenting quite weirdly. Even though he'd passed his most recent drug test, the way he was acting caused me to think there was something else wrong. So when he was being evacuated, I said, 'When you get him to hospital, please give him a thorough tox-screen blood test because I believe drugs are involved.'

And well, didn't the mining people give me a dressing down. 'You don't know us,' they yelled. 'You've only just got here. There's no drugs in this camp and there never has been.'

When the guy's results came back, they indicated that he'd been off his head.

'We're sorry,' they said. 'How did you know?'

I said, 'Well, that's what I do. That's my job.'

Up in the Highlands

While I'd been nursing out on the Queensland pipeline, one of the casual nurses, Deb, asked if I'd consider being her back-to-back when an exploration company set up its land-based gas and oil rig in the highlands of Papua New Guinea. It sounded like something different, so I said, 'Okay then. Just let me know.'

Anyhow, after my previous contract had come to its end, I'd planned to take a break for a month or two. But then I got the call from the exploration company: 'Deb's put your name up to come and work for us. How about it?'

'Yeah, I guess so.'

So Deb and I started our back-to-back, PNG, fly-in fly-out swings of twenty-one days on, twenty-one days off. I was there for the raising of the derrick and to date I've done eight swings. It takes me two days to get on site. First I fly from Adelaide to Brisbane, then from Brisbane to Port Moresby, where I overnight in either a security-guarded camp or hotel. Port Moresby's a place where you don't go out on your own. Just for starters, it's a bit scary when you see the local law enforcement walking around armed with AK-47s and chewing narcotic betel nut.

Then the following morning, a few of the workers and I get flown in a little ten-seater from Port Moresby up into the south-central highlands, where we land on a tiny grass airstrip near the Purari River. From there we get helicoptered up to the land-based rig. There's about a hundred and twenty people on site at any given time, including the skilled-labour expats. The expats come from places like England, Ireland, Scotland, Thailand, Spain, France, the US and Canada, plus there's five or six

Aussies. As a requirement of the PNG government, most of the unskilled and low-skilled labour is done by nationals, including the cleaning and the cooking. And the food! Pork! It's virtually pork 'n rice three times a day. But being the real sweet tooth I am, I'm just lucky that there's always a ten-litre container of ice cream in the fridge for dessert at dinnertime.

The rig site's just a clearing cut out of mountainous jungle. There's no roads or tracks in or out. All the equipment, plus our medical supplies and all the food, comes up the Purari River by barge and is offloaded to a supply depot. The supplies are then flown up to the site by large Vertol and Chinook helicopters. They don't land. They just lower their load down on ropes and cables, then head off to get another load. On a busy day we might get up to thirty deliveries, which means there could be five or six choppers in the air at any given time.

So it gets very busy. And it can be dangerous. See this photograph here? That's a Chinook that'd just made an emergency landing. It'd delivered a load, and when it turned around to head back down to the supply base, it started to lose its rear rotor. Luckily it managed to come in heavily on one of our emergency pads before it disappeared down into the jungle. And see this photograph of an overturned crane? One of the locals told everyone that he could operate it, and he couldn't. The end result: he rolled it, totally wrecked it, and he lost his job.

It's a pretty desolate place. There's nowhere to go. There's no television, radio or telephones. IT's limited so we bring back copies of TV shows and movies and share them around on our computers. Other than that it's mostly work, eat, sleep, work, eat, sleep. We don't even have a rec — recreation — room. There's no bar, no workmen's dry mess, no gym; nothing. We've got the steps though. I'm not big on steps, but there's about four hundred and fifty of them that go almost vertical, from the edge of the rig site, right up into the mountain to where the choppers drop us workers off. A new medic came out one time and the first thing he said was, 'Where's the gym?' So I took him over to the edge of the steps and I said, 'Go for it.'

For accommodation, Deb and I have a twenty-foot shipping container with a small bedroom at each end and an en-suite in the middle. Most of the expats have a similar setup, except for the managers, who get a shipping container to themselves, with an en suite, a bedroom and a small office. The other workers might have two to six people per shipping container, with shared ablutions. Then there's the accommodation for the local lads who have four-man tents set up inside big, open dormitories. All the containers on the rig have the referencing 'FUKU' — which we take literally when we arrive back on site.

The medical clinic's also in a twenty-foot shipping container. Deb and I decked it out. We've got a table and a desk. Then there's a full-sized medical bed, plus all the equipment and medications we'll hopefully ever need. So we're pretty well set up, with air conditioning and all. Seeing how it gets extremely hot and sticky and draining, we're always on about hydration and resting. Last swing I did forty-two days straight because the PNG government was its usual disorganised self in renewing Deb's visa. While she was off, trying to sort that out, the air conditioning broke down in our accommodation container and I spent nine days suffering in the heat. All the guys were asking me, 'Why don't you go over and sleep in the clinic?'

'No,' I said. 'It doesn't matter where you are in the world, if you're caught sleeping in the clinic bed it's immediate dismissal.' So I didn't. I just toughed it out.

Communicating can be a problem, especially with the locals. Apparently PNG has over seven hundred known languages, which is more than anywhere else in the world within the same-sized area. One of our initial concerns was that because the locals didn't like wearing shoes, they were forever getting foot injuries and so forth. We've now made it compulsory that they wear socks and boots during working hours. To make sure they do we run regular inspections. We also do random drug testing and if anybody's caught with anything, including betel nut, it's immediate dismissal. Another government requirement is that a locally trained doctor has to be on site at all times. And while they're lovely people, unfortunately they're not that highly qualified. To date we've had about sixteen local doctors come through and just about every one of them has thanked Deb and I for having taught them so much.

We have to be adaptable. At one stage we didn't have a barbecue and so an expat welder got a few of the guys together and they made one out of a piece of pipe. They were so proud of themselves. Another time the local cook decided to make a batch of lamingtons, which turned out like little bricks, covered in chocolate topping and coconut. Still, the thought was definitely there. Another time there was a stove that the electrician believed had asbestos in it and so it had to be securely wrapped up in something and removed safely from the site. That's when I got the idea of wrapping it up in a body bag. As you might imagine, everyone down at the supply depot got quite a shock when they saw a body bag being lowered down from the chopper.

With Deb and I being the only two women on site, and hardly ever at the same time, a little bit of chivalry does exist. We tend to get the co-pilot's seat on the plane and to sit in the front seat of the helicopter. Then, to our great relief, we get our bags carried up and down the four hundred and fifty stairs. Oh, and one of the cleaning supervisors always makes sure we've got a set of nice, clean white towels waiting on our bed when we arrive. If they're the small things we get as bonus then I'll take them gladly, because that's just about all we get.

Then I've got some pictures here of the amazing wildlife. There's a PNG hornbill. Beautiful isn't it? Apparently you can tell how old they are by the markings on their beak. That one had a partner, but she died. And now that Barry, the mechanic, has trained it to eat olives, Barry's its new best mate. I tried to feed it watermelon and apple, but it didn't even want to know me. But when Barry turns up with olives, it's happy. Then there's the moths. They're huge. Take a look at that photo. They're bigger than a dinner plate. Then there's the snakes. We have to be extremely careful of those. PNG's got the highest mortality for snake bites anywhere in the world, so whereas Australian clinics don't usually keep antivenin, we keep five vials, just in case. We've had death adders on the rig so I try to remind everyone to check their boots before putting them on, or, better still, keep their boots in their dongas.

Another thing we have to be mindful of is the crocodiles. If you take a look at this photo you'll see where the Purari River winds around. Well, the grass airstrip's tucked in tight between those two bends in the river. What you can't see is the crocodiles. If a pilot comes in too short, you end up in the crocodile-infested waters on the near side of the airstrip. If he overshoots, you end up in the crocodile infested waters on the other side. So when we come in to land, I usually shut my eyes and cross my fingers and everything else for that matter.

The weather can also play havoc. Just the other day four people died in a plane crash, during bad weather, only a couple of hundred kilometres from the rig site. So for safety reasons, night flying's been banned throughout PNG. The problem there is, if someone on site's been injured or they've had a heart attack late in the day and they need to be backloaded, you're in for a hell of a long night caring for them until a chopper can get in the following morning. And that has happened.

In 2015 I'd meticulously planned my swing so that I could be back in Australia for both my father's eightieth birthday and the Anzac Centenary. Anyhow, I was still stuck on the rig as Anzac Day dawned. As it happened, the person in charge of the rig, Garry, who's from Louisiana in the US, had organised a makeshift Anzac Day ceremony. I was walking back down the steps in the torrential rain when it started, and when I heard reveille being played I stopped dead. When I got to the group, Garry asked Stuart, a Kiwi, if he'd like to say what Anzac Day meant to him. When he mentioned the special relationship between Australia and New Zealand and how Anzac was named, he was in tears. I was then asked to say something. There were a lot of the local lads standing there so I spoke about the wonderful relationship that our soldiers had with the Fuzzy Wuzzy Angels along the Kokoda Trail. By the end I was also crying. And although the whole service only lasted ten minutes, it was the most moving Anzac Day I've ever experienced.

So that's where I am at the moment. But I do like coming back home. We've got a nice place here, and I'm very fortunate that I have a family who support what I do. Peter and I have now been married for thirty years. In many ways, from right back when we first met in the army, our lifestyles haven't changed that much. I still come and go in my work and Peter comes and goes in his. And it works. One time I was working in a single-nurse post over in the Pilbara region of Western Australia while he was working over in Hawaii. And I thought, Gee, we've got the best of both worlds. I love the Pilbara. He loves Hawaii. You can't get much better than that, can you?

Donna's Story
Payback

I grew up on the Eyre Peninsula of South Australia, around Kimba, Buckleboo. I have an elder sister and a twin brother. My parents owned a trucking company, and in the early '80s, they also bought the general store at Buckleboo, which they leased out. But the people who took over the lease ended up selling the shop and taking off with all the money. So by the time we moved to Roxby Downs we were virtually broke and we lived in a caravan for the next couple of years while my parents established Olympic Dam Transport.

Nursing runs in the family. Mum and her three sisters were all enrolled nurses, so it's just something I was always going to do. So after I'd finished Year 12 at Pembroke, in Adelaide, I began my three-year nursing course at Flinders University. With there being so much theory attached to the uni course, we didn't even get into a hospital until our second year. My first placement was at the Royal Adelaide, and that's when the reality of nursing hit. I just about spent the whole time dry retching in a pan room because I was struggling with the smells and the handling of bodily fluids and functions.

Another experience was watching a below-knee amputation. The man was diabetic and his leg was badly gangrenous. To begin with, the surgeons cut the tissue away and cauterised the blood vessels. And oh, the smell of burning skin was something I'll never forget. They then left a flap of skin below the knee and they looped a flexible wire-saw around his knee and manually pulled it back and forth until they'd completed the amputation.

After that they just folded the flap of skin back up over the stump and sutured it. But what I found astounding was that the man then had what's called phantom pain. He'd cry out, 'Oh, my toes are hurting. Don't touch my toes.' But there was no leg there for him to have toes.

After completing my RN I wanted to do my graduate program at either the Royal Adelaide or the Women's and Children's. So when I found out that I was going to Daw Park Repatriation Hospital, I was devastated because their primary focus was returned war veterans. But it turned out to be a great experience because a girlfriend who did her graduate program at the Royal Adelaide was bemoaning how she was just one of eighty graduate nurses, whereas at the Repat it was far more personal. I was Donna; one of just twelve graduates. What's more, I got to chat with all the old diggers. Another thing: I had a facilitator who had army experience and she was so regimented. It was, 'Right, this's what you do. This's when you do it, and this's how it's done … without fail.' And I think that manner of nursing really set up my career; the expectation of care was set at a very high level and that's continued.

As far as going remote, to be honest, I never really had a plan. Throughout my life, opportunities have just arisen. So then I met a farmer and I moved over to Ceduna, on the west coast of the Eyre Peninsula, and I spent eighteen months nursing there before going overseas. After my travels I decided to do a Bachelor of Midwifery. But prior to going to uni, Anne-Marie Borchers, from the Nursing Agency of South Australia — NASA — asked if I'd like to go out to Oak Valley Aboriginal Community for six weeks. The incentive was, if I went to Oak Valley, it'd help pay my uni fees, so I said, 'Yes.'

Oak Valley's one of the most remote communities in Australia. It's a good six-hour drive north-west of Ceduna. The company that contracted me drove me out there, dropped me in town and the next morning they loaded up the nurse I was replacing and took her back to Ceduna. So at the age of twenty-three I ended up as the sole practitioner in Oak Valley Aboriginal Community. I was it; the only nurse in town and it was a real eye-opener. My accommodation was a duplex-type setup within a compound. The front and rear porches were heavily gated and locked and I was adopted by two stray dogs who'd, thankfully, bark if anyone came near my doorstep. While a number of the Indigenous people had basic housing, quite a few of the more traditional Elders preferred to live in dome tents with their dogs and their outside campfires. And something that gave me a chuckle was that one old couple I took a shine to, Larry and Ada, were living in a dome tent close to the clinic and inside their tent they had a wrought-iron double bed.

At Oak Valley, if there was ever an emergency, the people would just pull up outside my place and honk their car horn. Late one night I was startled awake by this car horn honking. When I went outside they said, 'Bin a car accident out at the airport.'

With the airport being twenty k's away and their cars usually loaded with people, my first thought was, So, just how many casualties am I dealing with? This time there were only two: two young lads had been driving ahead of a second car. As it turned out, the driver of the second car was a brother and he owned the car that they were driving. Anyway, the brother was mucking around and he ended up running the car with the two lads in it off the road, into a ditch. It rolled and one of the lads was thrown out of the window and broke his leg. So, in effect, the brother had caused the accident of his own car.

Now something I soon learnt was that in any of these communities is to quickly identify myself with who has the weight and the power in the place. By doing that I knew they'd help me if any tricky situations arose. So I'd done that, and because I thought I was going to need an extra pair of hands, I grabbed a couple of hefty community caretaker guys to come out with me. So we headed out in the troopie-ambulance and we got the most injured lad onto the stretcher in the back of the ambulance, and his mate, who wasn't so badly injured, we put him into a car and we brought them both back to the clinic. I then prepared everyone for a long night while we waited for the RFDS to come in.

Meantime, the big issues arose that the brother — the guy who owned the smashed car and had caused the accident — was after payback, because in his mind the two lads had wrecked his car. So the two community guys, the traditional Elder and myself, ended up having to lock ourselves inside the clinic with the two injured lads, while the brother was outside, tossing steel bins into the wall and door in an attempt to break in and get his payback. When that didn't work, he pinched someone's car and started ramming it into the clinic. By that stage we'd called the police, but because they were in Ceduna, it was going to take them six hours to get to Oak Valley. Anyhow, the following morning, during a lull in proceedings, we managed to get the two lads out to the airstrip and they were flown out by the RFDS. The police then arrived and when they found the guy, they had to capsicum-spray him before they could arrest him. So that was my introduction to Oak Valley, and I can tell you, I felt much safer that I had those two community guys and the traditional Elder inside the clinic with me.

On a subsequent visit to Oak Valley I sought out an old Ngangkuri — a powerful Elder — named Willy Tinku. Willy and I got on really well. He drove an old Toyota that had a massive dent in it from when he'd hit a cow. Anyway, I was telling my dad about how Willy had these beautiful long spears that had been made from Western Australian trees. Dad was keen on getting some and so the next time I saw Willy I said, 'Willy, my dad wants some spears. Can I buy some off you?'

'Yep,' he said. 'No worries.' And I arranged to pick them up at some stage.

Then when I got to the clinic one day, the guys from the shop said, 'Donna you've gotta come over. Willy's on the doorstep.'

Now, most of the trouble in these communities is grog-driven, and of course most of the communities are allegedly alcohol-free. But they never are and so, as it turned out, two women had come into the community on the Sunday. They were drunk and we'd stitched them up after they'd been fighting. Anyhow, being a Ngangkuri Elder, Willy wasn't happy. He was after payback and when I got over to the shop, there he was, sitting on the front doorstep with his spears and a woomera.

I said, 'Willy, what're you doing?'

He said, 'I'm not happy 'bout these women bein' drunk. Oak Valley's dry 'n they've come in 'n shamed our community. So I'm gonna get 'em.' Willy's plan was to stop these women from buying fuel at the shop and leaving the community before he could get payback.

I said, 'Willy, how about we go over to the clinic and talk about it because I don't want blood on the spears that I'm going to give to my dad.'

So he came over and while he calmed down over a cup of tea and a few biscuits, I hid the spears out the back. So yeah, that's how I got out of that one, and my dad has the spears to prove it.

Ice to the Eskimos

After my first trip to Oak Valley, I went back to Adelaide and got my Bachelor of Midwifery and began working at the Women's and Children's. And I just loved every moment of being a midwife; every moment. Then one day Anne-Marie from NASA rang me ... again. I mean, that woman could sell ice to the Eskimos. She could make anything sound glamorous. She said, 'Donna, I've got some fantastic places for you.' So I listened to what she had to say, and after two and a half years at the Women's and Children's, I handed in my resignation. My first placement was to Oodnadatta, to relieve over the Christmas–New Year period, and I remember arriving in town and going, 'Hang on, how did I end up here?'

But I survived, and I spent the next eight years working all over the place. Primarily it's been South Australia. I've also been down to Tassie and up into the Territory. I've even been to Port Keats — Wadeye. With that one, I think I must've been very naïve because I was working in Gladstone, Queensland, when I got the call: 'Oh Donna, you're just the perfect person for this job at Wadeye.'

I thought, Wow, I must be really good if they think I'm the perfect person to go there. Anyhow, when I arrived, they were desperate. They were grossly understaffed and there was a lot of fighting in the community. There were something like fifty-four separate gangs in Wadeye, and what happens is, for example, the boyfriend beats his girlfriend. Then the girlfriend's brothers come and beat the boyfriend for beating the sister. Then the boyfriend's friends go and beat the girlfriend's brothers for beating the boyfriend. It was just that continual cycle of retribution; so much so that I've heard how, on occasions, the police have supervised 'arranged fights'. 'Just sort it out amongst yourselves.' Which they do. Then it's done. End of story. It's all over.

But Wadeye was a particularly hard placement. There were a couple of thousand people in the community. It was quite a large clinic. I was the midwife and I was flat out. I'd work nine to five, Monday to Friday, and I'd also have a period of on-call overnights. Then maybe I'd have a day off. Although we'd try to fly the mums out before the birth, that didn't always happen. The general belief was that babies who are born in Darwin didn't have that strong cultural connection to the earth of that land — their land. So while I was there, a number of premie and small babies were born.

One Monday I'd worked nine to five, then I was called back to the clinic later on when a sick baby came in. Anyhow, this baby really needed to be flown out. The problem was, being night-time, a plane couldn't come until the next morning. So I stayed in the clinic with the baby. Then another local girl came in. Her parents thought she was pregnant, which she was. Once that was sorted she went home. By about 2 a.m. the Aboriginal health worker was flagging so I sent her home as well. That just left me and the sick baby in the clinic. But then the pregnant girl came back complaining of cramps. So I rang the doctor in Darwin and said how I suspected that she may be miscarrying. There's nothing you can do to prevent a miscarriage. Nothing. It's just one of those situations where you have to let nature take its course, and so she went home again. It was now back to just me and the sick baby. Then the pregnant girl's parents came back. 'She's got pains,' they said. 'She's in the bathroom. Can you come and help?'

I said, 'Look, I just can't leave a sick baby. Can you drive her up to the clinic?'

The dad said, 'I can't drive a car. I don't have a licence.'

Anyhow, they went back home and I stayed on with the sick baby. As soon as someone arrived that morning, I jumped into the ambulance and headed off to the pregnant girl's home. On my way I saw a nurse walking to work, so I got her to come with me. When we got to the place it was just squalor. A dog had recently had a litter and there was dogs' poo everywhere. Most of the light globes were broken, so there wasn't much light. And when we got to the bathroom there was this poor girl; she was sort of standing upright, holding the baby in her hands. The umbilical cord was still attached, so I cut the cord and we got her into the ambulance and took her to the clinic. The baby girl would've been only sixteen weeks. She was still alive but there was nothing we could've done and I was so overtired and distraught that when she died, I broke down in tears.

Rhythm of Life

I work in these remote communities mainly because of the experience and lifestyle. The thing is, you get to go to places where most other people can't go and you do meet some amazing characters. In between remote placements, I work in a midwifery group practice in Ceduna. So one week I'd be in Ceduna, delivering babies and getting my fix of healthy women and a regular job schedule; the next I'd be out amongst the chaos of a remote community. That was the rhythm of life and by doing that I'd manage about eighteen weeks' holiday a year.

I only do six-week stints. I find that by week four I'm getting toward my limit and by week six I've reached it. It takes a certain character to be able to live in those type of communities, and because you give so much, you come out feeling exhausted. I remember idealistic me, going out to my first remote placement with the belief that I was going to make a difference and change the world. But, nah, it didn't happen, and I doubt it ever will. What frustrates me is that you're only giving bandaid treatment. In a number of these communities there's an element of people not wanting to help themselves. Like, if you refer someone to a larger town for treatment it'd be, 'Right, I've got you an appointment on this day. I've booked you a seat on the plane. I've got you all organised.' Then they don't turn up. And that really bothers me because it's a huge waste of resources and funds; just the airfares are expensive.

A much more enjoyable experience was at Numbulwar, in East Arnhem Land. Numbulwar's a small coastal community of around two hundred. To get there you fly to Nhulunbuy, then it's a couple of hundred k's south, down on the Rose River. While I was at Numbulwar I befriended two policemen. One was from Darwin, the other from Katherine. They were both Caucasian and they'd schedule their days off with mine so that we'd go fishing. So Numbulwar's where I caught my first-ever barramundi. There was also trevally and queenies. We got some crab pots, and so we caught mud crabs. Any excess from our fishing exploits we'd give to the Elders or the frail ones in the community.

We had four nurses, three Aboriginal health workers and two drivers. I worked primarily as a midwife and if you wanted to speak to a doctor you'd liaise with Darwin. The accommodation was the basic compound-type. All the windows were barred, and like in most places, there was some sort of weaponry, like a block of wood or an axe, beside the bed, just in case. The front and back porches of my place were supposed to be caged in and locked, but I didn't see the point. My back door wouldn't lock so I didn't bother about locking the front. My thinking was that if someone came in the back door and the front was locked, I'd be trapped.

I always try to maintain a reasonable fitness level and I enjoy running. But at Numbulwar I couldn't run through the community, because the camp dogs would attack me. I couldn't run on the beach, because crocodiles would get me. I couldn't run on the roads out of town because of the wild pigs, and you had to be careful in the bush, because of the buffalo. So I'd sort of run around the protected inside perimeter of the airport fence. Then there were the other obstacles. Like, you'd be driving to work and you'd have to negotiate your way around a pack of dogs that were out on the middle of the road, scrapping over the leftovers of a buffalo or a pig that someone had caught. And because the people there loved their dugong, you might come across a big flap of dugong blubber. I'd seen them go out in their boats, armed with their spears. I remember asking a woman how they actually tracked down the dugong and she said, 'When they make dust in the water, we know where they are.' And I thought that was the perfect description, because when a dugong swims it stirs up the sand.

Numbulwar was alcohol-free, and they kept pretty much to it. And they looked after themselves. Before coming to the clinic they'd wash their hair, and their clothes were always clean and colourful and vibrant. They'd have two skirts: one they'd wear around their waist and the other would be sitting up on their shoulders, a bit like a kaftan. While I was there they were going through a ceremony. It must've been more of a happy festivity with just certain elements of men's business and women's business. I was driving around town one night and there was this guy, dressed in his red loincloth. His body was painted white and he had feathers stuck all over him, and he was walking along holding hands with his little child, and I thought, That's just so awesome.

So Numbulwar had a good community mindset. The people were a lot gentler than in a number of other places I've worked. Someone once told me it's because it's a community by the sea. And the people I worked with were great. Like in a lot of other communities, the itinerants like the schoolteachers, the police and nurses get together.

So yes, I've now worked in quite a few remote communities. Another interesting place was Moomba. Moomba's a gas-field area in the far north-east of South Australia. I met a male nurse there that I affectionately named Ginja Ninja. It's not very often that you could pull the wool over his eyes. Anyway I had a guy come in one day who said he had something in his eye.

'Okay,' I said, 'cover your good eye and look at the eye chart.'

He said, 'Well, this is my good eye.'

I said, 'What do you mean?'

He said, 'The other one's fake. It's glass.'

Anyway, I was checking out his crook eye when in comes Ginja Ninja. So I said to the guy, 'Just go along with me here.' I said, 'Hey Ginja, can you check out this guy's eye for me please?'

Ginja's like, 'Yeah, okay, no worries,' and he comes over and he shines the torch in this bloke's eyes. The thing is, if the pupil doesn't respond to light, it could well mean there's some sort of brain injury. So there's the Ginja Ninja shining the torch in this guy's eye and of course, being glass, it's not dilating. So Ginja's getting quite worried. 'How long are you going to be out here for?' he asked.

The guy said, 'Another two weeks.'

'Oh gee,' Ginja says. 'Look, I'm not so worried about the eye you've got something in, I'm more worried about your other eye. The pupil's not dilating and that could well be something serious. We might have to fly you out to Adelaide and get a specialist to take a closer look at it.'

And this guy goes, 'Well, why don't you take a closer look yourself?' and he pops out his glass eye and he hands it over.

Well, you should've seen the look on the Ginja Ninja's face. He's never forgiven me for that.

Frances' Story
Privileged

My early childhood was spent in Lithgow, at the bottom of the western side of the Blue Mountains. My main memory from those days was the cold and also of the coal dust from the coal mining and the steam trains. Dad was in the railways back then and Mum worked at the small arms factory. There were three of us children: an older brother, me and a younger sister. Dad also had a market garden and chooks. I loved going there. I didn't even mind chopping the heads off the chooks and helping to pluck and gut them. Maybe that's where my interest in nursing came from. I don't know.

I did my primary schooling in Lithgow plus one year of high school. Then when Dad got a job in Orange with the State Housing Commission, we moved there. Orange was cold too, very cold. I did two years' high school there before we went to Dubbo. It was a bit warmer in Dubbo. Dad looked after the commission housing for the western areas, out in places like Walgett, Moree, Brewarrina and Broken Hill. Commission houses were usually set aside for people on lower incomes, which included a lot of Aboriginal people. Dad used to say how unfair it was that people in Sydney could make decisions for people they didn't know or probably didn't even care that much about. Funny how you remember things like that.

When I finished Year 12, we moved back to Orange and I worked in a whitegoods factory for five months. You know those old stove tops with a well type of thing in them so if a pan overflowed, it'd go into the well? That's what I did. I was on night shift, spot-welding the well-holders onto the top of the stoves. It was fun and I got to save enough to buy the set of regal-red suitcases that would hold my worldly belongings when I went to Sydney to start my nursing training at St Vincent's Hospital. I was eighteen and we lived in the nurses' home and we'd hear the nuns swishing along the corridors in their full dress. They wore a more casual headpiece than the Joeys — Josephites. Ours were more of the Sisters of Mercy order, and they were brilliant. Sister Bernice was the head, and while she was fair, she expected a very high standard. If things weren't clean and the patients weren't getting the best of care, we soon knew about it.

A lot of top people used to go to St Vincent's for surgery and people like Mark Shanahan and Victor Chang were working in the cardiothoracic unit. You may remember Victor Chang as being the surgeon who was involved in the first heart transplants in Australia and who later died after being shot in a failed extortion attempt against him.

Also, while I was in Sydney, I re-met my husband-to-be, Peter. By re-met, I mean we'd already known each other from our school days in Dubbo. We weren't going out or anything. We were just friends. He was sporty and a school captain, and after Dubbo he went into the navy in Sydney. Then one day he was looking for someone to go to a water polo game with him and a friend of ours said, 'Oh, Frances Ryan's in Sydney. Give her a ring.' So he did. We went to the water polo game and that was that.

After I'd completed my training I returned to Orange and did six months in theatre, as a scout nurse. That's where Peter and I got married.

Then we went to Nowra with the navy and I got work at Shoalhaven Hospital. Soon after that, Peter was posted to Exmouth, in north-western Western Australia, to work at the communications base there, in conjunction with the Americans. That worked out well because Exmouth was a remote placement and the navy counted it as time at sea. There were about forty

Australians in the navy up there, and while we all lived in town, the Americans lived on their base.

Exmouth was an amazing place. Socially, we had a ball. The Americans got all their supplies flown in from America or boated in by sea. They even drove around in their big left-hand-drive Chevys, and when we went out to their base, we'd eat American food. They had vending machines and a ten-pin bowling rink and a bar where you could drink duty-free grog. Coming back in to town was like going from one world to another. There was nothing in Exmouth apart from a pub and a shop where all the meat, milk and so forth came in frozen, and if you went to a party you had to take your own seat and cutlery and crockery. Like everyone else, we went up there with virtually nothing, just our clothes. Still, we got involved. Other than Peter's navy work, he instructed kids' swimming and I worked in the bar during my off-time from Exmouth Hospital.

Occasionally we'd have cyclones. But we got plenty of warning. They'd drive around with their speakers going, 'All hoses off your taps. Tape up your windows. Put everything inside.' I guess the hoses would whip around if they were left on their taps. It was all quite regimented as to what we had to do and I'd always take my photos and other precious items up to the hospital, just in case. But nothing ever got destroyed. The houses were well built and the hospital was sturdy, so it wasn't going to go anywhere. But it would still put the wind up you, so to speak.

Exmouth Hospital had about eight beds. I was very green in many ways so it was challenging at times. Our one and only doctor was an alcoholic. But we had a good team and we were lucky that the Americans were close by. Although they had their own consulting rooms on their base, their patients were admitted to Exmouth Hospital. So they had the right to practise there, but only on their own people. Anyhow, they knew what was going on with our doctor, and even though it was against the rules, they'd help us out where they could.

With Exmouth having a large fishery, we'd get a lot of fishing injuries and in appreciation we'd be given bags of calamari and fish. We were so spoilt. We virtually lived on seafood. Peter was even paid for doing swimming lessons in blocks of export prawns. But I did have a child die on me at the hospital. He was two and he choked. A bone or something had got stuck in his throat. I got the call when I was at a party and so I jumped the fence and ran up to the hospital where the matron and I gave him a trachy — tracheotomy. But it was too late. That was tough, though I guess we did the best we could at the time. The doctor would've come, but being night-time, he'd have been too drunk and shaky. My one regret was that I didn't give the mum the support I'd give a mum in a similar situation now.

Another time a friend's child got meningitis. It's still not known how people get it, but when they do, they get sick very quickly and they can die very quickly. It was touch and go. We eventually got her out to Perth with the Flying Doctor Service. A week later she was still alive so we drove down to see her. Luckily she survived, and she survived well, and that was a good outcome.

They also delivered babies in Exmouth. I wasn't a midwife at that time but the pregnant Indigenous women would come in from all over the place. They were just the most shy and lovely women, and quite scared about having been taken out of their own environment to have their babies. In fact, that's what made me decide to do midwifery.

So when Peter was transferred to Waterhen Base, on Sydney Harbour, I did my midwifery at Royal North Shore Hospital. I then worked for the neonatologist at Royal North Shore doing fetal monitoring for at-risk pregnancies. Most of the women who came in usually had some chronic disease, like diabetes, or they'd been smokers or drinkers or maybe drug users, and we'd do an assessment on them. I remember, very early on, when I couldn't find the baby's heartbeat in one woman, I went to the doctor and said, 'I can't find anything. Can you please come and have a listen?'

His reply was, 'Frances, you're just going to have to realise that the baby may not have a heartbeat.'

From Sydney we moved to the Gold Coast. Peter was out of the navy by then and we just didn't feel that we'd be able to get ahead in Sydney. We'd already had one son and the idea was for Peter to stay at home a bit more. But never a man to be held down, he got work which soon had him travelling again. Still, over the next few years we had another two boys and I got weekend work at the Tweed Heads Private Hospital.

There's one experience I'll never forget. One night I attended a birth in maternity and of course there's the tears of joy and all that. I'd just got that settled when word came through: 'You're urgently required in the medical ward. There's been a death.'

Later on I said to my father, 'Oh my God. All in one night.'

He said, 'You don't know just how privileged you are to be given the chance to be at a person's birth and a person's death.'

I've never forgotten those words, because he was right, it is a great privilege.

Learning Curve

No matter where you're nursing — city or remote — many of the challenges are the same. When our kids were at preschool I went to work in a general medical practice for my friend Anne, and her doctor-husband, Pat. I learnt a lot from Pat. Pat had an interest in mental health so we saw a vast number of mentally ill people. We even had a few younger ones come in who were seeing all sorts of illusions on the wall. But Pat was a very calm sort of character, and that's the only way you can greet and treat people who are at their lowest ebb. The thing is, when someone's hallucinating and psychotic they have no idea as to what's reality and what's not. Worse still, if you antagonise them in any way, they can easily turn violent. One young fellow had been walking along Nobby Beach in a psychotic state. He was about twenty-five and he came in carrying some sort of bag. He was a bit of a handful, which in turn caused the others in the waiting area to get a bit antsy. I told them, 'Just stay calm. It's all right. Stay where you are and we'll get this fellow sorted and treated in a minute.'

I then went out to Pat, who was in the treatment room. 'You'd better come quick. This boy's not well.'

Pat came in, and after he'd settled the young fellow down a bit, he said, 'Hey mate, what sort of work do you do?'

He goes, 'I'm a butcher in Adelaide.'

'Oh yeah. So what's in your bag?'

'My butcher's knives.'

Yikes. So I'm glad we'd all stayed calm. If not he could've easily taken out his butcher's knives and who knows what would've happened? Pat then drove him to the hospital. The thing was, the fellow didn't have a clue who or where he was. What's more, we didn't know who he was, and without identification, the hospital people refused to admit him. So Pat made a stand and said he wouldn't leave until he'd seen the fellow safely in a ward. So they relented. And things must've turned out okay because his family later got in touch and thanked us for looking after him. But he could've easily harmed himself, or, worse still, harmed someone else and ended up in jail. And unfortunately, with police involvement and incarceration, most times that's when mental illness is first detected.

So there were the stressful times. Pat had two surgeries: the one at Nobby Beach and another over near a state housing area. A lot of cases there involved families with very little money and/or education and/or health awareness. I remember a lady whose twenty-one-year-old came off his motorbike and had died. She said to me, 'Frances, I've got no money to pay for the funeral and I've got no one to come with me to the funeral. Can you come, please?'

So I went. It was so sad. She had no one to help her. I was pleased that a priest we knew had offered to take on the funeral. The service was a simple affair, held at the gravesite, with only the mother and me and someone else. I saw the mum quite a bit after that and she seemed to get on okay. But it must've been very tough. It was life at its very barest. I think that's what caused me to do my graduate diploma in mental health and start working in schools, with adolescents, promoting mental health and sexual health.

We dealt with a lot of suicides and stuff around parental separation. I was on the board of a suicide prevention charity and another group who worked with girls at risk of homelessness. We also ran programs for disadvantaged adolescent females. I was forever dealing with sexual abuse. In one case I put in eight notifications before Child Protection took it seriously. But that's not unusual, particularly with adolescents. Due to their workload, they usually assist the younger ones first; the ones who can't defend themselves. Though to my mind neither can a fourteen- or seventeen-year-old, especially if they've got no money and no home. Anyhow, Child Protection got into trouble over that one. But I was trying to do too much. In the end I got so overwhelmed that I said to Peter, 'Let's go remote. I want to learn and do more in the Indigenous health area.'

As quick as a flash he said, 'All right. That sounds like a good idea.'

Originally I applied for a couple of jobs over in the Kimberleys, but I didn't get them. Then I saw an advertisement for this job, up in the Gulf, and I thought, Well, it's probably better to come here and learn a bit more about Indigenous health first. By then Peter was working for the Indian government in a business that was set up to outsource all their back-of-house visa issuance. Now he works for the American government doing a similar thing. Each year they issue about 400,000 visas to the US from places like Japan, Korea, the South Pacific, New Zealand and Australia. His role is to look after the managers in each of those countries and to keep in contact with the embassies. He's still a traveller. He visits the countries once or twice a year. The rest is done via the internet, by teleconferencing and email. We don't tell many people about that side of things but it's amazing, isn't it, to be able to run such a huge business from a little remote place in outback Queensland.

And he loves it here. Other than his main job, he's very involved in the local community. When the pool opens he'll be over there as a swimming instructor and lifeguard, and he helps out at the sports centre and down at the local Indigenous gallery. He's also sorted out a traineeship for a young Indigenous girl at the gallery, and once she's done her three-month trial, he'll organise for her to go down to Brisbane for more training in hospitality. So it all works in well.

Anyhow, I just wanted to come and learn more about the Indigenous health side of things, and that's been a huge learning curve. There's a lot to running a hospital, and if you don't really love it and look after it and stock it and care for it and get to know the people you're dealing with, it will eventually run down. And that's not what I'm about. But living remote does have its challenges. Firstly there's the destabilising cycle of staff coming and going, so we lack that much-needed continuity. The doctors are on locum work and they change over every week or so. Then we get a lot of agency nurses who are only here for two to three weeks. And while we might only have the fourteen beds, we've got a very busy outpatients and emergency. We've got to be on the ball. Quite often our sickest don't even come in the ambulance; they'll just walk in the door, plonk themselves down and wait for the doctor. There's no big song and dance about how sick they are. One fella was having a heart attack and he thought he might just pop in and get it checked out. Just the other day someone else was sitting in the waiting room; next thing he was having a heart attack.

And if someone needs to be flown out, due to our remote location, it's at least an hour before the RFDS can get here. In fact, some of my most stressful times have been trying to keep people stable until a plane arrives. At the moment we're flying out a lot of station people and fishermen with various injuries. Late last year a twenty-four-year-old nurse was bucked off a horse and received a serious head injury. With that one, we were just lucky that the Deadly Ears team was in town. They're a group from Brisbane who come out and run programs on ear hygiene. They had an anaesthetist with them, and with the nurse having to be intubated and have a breathing tube, she had to be put to sleep. In the end she pulled through. She's still off work, but she's functional. Currently she's working on a property, but she hasn't got her higher-order thinking back yet, so she won't be nursing for another year or so.

We also deal with a lot of kidney disease. While heart disease is mostly due to poor diet and not looking after yourself, kidney disease is more complex. Trouble is, if people need dialysis they have to leave town and go to either Mount Isa, Cairns or Townsville, and it's hard for an Aboriginal person to have to go into a strange environment for their treatment. And we don't deliver babies here so the pregnant women have to leave town at thirty-six weeks, which, again, is hard on them.

So it's been a steep learning curve, and with a large population of Indigenous people, there's the sorry times. Recently we've had a couple of Elders die. That was particularly sad because they were pivotal in the community. Usually after someone dies they're flown out to the coroner, just in case, and when they're flown back in, there can be a couple of hundred people to meet them at the airport. Then as they follow the body up to the hospital morgue a lot of wailing goes on. The same happens when the body's taken from the morgue to the funeral service, at either the church or up at the sports centre, and from there out to the gravesite, still with all the wailing.

We've also had two young guys suicide in the last month. One was forty. He was mentoring young Indigenous people over in the Western Australian mines; he came back to town, said hello and goodbye to everyone, and hung himself. Nobody seems to know why. He had a stable job and he was doing something positive in life. The other young boy overdosed in Townsville and he had his funeral here. With all these funerals, the whole town shuts down. I think, with it being such a small community, everybody's related to everybody else in one way, shape or form so everybody feels the grief. The impact is far greater. But why do they suicide? I wish I knew and I know that quite a few other people wish they knew as well. Then, at least we might be able to do something about it.

I'm just glad that I had excellent basic training, followed by a lot of experience, because I can tell you, remote nursing pulls on every skill you've got. But one of the loveliest things about the Aboriginal people is that they're so family oriented; and their concept of family is so different to ours. Actually, it's something us whitefellers could learn a lot from. In an Indigenous group, everyone helps raise the children, not just the parents. An interesting expression they have around here is, 'Oh, who grew you up then?'

I didn't quite understand that at first, but I really like it now. So much so that just recently I said to my son, 'I want to grow up my grandchildren a bit more.'

His answer was, 'You're dreaming.'

I said, 'No I'm not.'

Glenda's Story
Bird Dreaming

I was born and raised in Kirkstall, a little town in the south-west of Victoria, near Port Fairy. It's an area with a strong Irish connection. We lived in the shire of Belfast and the nearby towns were Killarney and Koroit. My family were dairy farmers and I'm the first girl of six siblings, with an elder brother. Initially I went to the local public school. Then, as they started closing the smaller schools down, I transferred to a couple of different Catholic schools before going to a Catholic college in Warrnambool.

In my early twenties I came over to Adelaide with an old school friend. We liked the place and after she got a job there, I got a transfer in the bank that I was working for. Later I joined the YCW — Young Christian Workers — movement. In country areas there'd been a lot of fatal road accidents involving younger drivers, and, because of my rural background, they asked me to work with young people in the south-west of South Australia. So in the early '80s I moved to Mount Gambier, where we undertook a survey throughout the area. One of the major causes of the accidents was fast cars. Added to that was the long distances people had to travel to entertainment and sporting events, where alcohol was involved. From those results we began educational programs, getting the young people to consider how they could be more responsible within both their community and family structure.

After having been to the Philippines as a representative of YCW, I'd begun thinking about working in another country and experiencing a different culture. When I wondered what I could do of value overseas, nursing came to the fore. So I did my training at Queen Elizabeth Hospital in Adelaide, and following that, I completed a degree in nursing at the University of SA.

During that time I became aware of the poor health status of Indigenous Australians, particularly those in remote areas. I'd also begun to get interested in their spirituality, their Dreamtime stories and their strong connection to land. After completing my studies and working in Adelaide, in emergency and oncology, I wanted to further my interest in the Indigenous culture and health issues. One day I rang Alice Springs Hospital and the next week I was given a job. I went up to Alice Springs with the idea of staying for a year. Initially I worked in emergency; then, after staying on to do my midwifery, I decided to try remote area nursing. That's when I got the position as a coordinator of women's health in the APY — Anangu Pitjantjatjara Yankunytjatjara — Lands, for Nganampa Health Council.

I was based in Alice Springs and I'd drive out to the Lands in a four-wheel drive. My closest community was Iwantja, which is five hundred kilometres south of Alice Springs. The furthest was Pipalyatjara; a nine and a half hour journey, right over on the Western Australian border. I mostly drove out from Alice by myself to then met up with Pantjiti, my female Anangu Malpa — 'Anangu' being the people of the APY Lands and 'Malpa' meaning cultural co-worker. Pantjiti had done her health worker training on the Lands and had been working there for many years. She was very skilled and had a beautiful way of teaching. Her family had lived in Ernabella — Pukatja — so her childhood went back to the time of the Methodist missionaries. Actually, Pantjiti spoke positively about those days when they grew their own vegetables and had a decent diet, and the children went to school and received bilingual teaching.

Pantjiti was mainly based around Pukatja, but because the families throughout the Lands are all interconnected, she'd often be in one of the other communities. There was no mobile phone coverage back then so I'd ring around on a landline to find out where she was. If it was convenient, I'd drive out and pick her up and she'd come along as my offsider. We'd try to coincide our education times when something was happening in the community, like a sporting event or whatever — though never during times of sorry business, when someone had died.

Because women's business and men's business were quite separate, when we arrived, we'd gather the women and we'd head off to a place of their choosing, like down by a creek. Other than general health issues, sexual health was, and still is, a major concern in Indigenous Australia. And when a woman has had repeated sexually transmitted infections in her early life, her ability to become pregnant is often altered. So we'd discuss things like infertility and, if necessary, I'd try to help them on the pathway to IVF treatment in Adelaide. Other areas of concern were things like polycystic ovary syndrome and obesity.

With obesity: ever since Indigenous people have been forced to live in communities, their lifestyle has changed dramatically. They no longer hunt and gather in their traditional ways and so they no longer live an active type of lifestyle. These days they just go to the local store, like we all do. But of course, many of these community stores are managed by external non-Indigenous people who are out to make money. Add to that the huge transport costs and the food ends up being extremely expensive, which then forces the people to go for the cheap and not-so-healthy options, like deep-fried foods. So health education was also part of my job, and if there was no midwife in the community, I'd see the antenatal and postnatal women.

Occasionally a birth would happen. Though I must say, the women were incredibly obedient and obliging in that they'd usually fly out to Alice Springs at around thirty-eight weeks, to await the birth. It'd be a planned transfer; all the communities had landing strips, with mail planes coming regularly. The difficult aspect of this was, unless the women's costs were supported, most of them had to travel alone. And with some of these women having to come from as far away as Warburton and Warakurna, in Western Australia, Alice Springs was a totally different environment than what they were used to. Having to be so far away from their homelands and family while they waited to birth could be a very lonely and traumatic experience — especially if they had to share a small room in a hostel with another woman who they did not know and who could well be from another language group. What's more, it's not easy for such shy people to have to eat in a large communal dining room and be observed by strangers.

So when you're watching a pregnant woman get on a plane, to go and birth alone, and the family's all at the airstrip waving and crying, it's heartbreaking. Even more distressing is when a medical situation arises and a woman has to be flown out because she's unwell. There's a long history behind that, because quite often, when an unwell person is being flown out, they don't come back alive.

In all, I was in the APY Lands, with Nganampa Health, for five years. The special times were engaging with the women, particularly seeing young women move through a healthy pregnancy, having a healthy baby and doing well post-birth. Another great joy was being on camp with the women. One of my big projects was to organise the biennial breast screenings for the fifty- to seventy-year-olds, the special women who carried the stories of their people. Breast Screening South Australia had a big truck that would park in the far north of the state, at Marla. And the women just loved coming as a group to have mammograms. Healthy breasts were important to them. Not only were they necessary for feeding their children, but dancing bare-chested and painting their bodies was integral to the celebrations within their traditions.

Organising these screenings was a huge feat, not only for myself but also for the health staff in the communities, as we had to work out a process of moving the women from all across the Lands — from the WA border to the Stuart Highway and to the east. Normally it'd be a two-day trip into Marla. We'd round up whatever vehicles we could, then the health staff had to rise early and go from house to house, gathering the women up, along with all their medications and perhaps their dogs and sometimes their grandchildren. Many of them were disabled in terms of mobility, in as much as it was a real effort for them to get in and out of the vehicles. As the women were being driven in, I had to make their appointments at the screening mobile clinic. I'd be forever on the phone, trying to estimate their time of arrival, taking into consideration the likes of flat tyres or if they'd run out of fuel. One year it rained, and because the roads were wet, that presented huge problems.

We generally tried to make their main camp at Iwantja, which was the closest place to Marla. We also needed to organise their food, or sometimes they might've found a kangaroo along the way and put it on the roof rack. And with everything being shared amongst the family members back in their homes, they couldn't bring their own bedding. So I'd get blankets from St Vincent De Paul or Salvation Army and take them down to the camp. Others might've just jumped into the vehicle without giving a thought as to what they might need. A great aspect of the Anangu people is that they live in the moment, so there's little planning for the future. It's more, 'Oh, we'll deal with that when we have to.' Which causes problems for someone like myself who prefers to be organised.

Another of my great interests was learning about Indigenous culture, and on the APY Lands, the people have remained close to their traditional ways. In doing so, all the babies that are born have a special Dreamtime-spirit that's connected to the homeland of their family. In the early 2000s I became involved with a young Pitjantjatjara woman during her pregnancy. She was from a family that was a bit separated. Her mother lived in one community; her father was elsewhere. Anyway, she had rheumatic heart disease. That's when the valves of the heart aren't working effectively, and with the increased blood supply, there's a real risk of dying, especially when a woman's pregnant.

I'd supported the young woman quite a bit out on the Lands, and when she was to be flown in to Alice Springs for medical treatment, I discovered that she'd never been there. She also knew very little about money, which meant she didn't know how to shop, and so I decided to go with her to continue that support. In all it was a terribly lonely and traumatic time for her. To make matters worse, she ended up having to be transferred to the Women's and Children's Hospital, in Adelaide, to be closer to their intensive care unit. When she got to Adelaide, I kept in telephone contact with her. And because she didn't know anyone, I asked a friend of mine, who'd been an agency nurse and midwife out on the Lands, to keep an eye on her.

Anyhow, while she was in Adelaide, she progressed to birth. When I heard the good news I rang her from Alice Springs to congratulate her. While we were talking, she mentioned how her baby had the Dreaming spirit of the ring-necked parrot. The incredible thing about that was, at that exact moment, I just happened to look out of my office window and there were two ring-necked parrots sitting in the tree.

Twenty-six Weeks

While my work in the APY Lands involved general women's health issues, I was really keen to focus more on midwifery. So when I found out that the government-run NT Health Services was seeking outreach midwives, I applied for and got one of the positions. So I basically moved buildings and joined a huge primary healthcare service that covered the central region of the NT. In doing so I worked closely with the Strong Women, Strong Babies, Strong Culture program, which developed educational programs for the communities.

The Strong Women were women Elders who were based in Alice Springs, working as part of the Maternal Health team. They were trained by the NT Government, usually at Bachelor College. More often than not, the communities had Strong Women's centres where the women would gather and do all sorts of activities like teaching cooking, or they'd do art or crafts. And if we had antenatal women, the Strong Women would tell them their traditional stories, about what they should be doing with regard to their diet and their general behaviour. I admired the Strong Women greatly because they had to cover a much larger area than what I did, which was a huge challenge. There were also some part-paid Strong Women workers, based in the various communities. They were often older women who were great in terms of assisting us in our work and helping with language.

I travelled around the central and southern areas of the Territory, and while there were more different language groups, the work wasn't as intense as it'd been in the APY Lands. I'd mostly stay for a week in one of the larger communities, and because they weren't as widespread as they'd been in the Lands, I'd go out and visit the closer smaller communities from there. As for experiences: I guess the main ones you tend to remember are the more disturbing ones, like when a woman's unwell or when there's an unexpected birth in the middle of the night. One that stands out for me happened after I'd arrived in a community late one afternoon to do midwifery work. At that time most of the permanent staff were in Alice Springs for training, so there was just me and one permanent nurse left out there, plus a nurse who was new to the community and pretty new to remote area nursing in general.

I then got a call at 2 o'clock in the morning to come over to the clinic because there was a woman in labour. Off I went. It was in wintertime; freezing cold. When I arrived, there was the permanent nurse and the brand-new nurse and myself, who, mind you, hadn't really had a handover with regard to the woman in labour. Anyway, that was fine. It was a very early premature labour, but she progressed to birth. The baby boy, despite being very small, was alive and crying. Fortunately everything was fine with the delivery of the placenta and there was no bleeding. By now it was about 3 a.m. As is usual in these cases, an emergency retrieval was put into place to fly Mum and the baby out as quickly as possible. That was with the RFDS and so we had communications with the female paediatrician in Alice Springs Hospital plus the emergency services doctor who was planning to come out on the flight.

Like I said, the mum was good. I mean it was all a big shock to her; the fact that she'd gone into labour so early and the baby was born. Her husband was around. And it was great that he was able to be there because traditionally it's not accepted that a male partner be a part of a birth. Anyway, we had to ascertain the exact age of this baby, so there was a lot of telephone conversation going on between me and the paediatrician in Alice Springs as to whether they should send a paediatrician out on the emergency retrieval flight. Anyway, we finally worked out that he was about twenty-six weeks. Most of this time the mum held the little one and we just kept him warm and tried to get a manual expression of colostrum from the mum to feed him via a little cup or a syringe.

While we were waiting for the retrieval team to arrive, the dad went off and brought the little sisters and the brother over to see Mum and the new baby. Then a couple of aunties came over. But as time went by, the baby started to weaken so we wrapped him in cling wrap to keep him warm. All this time the mum was holding her baby. Then, unfortunately, the little one died while we were waiting for the retrieval team to arrive. I didn't say anything. There was still a kind of little nerve response in the chest, which made it look like he was breathing. But he wasn't. So I just let the mum continue on holding her little one, as if he was alive. She may have known, I don't know. Then as soon as the paediatrician arrived, he announced that the baby was no longer living.

The husband and the kids were still there. They were very silent. It was a very quiet time. I think some of it was shock and some of it was acceptance. They'd been with the baby for a few hours, and whilst in many ways it was disturbing, the good thing was that the family were able to be there while the little one was alive and they all got to see and hold him. We'd even taken photos.

In cases like that there's always a string of haunting 'ifs', such as 'if the birth hadn't progressed so quickly, and 'if the retrieval team had been able to get there earlier and had taken Mum and the baby off to Alice Springs Hospital, where the intensive care unit may have prolonged the little one's life. But that's one of the disadvantages of anyone having to give birth out in remote areas. I mean, if that baby had been born in a city, he probably would've lived. These days, babies are living at twenty-four and twenty-five weeks. So there's all those sorts of things that go through your mind. Then again, 'if' all that had happened and the baby had still died, the mum would've birthed alone in Alice Springs and her family wouldn't have seen their little one in his live state.

So anyhow, the mother and baby then went off in the RFDS aeroplane. When they landed on the airstrip in Alice Springs, the police were waiting for them. Someone had reported that there was an unknown reason for this premature labour and that domestic violence couldn't be ruled out. There'd never been any mention of that while I was in the clinic with the family, so I don't know where that came from. Anyhow, the police took the baby away from the mother and they put it in the local morgue. It was a shocking, terrible situation. And I only found out about it all when I rang a midwife friend, who was working in the maternity ward, to see how the mum was coping.

Fortunately my midwife friend had a close friend who was a police officer in Alice Springs. She called him and they managed to get the little one taken out of the morgue, and back with the mother. I mean, really, if something like that had happened anywhere else in Australia, it'd be plastered all over the headlines as being completely unacceptable and there'd be a huge uproar over it. Of course, we took our own action and we wrote letters of condemnation and so forth to all those concerned, but ...

Glynis' Story
A Day in the Life

Okay, before I start: some of your readers may think it's an easy sort of life working in an outback hospital. But it's not. I've just gone through one of my old diaries and this's what I'd written down under the title of 'A day in the life of a health service manager'.

Friday, 8:30 a.m.

Do general checks upon handover for any updates etc.

Death on arrival. Ring the ambos to make sure all ambulance sheets have been completed correctly re: correct times etc.

Get the body from the mortuary refrigerator, as relatives are arriving. Make sure it's ready for viewing and prepare the viewing room.

Get money from the safe for aged-care patients and give it to them, ready to go out with relatives, friends etc.

Read emails and respond where appropriate.

Commence reference checks for an RN who's coming up from Melbourne, as the wrong phone number has been given.

Speak with someone who knows the RN from Melbourne.

One person is on sick leave and another is off for another eight days so ring around and sort out replacements.

Adjust the roster for the two new RNs who are coming in to help out while others are absent.

Complete a survey for community health.

Accept to join the working party for drug and alcohol.

Order oxygen.

Communicate with the deputy. Discuss I-stat (hand-held point-of-care blood gases analyser) machine possible purchase.

Check if staff member can come in to help with the viewing of the deceased. Note: she apparently didn't finish until 4:30 in the morning so, unfortunately, can't start work until 1 o'clock.

12:33 p.m.

Haven't had anything to eat yet.

Speak to the family of the deceased with regard to the postmortem. Speak to the funeral parlour … twice.

Grab some lunch.

Make coffee for two police officers and chat re: mother requesting to speak to me about their thirteen-year-old, sexually active child.

Speak to ex-police officer and sergeant re: the possibility of an offender doing community service hours at the hospital.

Read emails and respond where appropriate.

Ring registrar re: request for staff to sign record of interviews.

Give sexual health list to clinic staff and explain process.

Mortuary door won't lock. Find maintenance. Ask to check.

Open postal mail. Give re-directed mail to the transport person and ask to take back to the post office.

Pay membership — College of Nursing.

Call from boss re: the circumstances of the death-on-arrival. Did the RN attend when circumstances, treatment, inspections etc. were carried out? Speak to the RN who was in charge.

Do the accounts and start sorting out the administration files. Put in new bookcase.

Call from rugby league re: wanting us to set up a first-aid kit for them.

Call from the Flying Doctor Service re: media attending on Monday. Will take photos. Get media-release forms signed by staff.

Call from RN in Melbourne re: working.

Sort out the logistics and put a call in etc. for the new pay system.

Await call from RN's other referee. Will call me back when she's finished ward round.

6:11 p.m.

Try to go home.

An enrolled nurse would like her mail ready for her to pick up, as she's waiting for an assignment.

Give up going home. Have a meeting with other partners on duty at the hospital.

Cover calls until 9 p.m.

So there you go, that's the day, and that's a relatively quiet one.

Camping

I was born here, in the far west of New South Wales, at Broken Hill, and this is where I grew up. Well, to be more exact, I really should say that I grew up in South Broken Hill, as there's a bit of a division at times. My dad was from a goldmining family, around the Daylesford–Ballarat area, in Victoria. Then, with the silver, lead and zinc mines opening up in Broken Hill, his parents packed up their horse and cart and their four children and they headed up here. Dad was two at that stage. That was in about 1916, and consequently, due to the lead, my grandfather ended up with lung problems and couldn't work in the mines any more.

There was no compensation in those days; instead, my grandfather was given the loan of a block of land down in the Riverina. That's where Dad started school. But things were tough. They were living in a hessian tent and it was a struggle to feed the family, so they returned to Broken Hill. Dad then finished whatever small amount of education he had at Marist Brothers College, which often caused him to joke how he'd had a 'college education'. But due to his deafness, Dad's opportunities were limited. Now, I'm not sure of the exact circumstances as to why, but when the rest of his family moved to Sydney, Dad stayed behind, working on the mines.

Dad was also a talented sportsman. He once played cricket against India in a country team and also against Bradman, back when Bradman captained South Australia. He also played exhibition tennis against the Davis Cup players when they visited Broken Hill. And I remember how he used to read about four books a week and was always quoting Confucius.

My mother's side were from farming properties in South Australia. Mum was born after her parents had moved to Broken Hill. They must've been a big family because my grandmother died giving birth to her fourteenth child, or thereabouts. The children were then separated and raised by aunties and uncles.

As for thoughts of nursing: when I was young I remember that Grandma — Dad's mum — had some sort of a heart condition and I was sometimes given the responsibility of sleeping over, just in case she had a turn. Perhaps that's where I began to develop an interest in caring for people. Also, back then, nursing was one of the rare occupations in Broken Hill that women were allowed to continue to do after they married. Anyhow, when I finished Year 10, I was too young to start nursing. So I did a year at day secretarial college, then, just after my seventeenth birthday, I started my hospital-based training.

Broken Hill Hospital was well renowned for its training. It was extremely regimental. Everything had to be as neat as a pin and our clothing was highly starched. And oh, there were so many pieces to that uniform. One flatmate I had would start getting undressed from the front door and she'd leave bits of clothing strewn all over the place. Even all the buttons came off. And we'd have regular inspections to make sure we presented well and that our dresses were the right length, with no petticoat showing. Mind you, that was done by an RN who often had her own petticoat showing. Still, at least we all knew exactly what was expected of us, and we were in absolute awe of Matron and her deputy.

Matron lived in a flat beneath our nurses' home, and to stir her up, we'd run up and down making noise. Then, before she could make it upstairs, we'd have tucked ourselves in bed, pretending to be asleep. It wasn't a hugely social life. Oh, there were the occasional dances and cabarets and parties but we'd have to be back in the nurses' home nice and early or we'd be locked out and be in big trouble. Still, every now and then you'd hear someone climbing up the trees outside, at some ungodly hour, trying to sneak back to bed. I never did that. I was one of the quieter ones, though I did spend a night or two out in the carpark, waiting for the domestics to open the place up so I could sneak in.

By the time I finished my training, Mum had been diagnosed with lung cancer and so I only worked at the hospital on and off over the next two years. I was married by then. My husband was employed by what's now known as Telstra. They were doing a lot of work out on the Moomba gas pipeline and he was out of town more often than not. But I always wanted to experience a town that was a bit different, and with Mum's blessing, I rang the matron at Wilcannia and asked if there were any positions available.

'Yes,' she said. 'Can you come out this afternoon?'

'Oh, okay,' I said. 'I'll catch the bus over.'

Wilcannia's a couple of hundred kilometres east of Broken Hill. I'd been told that someone would be waiting for me; the only trouble was, the bus was late, and by the time I arrived, nobody was about. I must've looked a bit lost because when a garbage truck came by, the driver stopped and said, 'Are you the new nursing sister?'

I said, 'Yes.'

'Good. Do you want a lift up to the hospital?'

So I got a lift in the garbage truck and when I got there one of the young Indigenous lads offered to carry my bags across to the nurses' home. I'd never had my bags carried for me before. I thought, Gee, this's good. Then, when I met Matron and the doctor, I was given a book on how to do a physical assessment and that night I was placed in charge of the hospital.

But they were very good to me at Wilcannia. By then Mum was seeing out her final days at home and they organised my shifts so that I could get back to Broken Hill and help Dad look after Mum. Now here's an odd thing: while the local Aboriginal people always used to ask about Mum, the non-Indigenous people avoided talking about it. Strange, isn't it? There was one man in particular; Brian. Brian was from an Aboriginal family. He worked as an ambulance driver, and when he heard that Mum was sick, he said, 'If you ever get called back to Broken Hill of a night-time, don't drive on your own. Come and knock on my window and I'll get up and take you.'

A week later I got a call to say that it didn't look like Mum was going to last the night. So I went and knocked on Brian's window and he got up, no questions at all, and he drove me back over to Broken Hill and he slept in our lounge room while I went up to the hospital. I still remember Mum saying, 'Please, don't forget to thank that young Aboriginal boy for what he did.' Not long after, she died.

Actually, for some reason, all of Brian's family took a liking to me. Because I worked Friday nights, his mother and aunties would often come in for a consultation after the doctor had left. Mostly we'd just chat, so it was social as well. They were good people and they helped me a lot. At one of the Wilcannia Balls a young Indigenous lad from the hospital got very drunk and so I offered to drive him home. The thing was, he was in a relationship with an older Indigenous woman, and when she overheard me offering to drive him home, she chased after me and king-hit me. *Bang*, down I went. I was a bit of a mess and I probably got a broken nose out of it. I say probably because, at that time, I was trying to get pregnant so I couldn't have x-rays. This's when Indigenous rights was a real hot issue, so there I was, a white person challenging an Indigenous woman, and I couldn't get a lawyer. No one would take me on.

When Brian heard about it, he told his mother. Next thing, he comes up to me: 'Mum wants to see you down home.'

I said, 'What's your mum want to see me for?'

He said, 'She's got a lawyer for you.' And she had. She'd organised a lawyer for me, and for those days of hot Indigenous rights, that was a real reversal, I can tell you. So that was that and things worked out for the best, given the circumstances.

And I was pregnant. But I continued in Wilcannia until I was six months, then I came back to Broken Hill to live.

I didn't see Brian or any of his family after that. Oh, I occasionally spoke to his brother because both our fathers were in Broken Hill Hospital at the same time — in fact, they were in beds near to each other — and he once said how Brian was working in town on the mines or on the council. But that's all I knew.

Anyhow, six months after my first daughter was born, I started part-time as a practice nurse for two local GPs. That lasted for ten years, during which time I had a second daughter. One of those GPs was particularly special to me. Not only had she delivered my first child, she was a person I absolutely idolised. But then she was killed in a car accident. It was just tragic. She'd been to Birdsville with her partner and their car rolled near Cooper Creek. She had children too so it was doubly heartbreaking. I was working for the government by then. I'd begun relief work as a family-planning community nurse, and after I'd done an online degree, I got re-graded to a clinical nurse specialist, which led me on to becoming unit manager of the Broken Hill Community Team.

By the early 1990s, I knew it was time to separate from my husband. I was thirty-eight, and with having the two girls to support, I needed a good job and one that came with a house. That's when I got the position in south-western Queensland as director of nursing at Charleville Hospital. Charleville was a fifty-bed acute hospital with a fifty-bed nursing home. I thought they'd be backward, but they weren't. They were very forward-looking and very well run. In fact, I put them in for an award and we won the best multipurpose facility in Australia.

My eldest daughter was in Grade 6 by then. She had a high IQ and one day I saw Geelong Grammar was offering scholarships. Having gone to Broken Hill High, all I knew about the place was that Prince Charles had gone to Timbertop, which was their Year 9 campus. So I thought it must've been good. Not long after my daughter had sat the test I got a call from the principal: 'Would you like to come for an interview?' So we did, and she was offered the second-highest Australasian scholarship to Geelong Grammar.

At that stage my youngest daughter was unhappy at school and so she went back to live with her dad in Broken Hill. But everything I was doing was for my girls and I was determined that she should get a comparable education. To do that we needed to get to a city. That's when I saw a job advertised in Hobart as director of an organisation that ran the state prison drug and alcohol service. I applied, and I got it. The thing was, I'd never lived in a city before, and now here I am, driving a packed ute the wrong way up one-way streets with everyone blowing their horns at me. It was terrible, and because I'd never lived in a place that had parking meters, I was forever forgetting to put money in the darn things.

As for my living: I'd put a deposit on a house but I had to wait until it was available. With having a mortgage and kids to support, things were tight, so I'd pre-organised accommodation at a place in Hobart where I was told 'college' students lived. It came with meals. Good. The only trouble was, instead of it being a college where university students lived, like I'd presumed, it turned out to be a 'college' for Year 11 and 12s. So there I was in amongst all these rampant fifteen- or sixteen-year-olds. Oh, there were parties every night, skateboards skidding across the roof and everything. It almost drove me mad. To make matters worse, my eldest daughter had come down to join me and we had to take it in turns sleeping on the floor.

She'd wanted to go to Melbourne University to do theatre studies so I'd invited her to join me in Hobart, but only on the condition that she worked and saved up to help pay her uni fees. Because she'd learnt some Japanese, she found a job as a trainee Japanese-speaking ghost-tour guide at Hobart Penitentiary. One night, not long after she'd started training, she was down there, ready to go on this ghost tour. Everything was in complete darkness when, all of a sudden, a chair spontaneously combusted in front of her. She was totally spooked and so that was the end of her career as a ghost-tour guide.

As for other memories: as I mentioned, the organisation I worked for was contracted to run drug and alcohol services in prisons. Risdon was one of the prisons, and that's where I ran into Mark 'Chopper' Read. I forget what Mark had been convicted for. It could've been for any number of things — assault, robbery, kidnapping — though I don't think it was for murder at that stage. But debating was part of prison activities and my eldest daughter and I debated against him. That was a real experience. The subject was something like whether or not the world would benefit from visitations by aliens. We were on the 'against' side and Mark and two of the other prisoners were on the 'for' side. It was an absolute classic. One prisoner came out dressed as Mork, from the TV show *Mork and Mindy*. Another came out as Superman, and Mark was Doctor Spock, with no ears, because his had been chopped or bitten off. Well, they really shot us down. It was like a stand-up comedy act, with all their mimicking and going on.

But oh, Mark was character. I actually got to know him well. We debated against him another time. Again it was all fun and games, so much so that when we got home my daughter said, 'Isn't it funny how such nice people end up in a prison like that?'

The next day, when I told Mark what she'd said, he said, 'Glynis, you go back and tell your daughter, just because we can be civilised for one night, it doesn't mean that we're nice people.' So I did. I went home and I told her what Mark 'Chopper' Read had said.

So that was one memorable experience; then there was the Port Arthur massacre on Sunday, 28th, April 1996. That's when Martin Bryant went on a rampage in the Broad Arrow Café, fatally shooting thirty-five people and wounding another twenty-three. It was just horrible. I'd done a bit of debriefing training, and as soon as I heard what had happened, I rang and offered my help. Two hours later I got the call: 'Could you come straight down please?'

The initial coordination centre was at Rokeby Police Academy. Martin Bryant hadn't been captured by then, and because the Broad Arrow Café remained a crime scene, no one was allowed back inside to get their belongings: you know, things like babies' bottles, car and house keys, passports, wallets and purses. So we had to help the best we could with all that, as well as gather everyone's information on databases. The relatives also had to be brought in to identify bodies. Help and advice lines had to be set up. The army came in with their counsellors and were trying to organise as many one-on-one sessions as possible. We were receiving phone calls from all over the world from people wanting to help. We had tourists in motels trying to find out who was missing and who wasn't. Consulates were ringing to find out if any of their citizens had been involved.

It was an absolutely huge operation. Virtually overnight we had to create a whole new department of three hundred and fifty people. Of course, we then had to screen everyone, just to make sure they were who they said they were and that they had the qualifications they said they had. Then after we got all the managers together, I debriefed them on what we'd already done. By about the Wednesday, the poor guy who was doing the majority of the work was completely exhausted so I took charge for the day to give him a break. In fact I've got a letter here thanking me for my response.

Yes, so I was living in Hobart. I was busy. I was seeing someone, a friend, and things were very comfortable. I'd had very little contact with Broken Hill, just a couple of phone calls. That's how I heard that they were going to have an opening for the newly renovated Wilcannia Hospital. It'd been over thirty years since I'd been to Wilcannia and I began thinking how it'd be good to get some of the old crew back together for the occasion. So I rang around and found out that Brian was living with family in Albury. I gave him a call and said, 'It'd be great if we could all get together and go along.'

'Yeah, okay,' he said. 'I'll see.'

After that sort of response I wasn't sure if he was too keen about it, so I kept ringing him and during one call he said, 'Would you like to go camping up the Murray River?'

Now I'm not a camper, not at all, so I really don't know why, but I said, 'Oh yes. Okay.'

Around that time I'd been watching the television show *Bush Mechanics*. It's where a group of Aborigines from Yuendumu drive through the desert in an old bomb car to pick up their mate from Alice Springs jail. All along the way their car kept breaking down and they kept coming up with different ways to keep the vehicle going. So when I sussed out that Brian had an old Holden, I started having second thoughts about going bush with him. But I'd committed, so I flew to Melbourne, hired a car and I drove to Albury where I went to his brother's place and had a nice barbecue.

I'd organised my own accommodation, so the next day I turn up all prepared to go on this camping trip. I'm dressed to the nines, jewellery and all, hair done, smelling of Chanel No.5, and just in case Brian had forgotten, I'd bought along my own camping shower. When he saw me he looked a bit shocked, but he was patient with me. So we headed off to Corowa. That's when he found out that I didn't know the first thing about fishing. But he was patient with me. Worse still, when he was showing me how to fish, I ended up hooking him sideways in the lip. Again, he looked shocked, but he was patient with me, and I am a nurse.

That night around the campfire we got chatting, catching up on the years. Thinking back, I guess I'd been quite naïve. He said he'd always liked me. He told me that after I'd had the two girls and I was living back in Broken Hill, he was working in the council. He knew I was married but he just wanted to see me.

Thinking that I might come out of my house if I saw a broken-down car outside, he'd parked his council vehicle near my place and he'd put the bonnet up. There he was, with his head stuck under the bonnet, waiting for me to appear, when one of his colleagues tapped him on the shoulder and said, 'Brian, you'd better take that car straight back to the workshop and get it checked.'

But it was a wonderful night down by the river. And that was our first real date. His brother later told me that after my initial call, Brian had put down the phone and said, 'That's it. I'm getting married to that woman.'

So the romance was on and by the time of the Wilcannia Hospital opening, we were partners. But it would've been very difficult for us to make a go of the relationship in Hobart. To begin with, Brian wouldn't drive in a city, and of course he'd be socially isolated. By then both my girls were living independently in Tasmania, so I decided to return to Broken Hill. Now I've done the round trip: Broken Hill to Wilcannia, Wilcannia to Charleville, Charleville to Hobart and from Hobart back to Broken Hill. Along the way I'd achieved great things, and when I came back, I had to start all over again as a casual Year 8 nurse.

But I was used to working my way back, and with the love, help and support of Brian, I have. In 2004 I was awarded Nurse of the Year at Broken Hill Hospital and now, in 2015, I'm about to take on the appointment as a casual health service manager for western New South Wales. I'll continue my work for the RFDS as well as in triage and intake mental health and teaching several subjects online. So nursing's been very good to me and perhaps in some small way I've been good for nursing. Actually, just a few weeks ago, a psychiatrist I'd once worked with said, 'Thank you very much, Glynis. I wouldn't have survived those very difficult times without you.'

I can tell you, it's very humbling for a nurse to be told that.

Jane's Story
Joys and Pitfalls

I grew up in Brisbane, so you could say I was a city girl. But due to my father's occupation, we were fortunate enough to own a small property outside of the city, where we'd spend the weekends. Perhaps that's why I originally wanted to go jillarooing. But no, my parents were keen that I have something solid behind me. So, not wanting to have a job where I'd end up sitting behind a desk, putting on weight, I decided to try nursing. As soon as I started my training, that was it: nursing was all I wanted to do. I did my three years of general in Maryborough, up in the Fraser Coast area of Queensland, followed by twelve months of midwifery at Nambour, just north of Brisbane. I then went over to the Northern Territory where I did my intensive care in Alice Springs.

Alice Springs was my first big job out of training. That was in the late '80s. I was still quite green and I was working in the ICU. It was a huge cultural learning curve because I'd had very little to do with Aboriginal people. Being in Alice Springs we'd get quite a few in at the hospital. Then there were the ones from the outlying mission-communities, who were still living in more of their traditional manner. With most of those being non-English speaking, communication was difficult. So I had to learn cultural things like how a women wasn't allowed to look an Aboriginal man in the eyes and how you had to bow your head when you talked to them.

It was quite fascinating really. I remember when one of the community clinic doctors flew an Indigenous male in to us. When he arrived in ICU he was unconscious. There was nothing untoward in his pathology, nor were there any obvious indications of injury or disease. We then managed to get it out of his family that he'd recently married outside his tribe, which is very much against their culture, and so his wife's tribe decided to 'sing' him to death. Anyhow, we put him on the ventilator to keep him breathing and we gave him intravenous fluids to keep up his nutrition. But we were getting nowhere. He was just lying there unconscious, with no improvement or deterioration. After some discussion it was decided to send the clinic plane back out to the man's community and bring in their witch doctor — kurdaitcha man — to see what he could do. The thinking was that perhaps he might be able to somehow reverse the curse that'd been put on this man.

It was quite a scream really. When the kurdaitcha man arrived, he was in the full regalia. He'd brought along some sort of special rocks and he was covered in feathers, literally. He had feathers on his arms, his ankles, his wrists, his head. He wore a skirt of feathers. He had a mass of large feathers and bones hanging around his neck. Then before he went in to see the man, the room had to be darkened. So all the lights were turned off. Curtains were hung over the windows. Then we all had to wait outside. So I don't know what went on with the feathers and the rocks but sometime later the kurdaitcha man reappeared.

'No good,' he said. 'He's fucked.' Then he left.

And that was that. The fella was even beyond the help of the kurdaitcha man.

Of course, the doctors were quite sceptical about all this and so we continued to monitor the man and feed him and artificially breathe for him with the ventilator. But still no change. Then a day later, all these old, battered and bashed vehicles arrived outside the hospital, packed to the hilt with his tribe. I can't remember what community they were from, but they'd driven a long way. There were about fifty of them. They all came into the ICU and they took up their position, sitting down along the corridors outside his room, and then they started wailing. And they wailed and they wailed for a full twenty-four hours.

These people weren't shushed or asked to leave. They were allowed to go through their traditional grieving process, and the other patients in the ICU just had to bear it. Throughout this process, not one of them went into the room to see him, not even any of his relatives. They all just sat in the corridor and wailed. I'll never forget it. It was the eeriest of sounds. Then the strangest of things happened. Just as the wailing reached its crescendo, the man passed away. And with no one else in the room bar us, there was no way that his actual passing could've been known by any of them. But the moment the ECG monitor flatlined, they all got up and walked out of the hospital. Just like that, and that was the end of it. We couldn't believe it. We just stood there, aghast. The man had been sung to death.

After Alice Springs I began doing three- to six-months stints of remote relief. Weipa was another experience. That was in the early '90s. Weipa's in the Gulf of Carpentaria, on the Queensland side of Cape York Peninsula. It's a big bauxite-mining town. Apart from a state government–run hospital and the huge Scherger air base that they were building, the rest of the place was pretty much owned by Comalco. I arrived just at the end of the wet season. It was still incredibly humid and the downpours were amazing. People were walking around the supermarket absolutely saturated, doing their shopping. The population was roughly two thousand. It was a twenty-bed hospital, then we had a few long-term patients. There was just one doctor in the town and he'd only come if we really needed him. He was employed by Comalco and they had their own medical rooms, separate from us, so the employees would go to him on site. But we managed to do most things ourselves. We even delivered the babies. Anything major was sent to Cairns, which was a bumpy 650-kilometre flight.

You were either dead bored or dead scared in Weipa. There'd just be two of us on duty: a registered nurse and an enrolled nurse. I remember when the ambulance people called us one night. They said there'd been a family dispute and they were bringing in a female who'd received head injuries. When they arrived at casualty, they opened up the back of the ambulance to pull out the trolley and there was this female with an axe stuck in the middle of her skull. Her boyfriend was with her, and he was looking pretty sheepish. They'd obviously had quite a few drinks, and they'd had this big argument — which was continuing. She certainly wasn't too compromised by having the axe stuck in her head because she was calling her boyfriend all the names under the sun.

Being a major injury, we decided to call in a retrieval plane from Cairns. When it arrived we struck a problem. We couldn't fit the woman into the plane with the axe still sticking out of her head. So we sedated her some more, then we got to it and sawed the axe handle off. That done, we bandaged down the axe head so it wouldn't move about during the trip and off she went to Cairns. Believe it or not, a week later she was back in Weipa, and all was well. Last we heard she'd got back with her boyfriend and it was 'happily ever after' ... hopefully.

So it got to be a pretty wild place at times. We'd even get the occasional request to patch up a wounded pig dog. Pig hunting was big in Weipa, particularly among the white population, and it was dangerous. The pig dogs came in all shapes and sizes. There were the border collie–cattle dog crosses. Then you'd get your big-chested, solid-headed bull mastiff–Great Dane crosses. They were massive. Some were up to a metre tall. But with wild pig's meat not being fit for human consumption, if the dogs won, the pigs were either shot or they'd have their throats cut, and be left out in the bush, or they might just chop off a leg and take it home for the dogs to eat. Mind you, some of the pigs were pretty massive as well — and with huge tusks — which is why the dogs got so badly gored. So we'd get a call, and if things were quiet, we'd let them bring the dog in. We'd open up the morgue, pop the dog on the slab, sedate it and off we'd go, practising our surgical skills. Most of them had been gored around the abdomen, or they'd been gashed around the throat. A lot of them survived. Some didn't. Sometimes they'd been ripped open from head to toe and were already too far gone.

As for other memories: the council used to run outdoor movies, down on the beachfront. That was fun. You'd grab a chair, a few beers and set up in the sand, out in the open air, under the stars. They had a big screen mounted on the back of a truck and the movie would be projected onto that. One night we were watching that movie with Demi Moore and Patrick Swayze in it; *Ghost*, I think it was. It was the one where Patrick Swayze died in a car accident and he kept visiting Demi Moore as a ghost. Anyhow, just as it got to the exciting part, we were interrupted by an announcement: 'Can you please evacuate the area? A crocodile's been seen coming up the beach.' So we all packed up and we went home, and I never saw the end of *Ghost*, not until years later when I got it out on video. Though for some reason it just didn't seem to have the impact that it had when we were on the beach that night, up in Weipa.

After Weipa I did a lot of relief work around places like Roma, Blackall, Ayr. I've also been out to St George and I was at Moree for quite a while, in northern New South Wales. Then I did a stint as an emergency flight nurse with the Royal Flying Doctor Service, at both their Broken Hill and Dubbo bases. One time we got a call from the nurses at Tibooburra saying how they'd just been out in the ambulance to pick up a man who'd been wandering down the highway in a distressed state. It was extremely hot at the time, and as it happened, this man was schizophrenic and he'd either broken out of, or been released from, a psychiatric hospital near Morisset, just south of Newcastle. How on earth he found his way out to Tibooburra is anyone's guess. Anyhow, he'd told the nurses that he'd come up there to pick pears. Mind you, we're talking about the far north-western corner of New South Wales where the nearest pear orchard could've been a thousand k's away.

But what really got the nurses going was that this poor man had not only come to pick pears in an area that had no pears, but he'd also somehow got it in his head that he was the Easter Bunny. So when they found him out on the highway, he was stark naked, apart from wearing his underpants on his head, and, for added effect, he'd stuck a carrot up his rectum. He wasn't at all violent, because when the nurses had asked him if he'd like to get in the back of the ambulance, in he hopped, no problem at all. We then found out where this man's father was and we contacted him, thinking that he might be worried about his missing son. But when we explained the son's circumstances, all the father said was, 'Yes, he does that kind of thing quite a bit. You should've seen what he did last Christmas.'

But, oh, when we got to him, he was totally off the planet. He had no idea where he was or who he was, other than believing he'd come out to Tibooburra to pick pears and that he was the Easter Bunny. What's more, there was no way he was going to let us take his underpants off his head or remove the carrot from his rectum. In his mind, he was the Easter Bunny and that was it, carrot and all.

Not long after that I got married and we moved over here to Walgett, in the central-north of New South Wales. I'd first met my husband-to-be when I was working over in Moree. He was a stock and station agent there, then he moved to Walgett. Then after he'd seen a story about me in one of the newspapers, he got in touch and we caught up in Dubbo, and it just went from there.

I've now been in Walgett for nearly ten years. Walgett's population is around two thousand and there's a multipurpose medical centre with ten beds. I did my early childhood nursing here. Part of my job these days is to go out to the Aboriginal communities around the north-western and central-western areas of New South Wales and immunise the babies and the children. It's quite easy to keep track of them really, because once they're born, they go onto a national register. So say if they're born in Dubbo, the paperwork would come back stating their birth date, where they're living and so forth, and you add them onto your list. Then because they rarely come to town, on the date they're due, we travel out and immunise them.

One community we visit is only about twenty k's out of Walgett. It was from the days when the Aboriginal people weren't allowed to live in town. I always have an Aboriginal health worker with me when I go out to immunise. When we arrived, the family was outside in the dirt, in their front yard. Mum was hanging onto the baby. The other kids were running around. I don't know where the father had got to but Grandpa was sitting there smoking. Mind you, I wasn't quite sure what he was smoking but it certainly wasn't tobacco. Anyhow, I was bending down, talking to the mother and examining the baby on a sheet that I'd placed on the ground. I was just getting the needles ready when the Aboriginal health worker called out, 'Jane, Jane.'

I said, 'Look, I'm nearly there. I'll be finished in a tick.'

Then I heard the grandfather say, 'Ah, 'e won't hurt ya.'

When I looked around, I swear, there was this pig: it would've been as big as a razorback. And it just barged in and bowled us and the medical kit over. I don't know why; it might've been hungry or something because there was not a blade of grass to eat. The yard was a dust bowl. But gosh it was big, and it sort of barged through the whole works and sent everything flying, including us. And there's Grandpa, off with the fairies, contentedly smoking away, watching, while the kids are trying to drag this pig away. It was chaos. In the end we immunised the baby, then we packed up everything we could pack up, and when we were leaving, Grandpa asked, 'Hey,' he said. 'You wanna have some smoke with me? 'N what'a about any of them needles 'n syringes; can yer leave 'em here?'

I said, 'Nah, mate, I might just go home now. I've had enough for today.'

So working out in the rural and remote areas has its disadvantages and its advantages. Of course, on a more serious level, there's the ongoing problem of not having the same resources you'd have in the city, where you can just refer a patient on to someone else. Then there's things like the lack of CAT scans, x-rays, pathology, theatres and so forth. But I guess, if you're in the business of saving people, you just have to get to and do the best you can. There's been times when we've had to carry a woman in labour up the stairs to a theatre, because the lifts are out, due to a power failure. Or when you go out and chop a load of firewood for a family that's due home from Sydney with a newborn, late on a freezing winter's night. And you've got to have that little bit of extra ingenuity too; like the time we took the front door off a house to use as a spinal board for someone who'd had a horrific motorbike accident.

Then I don't know if this is really relevant or not, but as I said, I was the only early childhood nurse and midwife covering the area from Walgett to Lightning Ridge to Dubbo. No one else was qualified. I was it. I was the one who was supposed to have all the answers. Then, when I was having my first baby, I had to be flown out to Brisbane with an emergency delivery. If that wasn't traumatic enough, I returned to our property with a newborn who was on second-hourly feeds, twenty-four hours a day, and a husband who left for work early in the morning and didn't get home till after dark. And there I was, still trying to work around the place, doing the usual washing, the ironing, the cooking, the feeding, the cleaning, the gardening. On top of that there were the dogs to care for. There were sheep that needed looking after and their water checked. Then the pump would break down and we'd have no water, so I'd have to go out and try to fix the pump or clear the blockage or try to source water from somewhere else. And because I was the only person within cooee who had early childhood nursing experience, there was no one I could talk to. Not a soul.

I mean, I can understand how it happened. It was purely from the exhaustion of trying to do everything that I fell into a massive heap of postnatal depression. It got to the stage where I could hardly even make a cup of tea. I was useless. I couldn't even drive the car. And I certainly wasn't going to walk into town, looking like I'd lost my bundle, especially when I was supposed to be the one that everyone comes to for help in early childhood situations, exactly like I was in. And when I did eventually get in to see the doctor and say, 'Look, I need help. I'm depressed. I need something,' all he said was, 'Well, do you want to talk about it?'

I said, 'Nope. I just want a tablet so I can hurry up and get back to work.'

'Oh, okay then.'

It all points to the fact that, yes, while it's good to be living out in places like this, sometimes it does get difficult; very difficult. Anyhow, thanks largely to my amazing mother who came and stayed for a while, I did eventually get over it. So I don't know if that's relevant to your book or not, but there it is. That's the joys and pitfalls of rural and remote nursing for you.

Kaisu's Story
Mad, Mercenary or Missionary

I was born fifty kilometres south of the Arctic Circle, on a minus forty degree Celsius day, in Finland. Because of the impact the Second World War had on the country, my parents were keen for us to immigrate to Australia. But at the age of twelve, the last· thing I wanted to do was to leave my friends and move to a place I knew nothing about. So to entice me, and avoid a tantrum, my parents told me that I'd be able to go to school in the pouch of a kangaroo and I'd be able to live in a wurley-wurley with the Aborigines. And that got me. Of course, I soon discovered that it was absolute bullshit. Instead, after we arrived in Sydney we lived in a range of migrant hostels before my father got work at Holden, in South Australia.

I couldn't speak English, so when I went to Findon High, it was either learn the language and assimilate or be discriminated against and be called a wog because I was a migrant. But Finnish people tend to be tenacious. They fought the winter war against the Russians, one soldier to ten Russians, and defeated them. So with the desire to assimilate being so strong, I learnt the language by listening to the radio and reading newspapers and by the end of the academic year I came second in English. But Findon High wasn't a particularly aspirational school. This was in an era where the women who wanted to work outside of the home became secretaries or primary school teachers or went into a typing pool or did nursing. I decided on nursing. Actually, in many ways it felt a bit like my calling in that I had a deep need to care for people.

I was seventeen at the time, and being a bit of a bushie at heart, I did my training down in the south-east of South Australia, at Mount Gambier. After that I went to Melbourne where I worked in an intensive care unit, then I travelled the world. Upon returning to Adelaide I did my midwifery. That would've been in about 1973. Then I got a scholarship through the Lyell McEwin Hospital to do my Diploma in teaching nursing education. After that I taught at the Lyell McEwin before getting the job as matron, up in the Barossa Valley. But there was little accountability and I felt that some of the doctors were incompetent in their delivery of babies. I saw some atrocious stuff, and not wanting to see any harm be done, I reported one of the doctors to the Australian Medical Association and the hospital board. When nothing happened I got so frustrated that I applied for, and got, the job as principal nurse-educator and deputy matron at the South Coast District Hospital, in Victor Harbor, and later became matron.

I loved the dual role of management and of making learning a joyful experience. But what was really lacking in the general hospital environment was their poor approach to primary prevention, and I decided to do something about it. So, at the age of thirty-three, I went back to university to do my Masters of Health Administration. During that time I had a big rethink as to my direction in nursing. And so, in early '87, when an opportunity came up as community health nurse-midwife for Nganampa Health Council, I got the position.

At this point I'd like to refer to two significant anthropologists, John Tregenza and Stephan Rainow. John and Steffy not only documented language and history throughout the APY — Anangu Pitjantjatjara Yankunytjatjara — Lands, but they were incredibly supportive in encouraging those people whose historical homelands had been Kalka and Pipalyatjara to move back to country. In doing so, they, along with Dr David Scrimgeour and key Aboriginal leaders such as Donald Fraser, Yami Lester and

Ivan Baker, received funding to establish a small mobile health service to serve a fifty-thousand-square-kilometre area out from Kalka and Pipalyatjara.

Nganampa Health Council grew out of that. As an Aboriginal community-controlled health service it covered an area of 104,000 square kilometres of the APY Lands in north-west South Australia. By 1983 there were about eight separate community-based clinics throughout the Lands. I was allocated the Kalka–Pipalyatjara communities, which are right over on the border of South Australia, Western Australia and the Northern Territory. So I went from a hospital-based environment into the vast remote outback. In some ways I guess I was fulfilling my childhood desire to go and live with Aboriginal people.

To take up my appointment, I flew from Adelaide to Alice Springs, then via light plane out to the little dirt runway at Pipalyatjara. Both Kalka and Pipalyatjara are very small communities compared to Ernabella (Pukatja), Fregon (Kaltjiti), Indulkana (Iwantja) and Amata, where, during the drought years of the 1930s and '40s, the Aborigines were rounded up and moved into communities by the church and various government agencies. The Department of Welfare, for instance, has had a significant and painful history throughout the APY Lands for the taking away of children from Aboriginal women.

I was based in Kalka and I covered eleven homelands, some of which had only ten people. In all I'd estimate the total population would've been around five hundred. My home was a two-room caravan — a Silver Bullet — which had a verandah, a bathroom, a bedroom and a gas stove for cooking. Then, because the gas would invariably run out, I'd have, at the ready, a halved forty-four-gallon drum and some wood. The clinic at Kalka was a pre-fabricated building of two small rooms. There was a small treatment area and a medicine store, and there was a general office–cum–waiting area. At Pipalyatjara our clinic was a transport container.

While we couldn't do anything too sophisticated, we still managed all sorts of medical issues. As a midwife, I delivered quite a few babies. At one time we had a country and western show in the Pipalyatjara school hall. The place was packed. People were having a great time; the kids were dancing and grooving around. I'd previously checked a pregnant woman out. There were no palpable contractions, then, lo and behold, she went into rapid labour, and that was the end of the concert. The music stopped. Everybody vacated the hall. The men shot off the quickest because of the women's business–men's business stuff, and I managed the delivery on the floor.

If someone needed to be evacuated we'd call the RFDS on our CB radio. So, say if we'd assessed a woman in labour as being in difficulty, after we'd contacted the RFDS, we'd take her in the Land Cruiser troopie over to the nearby dirt airstrip at Pipalyatjara and wait for the plane. If it'd rained and the plane couldn't get in, we'd have to manage the situation ourselves, with advice from the RFDS doctor given over the radio. I say 'we' because Dr Niall Quierey was there. Niall was fantastic. We worked well as a team. When he'd take a break, I'd be there on my own, then we'd swap around and I'd take a break.

We were also lucky in that we had some excellent Aboriginal health workers. Invariably I didn't travel by myself on mobile clinic visits out to the homelands. I'd try and take a couple of the health workers with me, usually a male and a female, even though, because of kinship, there were some people they couldn't treat. The communication centres in the homeland communities were nothing flash, just lean-tos basically. We'd get on the CB radio: 'We're coming. Anybody there? Any problems?' Then we'd jump into our troopie and head off. It wasn't easy work. It was tough, and we dealt with some very difficult situations. Other than the usual raft of health issues, there were a lot of traumatic injuries through motor vehicle accidents and such, where we simply had to do the best we could with limited resources.

The living conditions of the people in Kalka and Pipalyatjara and throughout the homelands was terrible. Many were living in wurley-wurleys or in unlined corrugated-iron sheds that didn't have water. So the washing machines didn't work, the toilets didn't work, the showers didn't work. At the store you'd pay six bucks for a loaf of white frozen bread. You'd get onions and maybe carrots and pumpkin, but there were no fresh green veggies. You might get oranges, but not any other kind of fruit. The meat that came up from Adelaide was basically the fattiest lamb and mince and sausages. And these are the determinants of health in a remote context. As to medical issues — you name it, we saw it, and they were exacerbated due to poor health infrastructure. As far as diseases like measles, diabetes, and high blood pressure went, what us white fellers were getting in our seventies and eighties, these people were getting in their forties and fifties.

So, other than acute medical intervention, Dr Niall Quierey and I decided on a primary prevention strategy. We worked toward a high rate of immunisation against preventable diseases such as whooping cough, measles and mumps. We began a school lunch program where the women cooked nutritious food. We helped the school buy towels so the kids could have a shower of a morning. Most of the children also had suppurative otitis media, so their ears would pour with pus, due to an inflammation of the middle ear. When that happens they can't hear soft sounds, so they struggled to learn the English language and so we'd try to syringe their ears daily. Then most of the dogs had no fur, due to scabies. Traditionally the Aboriginal people love their dogs, so, with the dogs being part of the family, they slept on the same bedding as everybody else did. And because people didn't have the facilities to wash their bedding or clothes, scabies was rife.

It's said that to work in remote Aboriginal communities you have to be either mad or a mercenary or a missionary. Those of us like John Tregenza describe ourselves as being missionaries because we're definitely not mercenary and we're not bloody mad. But I do think, if you're a white feller who's going to work in an Aboriginal community, the first thing you need to do is to sit down with them and shut up and listen and learn. Otherwise you're just going to alienate yourself and you'll never get anywhere. Secondly, you've got to learn some of the language and try to understand contact history and culture. Following on from that comes the community politics and the politics of Aboriginal health.

So it was exhausting work. We were on call 24/7, and in one of the most remote areas of Australia. But that's just how it was. But see, the fortunate thing for me was, I fell in love with the place. I really did, and so I wanted to learn the language and the culture. I wanted to understand their contact history. I wanted to listen to their stories. I wanted to attend their corroborees — 'inmas'. I wanted to be with the women when they went out gathering bush tucker or to find lizard or to shoot kangaroo, because I knew I was in a really rich cultural environment. I wanted to be immersed in all that sort of stuff. I wanted to soak it all up.

And because they could see that I was interested, they took me in their embrace. I felt their warmth. They cared for me; looked after me. They told me their stories. I was invited to their community events. I was told who my Indigenous family was and so I got to know about kinship. And while I served my role in terms of service provision, they taught me what my responsibilities were to them and what their responsibilities were to me. They helped me work all that stuff out and so I learnt a lot. In fact, in my forty-seven-year history of working in health, my time out at Kalka–Pipalyatjara was one of the most fabulous experiences I've ever had.

Closing the Gap

After a year out at Kalka–Pipalyatjara a vacancy came up as health services manager for the APY Lands. Seeing that I had a strong affinity with the people and was ably qualified, I applied for and got the job. So I left my Silver Bullet caravan out in far western South Australia and moved into an Alice Springs-based office. I was now in a position to work with both Aboriginal and non-Aboriginal people to get a broader health strategy in place for the Lands, and to develop standards of care. I was involved in political advocacy and lobbying where I'd get people like the then Minister for Aboriginal Affairs, Jerry Hand, to come and visit the Lands so he could see for himself what the social determinants of health were. We also recruited high-profile people to help as advocates; people like Hazel Hawke and Don Dunston who'd also been involved in the APY land rights movement.

Due to my experiences of the inner workings of the politics of Aboriginal health, I was able to sort funding for a number of projects. To be closer to the Lands, I got money to build a head office and staff housing between Fregon and Ernabella, at Umuwa, and we put in place a high level of accountability for what we did. We received a substantial amount from SA Health to do a major survey of health on the Lands. Along with people like John Tregenza, Stephan Rainow, Paul Pholeros and Suzy Bryce we wrote a report titled 'Together we will become healthy'. In it we detailed the appalling health situation and what was required to address it.

We got money for a dog health program and to have vets visit the Lands to try and stem the rampant scabies. We started to address the issue of getting decent food into community stores. After an outbreak of meningococcal meningitis, we got funding through SA Health and Northern Territory Health for a mass immunisation program. Then there were the health issues around rubbish and rubbish removal. When people visited the communities, they didn't see the beautiful blue sky or the beautiful red soil. All they saw was rubbish lying around everywhere and they'd say, 'These fuckin' Aboriginals are hopeless. They can't even put their rubbish in a bin.' But rubbish bins weren't available in the communities. Even if they were, nobody had the responsibility of taking them away.

Other projects we started were to bituminise the dirt roads around the communities so the dust hazard was reduced, and to have street lighting installed for increased community safety. There was the ongoing maintenance and development of housing infrastructure. We sought the assistance of ATSIC — the Aboriginal and Torres Strait Islander Commission — to start building decent community housing, and not the sort of shit that was being put up. We also got water and basic amenities into those houses so the people could have decent drinking water and they could do their cleaning, washing and have a shower. Look at it this way: if us white fellers were to stop building public housing in our towns and cities and we didn't have water for drinking or showering or washing and there was no lighting in our streets and our roads were crap, I tell you one thing — we'd be in the exact same situation as they are.

The thing is, in Australia we have a well-documented history of funding stop-start one-off pilot projects. Remember that so-called 'great' speech by Labor prime minister Kevin Rudd about closing the gap? You know, closing the gap between Indigenous mortality — where an Aborigine's lifespan is twenty years less than an average Australian's — and closing the gap in terms of literacy, health status, access to necessary health hardware? Turns out it was all crap. In 2010 a Department of Finance report was leaked which detailed the successive failures by state and federal governments to properly address the issues that are the self-determinants of health within Aboriginal communities. It came to the conclusion that all the associated government departments were fundamentally responsible for the total fuck-up in Aboriginal health. If you don't believe me you can read the report by searching for 'Strategic Review of Indigenous Expenditure'.

Number-one major fuck-up was that the government doesn't listen to the needs of Aboriginal people. They make up their mind as to what they're going to fund and how they're going to fund it and away they go, without consultation. And that's the wrong way to go about it. Take the Northern Territory intervention policy for example: that's been a basic case of miscommunication and misinformation. So now more children are being taken away and put into welfare and in foster care than there has ever been. Even today, Aboriginal children are being taken away. Right now, and it's all because of this one misguided interventionist policy.

But within the Aboriginal community, what really saddens me is the significant loss of leadership and self-determination, within males in particular. Most of the community leaders died in their fifties, and with petrol-sniffing, and drug and alcohol abuse continuing to be a significant problem, the young men just aren't coming on as leaders.

Anyway, in 1994 I took up the position of CEO with what's now known as SHINE SA — Sexual Health Information Networking and Education, South Australia. Initially it was a very middle-class white organisation so one of the things I did was to refocus the service on those in the most need, in particular the Aboriginal people. Through Close the Gap funding I got a grant of $3.5 million, over a three-year period, to begin implementing a number of sexual health initiatives. We started training the teachers who were working in Aboriginal schools. We started training Aboriginal health workers and Aboriginal teaching assistants. We started talking to the children and their parents. We even had an ongoing research program with Flinders University with regard to the impact we were having within the communities, and that research was showing positive signs.

Then in 2012–13, the federal Liberal government decided to stop funding Close the Gap initiatives. See, once again it's a stop-start one-off pilot-project funding. It's all to do with populist politics. Take Tony Abbott for example. When he came into office he was all about being the Minister for Indigenous Affairs and he'd visit Aboriginal communities. Well, I'm sorry, but that's the biggest load of crap I've ever heard. Oh yes, he did get to visit Nhulunbuy, once. But he no sooner arrived than he said he had important business to attend to back in Canberra.

Anyhow, fortunately SHINE SA was able to maintain state government funding because they could see from the research that there were reduced rates of Aboriginal girls getting pregnant and/or having abortions. But as of the 30th of June 2016, that funding's going to stop. Another example of stop-start one-off pilot-project funding. And that's a bloody shame because there's a huge crisis out there. Out in some of these communities there's ten-year-old girls giving birth. Yes, ten-year-olds, and it's still happening now; still.

The thing is, there is not, I believe, any commitment at a community or a political level to actually address Aboriginal inequity and inequality. One of the barriers to that is, as a country, we don't have an articulated reconciliation plan that's been negotiated with Aboriginal people. Nor do we recognise Aborigines as the nation's first people. And all that has to be a part of our constitution, otherwise we'll never get anywhere. And we're currently not getting anywhere. I mean, if I was going to take a cynical view of all this, I can almost hear a few political voices saying, 'Why bother? They're going to die out anyway.'

Anyhow, in September 2012 I finished at SHINE. I had three deaths in the family, all in close succession. Could you please turn that recorder off now? I've said enough.

Kerry's Story
Dreams

After I matriculated, I was offered a Commonwealth Scholarship to go into medical laboratory technology at RMIT — Royal Melbourne Institute of Technology. But the more I thought about it, I just couldn't imagine myself staring down a microscope all day. Being more of a people person, I wanted to look outward and that's when I decided on nursing. Problem being, when I applied at the Alfred Hospital in Melbourne, their response was, 'But you're too highly qualified.'

'Well, maybe I am,' I said, 'but I'd still like to do nursing please.'

So I got accepted, and then Mum died three weeks before I started. I was seventeen, and, with being an only child, that was quite tough. But that's just the way it went. You can't predict these things. So I left Dad at home and went off to board at the hospital along with the other trainees. Then Dad got sick. So I got permission to go back home and care for him while I continued my training, and Dad ended up dying halfway through my second year, which was another tough time.

But thanks to the great support of the nurse educators at the Alfred I survived, and after I'd finished my general training, I began a staffing year. During that year I dreamed of working in remote areas, and with that in mind, I decided to do midwifery. In those days the top hospital for midwifery was Crown Street in Sydney, but, seeing as they had a huge student intake, I chose the second-best hospital, King Edward Memorial in Perth. Looking back as I am now, the drive across the vast space of the

Nullarbor was something that made a huge impression on me. In fact, I'd say it was one of the experiences that led me to the gypsy lifestyle I now live.

After midwifery I returned to Victoria where I ended up getting married. My plan was for us to island-hop across the Pacific, to be in Rio de Janeiro for their three-day festival, then go on a camping trip through South America, the United States and Canada, then jump across to Europe. But my husband had no interest in going overseas. None at all. Instead, we bought a four-wheel drive and a caravan, and as so often happens with women, I followed my husband's dream and tried to forget my own.

So we took off on a three-year trip around Australia, finding work along the way. I didn't want to do any nursing so I did some fruit-picking, motel-cleaning. I even worked in a fish and chip shop and when we got to Darwin I scored a job with a book wholesaler. That was great because they provided me with a car. Until then my main mode of transport was a motorbike which wasn't really suited to the wet season. In fact, earlier on in Darwin, I went for an interview at a bank and the heavens opened up on the way. Even though I had my Japara on, I was absolutely saturated by the time I arrived. Not to be deterred, I wrung out my long hair, wrung out my skirt and I slopped into the interview. And didn't they give me a dirty look.

'Well,' I said, 'at least I'm on time.'

After our travels, we settled in Brisbane where we had our two children, a boy and a girl, and we stayed put while they were growing up. But again life threw up some challenges. My husband got chronic fatigue which meant he virtually couldn't work. At that time we were in a partnership in a building business, and when we found ourselves stuck between insurance claims, with no income, things became extremely tight. That's when I decided to go back to nursing. I applied at three hospitals. Two offered me a job: one was a day shift, the other one was a night shift, and, seeing how we were struggling economically,

I took both. Then when it became obvious that I couldn't keep that up, I simplified things by going to a repatriation hospital where I ended up working in intensive care.

To cut a long story short, the children left home at about the same time my husband and I separated. I was kind of itching to get out of Brisbane, but seeing how my sixteen-year-old daughter had chosen to go out and live on the streets and live the sort of life that that entails, I stayed on. It wasn't until she was a bit more stable that I actually did my first rural contract. That was up at Ayr, which is a thousand or so k's north of Brisbane. And oh dear, that was a big move. With things being as they were in Brisbane, I was so nervous about it all that I was almost throwing up as I drove out of Brisbane.

See, the other thing was, I'd always tried to avoid being pigeonholed — like having to have a nursing specialty — but as it turned out, in a rural placement like Ayr, they had a much broader perspective. And that's what I liked.

After that contract, I returned to Brisbane until my daughter was truly back on her feet. When she was, I moved up to the Sunshine Coast where I began a counselling course and did some ad hoc shifts at various hospitals and took on a few rural short-term contracts during people's holidays. And it was while I was out in central Queensland, at Aramac, that the dream of remote area nursing returned. I remember waking up on the Christmas morning with the clear direction of where I should head. So, when I returned to the Sunshine Coast, I finished my counselling course, then, to really test my resolve, I took off on a six-month contract out in the centre of the Northern Territory, in Tennant Creek.

Initially, Tennant Creek was a real culture shock. It was an extremely long drive just to get there, and when I finally did, I was confronted by shop windows covered in metal grilles. And with never having lived in a place where there were so many Indigenous people, my first fleeting thought was, Oh dear, they're all so dirty. Then I realised that if I was living in such a dusty environment, where I didn't necessarily have working showers or many other modern amenities, I'd be pretty much the same. Another eye-opener was when someone told me how I should always check under my car before I drove off anywhere.

'Why?' I asked.

'Because they sometimes sleep under there, to get in the shade.'

But really, it was a case of me having to come to terms with living in a different culture instead of assuming that they should live within mine.

And of course, like in so many other outback places, various governments had, in their wisdom, tried to settle different Indigenous tribes in the one town. With them being warring factions before they even got together, and to then bring in the alcohol, things sometimes got quite nasty. I don't know if you've ever heard about 'payback' or not, but payback's the term used for when Aboriginal people sort out their grievances, either through spearings or other sorts of punishment. In Tennant Creek it was very much alive and well. When everyone came to town for footy or other occasions there'd be a special area put aside, just out of town, where all the payback happened. And I'm not only talking about payback between men. It also happened between women, and oh my goodness, that could become vicious.

So Tennant Creek really tested my resolve for remote nursing, and now none of that sort of stuff fazes me. I learnt to accept it.

Most of us nurses lived in individual flats, on the hospital grounds, and I worked between the emergency department and midwifery. I got on really well with the pregnant ladies. We only had an antenatal clinic at Tennant Creek, so we'd send the ladies to Alice Springs to await the birth of their babies. Even so, I attended three deliveries. The first was a young lass who hadn't had any antenatal care and was brought in to hospital in strong labour. The second was a young lady that I'd already sent to Alice Springs. Problem being, she wanted me to deliver her baby, so she took off from the Alice and came back and waited until I was on shift. The third delivery was non-human, which might need a bit of explaining.

That particular one was an egg-bound seven-foot-nine-inch python, belonging to a snake breeder. It was the snake's first time; she'd already delivered eight eggs but there were still four more to go. So the breeder got in touch with the vet, and, in an attempt to help with the delivery, the snake was injected between the scales with syntocinon and calcium gluconate. The vet's instruction were that if she hadn't delivered within forty-eight hours, the owner might have to take her to a reptile specialist over in the eastern states for the equivalent of a caesarean. Anyhow, after the forty-eight hours, I went around to the breeder's place. Seeing that the snake still hadn't released the last four eggs, we decided to place her on the kitchen table and start working with her.

I hadn't had any experience with snakes. But I had trained in healing touch, which is an energy therapy that originated in nursing. So in an attempt to keep the snake calm, I began working up near the head while the breeder used an instrument to stimulate her through the cervix. It took a while, but with the eggs being so soft, he squashed them down just enough to get them to come out, which was a great relief to all concerned. In fact, the snake breeder was so thankful for my help that he offered to give me a snake to keep in my car as a guard. I mean, I could just imagine driving along and having this snake slither up and curl itself over my shoulder or around my neck.

'I very much appreciate the offer,' I said, 'but no thanks.'

Travelling North

From Tennant Creek I went north to Nhulunbuy, a big bauxite-mining place in the Northern Territory, out on Gove Peninsula. I worked in the maternity ward and one experience I vividly recall was from an energetic side of things. Now I presume you're aware that spirits often hang around places like graveyards and hospitals. This time a part-Indigenous midwife and I were on night shift when I felt an extremely angry energy coming from the other end of the ward. As it happened, the part-Indigenous midwife had the ability to see spirits and when she saw this one she became terribly distraught. The only thing I could think of was to throw some protection around her. The obvious question you might be asking is, 'How did you do that?' Well, over my time I've studied a lot of alternative and complementary therapies and so my perspective on things may be a bit broader than a lot of people's. So I guess you could describe what I did was like casting a fishing net of protection around the terrified midwife; like a bubble of energy.

Anyhow, the spirit then retreated into the room where all the pregnant ladies were staying for the last couple of weeks before they gave birth. Being Indigenous, they also became aware of the spirit, and before long, they'd all gathered up at the nursing station with us. So we found them somewhere else to stay. Then, a couple of days later, when they still wouldn't go back to their room, I thought, Okay, if they don't consider it safe back in there, the spirit's going to cause problems elsewhere in the hospital. So I rang a ghostbusting friend of mine who said that the hospital should be cleared of the spirit by means of a smoking, and that it preferably be done by an Indigenous person. Problem being, it's a bit difficult to do a smoking in a place that's got smoke detectors. Anyhow, after I explained the situation to our Aboriginal liaison officer, she organised for the clearing to be done, and after that, the ladies were happy to go back to their room.

I find all that sort of stuff absolutely fascinating. While I was in Nhulunbuy I met with three witch doctors. One told me that he only worked at night, and only after he'd had his fill of gunja — marijuana. I thought, Well, that's certainly a different approach. The other two were more fair dinkum. They didn't need a crutch. In fact, while I was chatting to one of them it struck me that in many ways, their methods weren't that much different from some of the various therapies I'd learnt.

Now I know I'm jumping around a bit here but I once went to a holistic nurses' conference in Brisbane. Bob Randall from Mutitjulu, the community next to Yulara, was speaking there and he said that at the Mutitjulu clinic, they offered the services of both a white doctor and an Aboriginal medicine man. And that's how it should be. There should be a choice and that's why I've always tried to encourage the older Aborigines to pass on their different therapies and medicines to the younger ones so that that side of their culture doesn't disappear.

Anyhow, while I was at Nhulunbuy, one of the doctors introduced me to the clinic manager from Elcho Island. Elcho's just off the coast of Arnhem Land, at the southern end of the Wessel Islands group. Through that meeting I was given my first opportunity to work in a truly remote community, where the Indigenous people lived much closer to their traditional ways. The population on Elcho was near on two thousand. The main community is Galiwin'ku. The island itself is about sixty-five kilometres long and about five k's wide. Very few white people lived there. In our clinic we only had about five white people. Another clinic that covered the areas outside of Galiwin'ku had three or four white people. Then there would've been a couple of schoolteachers and two or three police, one of which was female.

Elcho was extreme culture shock. Other than the living conditions, the first thing that struck me was the number of camp dogs. I don't know if they can smell the difference between a white person and an Indigenous person, but I suspect they do because I never felt comfortable around them. And they acted as if they owned the place. They'd lie out on whatever little bit of tarmac there might've been on the road, and that's where they'd stay. So if you were driving along, you just had to drive around them.

After recovering from all that, I then had to try and figure out the most effective way of working with my colleagues, both Indigenous and non-Indigenous, and also those within the community, plus learn a completely new computer system. On top of that, the workload was huge. Sometimes there was a doctor, but not always, so I was expected to be on call for general emergency. With my main job being the women's health program, I was virtually it, which meant I was also on call twenty-four hours a day for midwifery. I had thirty antenates, and they were only the ones I knew of, plus there were five hundred ladies on the list for pap smears. Most of my antenate support was from Nhulunbuy, and to get to Nhulunbuy, there was a four- or eight-seater charter flight. If anyone was at particularly high risk, I contacted Darwin because that's where they'd be birthing and there was a commercial Airnorth flight that went from Elcho to Maningrida then on to Darwin.

Language was another problem. I sometimes had an Aboriginal Strong Women with me — an Elder — who spoke some English, but not a lot. The Strong Women's role was to help within the women's health program. When I first arrived this particular lady said, 'When we drive out into the community, if I say, "Turn right," but I point my finger to the left, then follow my finger.' Another time she said to me, 'Ladies big belly come quick.' I got that message.

I also had to come to grips with having to shop in a place that had very few prices on any of the items. I once saw some blueberries and thought, Oh, they'd be awesome. I knew they were normally quite expensive, but, when I went to pay for just a small bag, I was asked for seventeen dollars. And I tell you what, I enjoyed every single one of them. Another time I saw some medium-sized chocolate mud cakes. As usual, there was no price on them, but people were buying them. Later on I discovered that they were something like eighty dollars each.

In all I was faced with a complete different way of doing things, in a completely different culture, and I was working up to eighty hours a week. I lived in multiple places before I eventually moved into one of two brand-new duplexes, right on the headland. The duplexes had been built for people like myself at a cost of $1.2 million. That was mainly due to everything having to come in by barge, including all the building supplies, all the workers and all their food and so forth.

As with everywhere I'd been, I tried to encourage the younger ones to learn the different techniques of healing and medicine-making from their Elders. One old lady had the knowledge. She'd go out and collect whatever barks and leaves and plants that were needed and she'd brew up the different concoctions out the back of the clinic and give them to people to treat their ailment. I once said to her, 'What you're doing is just so valuable. It needs to be preserved for future generations.'

Although I was ready to pack up and leave within the first two weeks, I was glad that I stuck with it because Elcho turned out to be a great experience. It's a place rich in artistic talent. Have you heard of the Chooky Dancers? They're from Elcho. A few years ago they were on *Australia's Got Talent* where they did a traditional sort of dance, but to the tune of Zorba the Greek. You can see it on Youtube. It's fantastic. Anyhow, they've since toured the world. Another very artistic person from Elcho is the blind musician Geoffrey Gurrumul Yunupingu. Then some of the members of the Saltwater Band, they're also from Galiwin'ku.

And the more I got involved within the community, the more I started to feel my way within my women's health role. Being closer to their traditional ways, they still held smoking ceremonies for the newborn babies and the mums. As time went by, I was involved with those. And I felt very privileged to be so. So I did end up overcoming that initial cultural shock. Only just last year, when I went back to Elcho, I got greeted with cuddles from a lot of the ladies. And some of the mums that I'd looked after antenatally came up and introduced me to their little ones. And that was beautiful. It really was.

Gypsy at Heart

Toward the end of my time on Elcho Island I was starting to feel quite burnt out, which for me is the sign to move on. I've seen it with other remote area nurses where they haven't taken the cue and they've ended up having to go out on sick leave. So being a gypsy at heart, it wasn't long before I started doing short-term remote relief work. That was in 2012 and since then I've worked all across the Top End, I've been to the Kimberley in Western Australia and out to the Great Victoria Desert, and I've done a few stints in South Australia and Queensland.

One unique place I went to in WA was away out in the Great Victoria Desert, at Tjuntjuntjara. Tjuntjuntjara's about seven hundred k's north-east of Kalgoorlie. Only about a hundred and fifty people live there, and when you fly out in the mail plane, you see all the old rusted vehicles, left deserted along the way. The odd thing is, the Indigenous people are such innovative mechanics. When we landed on the dirt airstrip, the first car I saw was a beaten-up old sedan that didn't have a roof. It'd been in an accident and after they'd got it back together with bits and pieces from other wrecks, they'd cut the roof off at door height and left the windscreen. So basically it was now a convertible and it'd been driven all the way to Kalgoorlie, all around Kalgoorlie, then all the way back out to Tjuntjuntjara, without missing a beat. Another fella wanted to work underneath his old four-wheel drive, so he just pushed it over at twenty-five degrees, propped it up with a couple of star pickets and away he went.

Also, when I was at Tjuntjuntjara, I got to meet a group of full-blood Aborigines who'd walked in from the Great Victoria

Desert, back in the mid-1980s. Before then they'd never even seen a white person. Most of them still didn't speak English. I'd say they would've been in their late seventies, early eighties, and with having lived most of their lives in their natural habitat and in their natural ways, they were still a lot fitter and healthier than a lot of the younger ones. So that says something, doesn't it? And news travels. I've heard that there's still some desert people living out from Docker River and the message has been sent to them: 'Stay out there. Don't come in.'

So that's just another experience I've had with this relief work. The agency does a good job. When I was due to fly out from Tjuntjuntjara, to take up my next relief at Fitzroy Crossing, the mail plane couldn't get out because it'd been raining. Nor could it get out the next day. By then I was supposed to have already been in Fitzroy Crossing. Anyway, a contractor who'd been working out at Tjuntjuntjara was about to drive back to Kalgoorlie, so I asked him if I could catch a lift.

'Yeah, okay.'

Like I said, it's a seven-hundred-kilometre trip back to Kalgoorlie, so I rang the agency and left a message: 'Need accommodation in Kalgoorlie tonight. Need flight from Kalgoorlie to Fitzroy Crossing tomorrow. Will get mobile service when I'm closer to Kalgoorlie.' And it was all organised, no problems.

But you take the good with the bad. I went out to Wadeye once and I've chosen never to go back there again. Wadeye's a coastal community in the west of the Northern Territory, over near the West Australian border. Yet again it's another of those dysfunctional communities where various governments, in their wisdom, have thrown together a number of different tribal groups in the one place. It was terrible. While I was there a police taskforce was brought in due to the rioting. I honestly don't know what the solution is. With places like that, if it's ever going to be fixed, it's going to take generations and generations. It's like a cooked noodle. If you push it too hard, it'll just go all over the place, and if you get on the other end and pull it too hard, it'll break. Anyhow, enough of that. Needless to say I won't be going back to Wadeye again.

On the other hand, I did a fantastic relief on the Cocos Keeling Islands. They're out in the Indian Ocean, about three thousand k's north-west of Perth. You fly out from Perth International Airport to Christmas Island, then it's another nine hundred k's west of there. It's a beautiful group of little coral islands. Only two are populated: West Island and Home Island. West Island's around six kilometres in area with a population of around a hundred, whereas Home Island is less than a square kilometre and it's got a mainly Malay Muslim population of around five hundred.

It's an idyllic place. John Clunies-Ross first discovered the islands back in the early 1800s when he was sailing by on a trip to India. His plan was to return to live there, but before he did, a bloke by the name of Alexander Hare arrived and settled in with his harem of Malay women. Thus the Malay connection. Then a couple of years later, Clunies-Ross returned with his wife and family, kicked out Hare, and took over the running of the place. In fact, right up until the islands became a territory of Australia in the 1980s, the currency was the Clunies-Ross family's self-minted tokens of Cocos rupees.

I was based on Home Island, and with the Cocos Malays being Muslim, it was a vastly different culture from what I'd been working with, which was refreshing. There was a full-time doctor and two nurses on Home Island and two nurses on West Island. We all worked between both islands. I lived in a flat at the back of the medical clinic and the only vehicles were like quad bikes or golf buggies. Some were electric, some were diesel. If I was going over to West Island to help out at the clinic there, I'd drive a buggy down to the ferry, I'd leave the key in it, jump out, get on the ferry and go the eight kilometres across the lagoon. I'd then get off the ferry, jump in another clinic vehicle, which already had its key in it, and I'd drive to the West Island clinic and do whatever I had to do before I'd reverse the procedure when I came back to Home Island.

Home Island's only a metre above sea level, which is all well and good until a cyclone hits. I was lucky in that one only came within a couple of hundred k's, and even then the waves were crashing right up and over the road. Also, with the place having lots of coconut palms, whenever there was a cyclone or high winds, we had a spike in head injuries caused by falling coconuts. But I guess one of the different things we did was that if someone was ill on a passing ship, we'd get the call and the doctor and a nurse would go out on one of the ferries and bring the person back in. The incident that I was involved in happened after one Filipino sailor had died from a type of malaria and his mate was sick and needed to be evacuated. Then, after we got him back to the clinic, instead of sending him to Australia, it was quicker for him to be evacuated to Singapore. And in that case he did survive.

But probably the thing that made the greatest impression on me was not so much the clinic work, but more the culture. Having worked in Indigenous areas where you had to adapt to a very much 'men's business–women's business' culture, the people on the Cocos Keeling Islands were just the most beautiful, easygoing and peaceful human beings — and very enterprising. The number of small businesses that'd sprung up was amazing. One health worker also doubled as the dentist. Lots of the women did dressmaking, and because food's very much a part of their lives, there were lots of little street stalls. Over on West Island some of the white people were creating art out of the rubbish, like the fishing nets and thongs, that'd been washed up on the beaches. I never realised there were so many different coloured thongs. People would clean them up and they'd make them into all sorts of shapes and designs. And their sense of humour's fantastic. One guy had a sign outside his shop that read, *If we're not in, we've gone fishing.*

I was also invited to two weddings, which was just a most humbling experience. Both of them went for seven days. Then there was the huge amount of crabs. One time I was just about to step out of the flat when this massive crab came marching along. So I sort of closed the door and waited for it to go past. And unlike the Top End of Australia, there's no crocodiles and there's no mosquito-borne illnesses. And the turtles are absolutely everywhere. They're huge. They're the best part of a metre long, and because of the Muslim religion, the Cocos Malays don't eat anything that lives both in the water and on land, and so the turtles are safe.

So the Cocos Keeling Islands was a good one, and being a gypsy at heart, I do love seeing new places. I love meeting new people, and I'm now comfortable living out of a suitcase. Though, mind you, it sometimes does get a bit challenging when you're limited to just thirteen kilograms checked baggage and four kilos of hand luggage. It's not insurmountable though. Like they say, 'Where there's a will there's a way.'

Marcel's story
Irish Stock

I've recently returned from Cambodia where I run my charity Supporting Silk Sisters Project, which is supported by Rural and Remote Nurses Cambodian Volunteers. Check us out on Facebook. For me, Cambodia's a country that you can so easily fall in love with, yet it can break your heart. I'm feeling a bit pissed off at the moment, because before I came home, a man tried to rob me in Phnom Penh. And mind you, that's not the first time something like that's happened. And now, while we're on about crime, are you aware of what happened to remote nurse Gayle Woodford out on the APY Lands? Such a tragedy. To be honest, I don't think the public have any idea of the dangers faced by our predominantly female staff. The safety of remote area nurses is long overdue for attention, and while they'll never tell someone like you about it, just about every nurse I know has a story of assault or knows of rapes, many of which are hidden by authorities.

That said, I grew up in Melbourne. I come from fairly boisterous Irish stock who grew potatoes in the western district of Victoria. They were all country people who, like myself, never liked the city much. I always wanted to go to the outback and ride horses, and so when I was seventeen, I went governessing out on a station property, in the Channel Country of western Queensland. It was a wonderful experience and for me it was a great finishing school. I was introduced to a huge range of experiences that I wouldn't have had if I'd been working as a typist or something in a Melbourne office, plus I got to live in that beautiful wide open red-dirt country and ride horses every afternoon.

My living quarters were fairly basic, but clean. I slept out on the fly-screened verandah, close to the kitchen, and I'd have meals with the family. We had an old Irish cook called Mickey. Mickey was short-tempered. He'd start cooking breakfast at 4.30 a.m. and I could gauge his mood by the racket he was making. On a bad morning just about every saucepan and lid got a real going over. To get on the good side of him, I'd go and sit and have a cup of tea and a yarn with him. With Mickey, things were never quite right. But we got on okay. He had a good heart. See, there's two conflicting things that happen to white people when they live in remote places. It either brings out the best in them or it can bring out the worst in them. And that's because they think they're living in a less structured environment where their actions will be less scrutinised.

After my governessing stint, I returned to Melbourne to do my nurse's training. Like many other Australian girls, I decided on nursing because it'd allow me the opportunity to travel. So I did my basic training, then I met someone, fell in love, moved to Sydney and I stopped nursing and had two children. It wasn't until four years later that I went back and did my three certificates. I did my mental health certificate, which I consider to be my most valuable because it taught me so much about human behaviour. Then I did a bridging course into my general nursing, followed by a postgraduate in geriatric rehabilitation. I loved that as well, because to have someone come in paralysed and then to see them walk out and return to their own homes was a wonderful achievement.

From there I went down to the Snowy Mountains. I was district coordinator for Snowy Mountains Community Health Services. I was based in Cooma and my area took in the slopes and the snow fields, right down to the Victorian border. Some of the Aussie nurses I worked with followed the ski season around the world. They'd start out in Europe or the USA, then they'd come home and work around the Snowies for a while, then have a skiing holiday before heading back overseas again. And because of their experience in other countries, they were very skilled.

By that stage I was separated with two primary school children. We lived in the nurse's cottage at Nimmitabel, one of the highest towns in Australia. Nimmitabel's about thirty-five k's from Cooma and I used to drive to work and back every day. I'd drop my son off at a friend's place and they'd go to school together. Then I'd drop my daughter off at child care and they'd take her to primary school and I'd pick her up from child care on my way home. That was no problem. It's what every single working mother does.

But I just loved driving through that mountain country. When it was dry and burnt, it was a quintessential Australian landscape. When it was covered in snow, it had its own special quietness and beauty. What also intrigued me was the contribution that the migrants had made to the area. After they'd finished building the hydro electric scheme many had stayed on and bought taxis, built flats or set up little businesses. Some opened restaurants, so the food was interesting, and, if you went somewhere, you'd always find someone different to talk with. So it was quite cosmopolitan in a way, yet at the same time, there was a lot of old squatter money around the area, with the conservative types who thought they were a cut above the rest.

And that's what really excites me. It's not working in a hospital, but being out in the bush, talking to people over copious cups of tea. Many of them were stricken by loneliness. So I'd sit around their big farmhouse tables and we'd chat under slats of aged sticky flypaper with generations of dead blowies on board and I'd never know when one might unstick itself and fall down into my tea. I also drank black tea because I didn't have to worry whether the milk was off or not. And I'd meet such wonderfully strange characters. One such man would've been in his late twenties. He was an only child. He wouldn't have harmed a fly but he was quite unwell and psychotic. He'd been in a seminary, as a trainee priest, and he'd had a breakdown which led to the onset of his illness. So he'd gone back to live on the family sheep farm. Then after his elderly parents had died, he was left on the property to run the flock, and out on that treeless country, when those winds blow up the Kosciuszko, you get frosts that'll kill you. So there he was, living alone, in this isolated, bleak area, in a house that didn't have a woman's touch. It was a bare and pretty basic old joint where the winds would whistle through the walls and up through the floorboards.

Every three months I'd drive out and take him into town to see the psychiatrist and have him reviewed. I'd also visit him every two weeks to give him his anti-psychotic injection. Because I'd spend so much time with him, it'd often be a full day's trip. He used to write poetry. It was mostly about his loneliness and how he'd like somebody in his life. I think he had a few things mixed up in his thought processes because he also used to reflect a lot on God. It'd all come out in his writings. So he'd read his poetry and we'd talk about it. And at every visit, he'd give me a lamb that he'd slaughtered. He must've cut it up with a chainsaw because all the bones would be shattered. I'd never eat it. I couldn't. I'd give it to friends who had dogs. But that was his thank-you to me for coming all that way to visit him and for listening to his stories and his poetry. But there was little else I could do for him. Due to his desperate situation, after I left him, I'd often shed a tear. Like so many, he just needed a little love and human contact in his life.

Scapegoat

From the Snowies I moved up north. I won't say the name of the place for reasons you'll find out later, but it's where I met my second husband. I was applying for a position in mental health so I thought I'd pop up there for a weekend to see what the town was like and what it had to offer. A friend picked me up at the airport and my husband-to-be was with him. He computerised financial systems for hospitals and he offered to drive me around and show me the place. He even ended up showing me where he was born and where he'd grown up. Anyway, it was a nice town. There were lots of sporting activities for my kids and the local college had a good reputation. Two interviews later, I got the job and things went from there.

My husband and I ended up buying a small grazing block and we built a log cabin, high up, that had a three-hundred-and-sixty-degree view over a valley. When we laid in bed and looked out through the French doors, it felt like we were living in the clouds. Then as the sun came out, the mist would melt away. There was a real sense of energy and magic about the area. No wonder it attracted such a diverse and interesting lot of people. I was working in a Life Be In It program and I also conducted hydrotherapy lessons for women. As a sideline I became a goat farmer, which, in turn, subsidised my venture into endurance riding, which, in turn, I became all the poorer for.

While I've always loved my horses, the goats proved to be an experience. We were trying to breed them for their wool. We had one old billy goat: Billy Goat Gruff. Every six weeks he had to be wormed and have his hooves trimmed. The thing was, he was so hard to catch. My husband and my son would have to chase him around the yard and tackle him like in rugby. Then, when they finally knocked him down, his pheromones would kick in and he'd start urinating all over them, and oh, the smell was unbelievable. I'd have the washing machine at the ready, full of hot water and detergent and disinfectant, and they'd come round the back of the house, take their clothes off and go and have a shower. I'd then put the clothes in the washing machine with a long stick and give them a thorough wash. The stink was just dreadful. In the end we sold the goats as a flock.

While I was there I also did a stint as a community nurse up in the mountains. On some days I'd do my home visits on horseback. That's where I met an old guy. He'd lost an arm in the Great War, and he and his son ran cattle. There were no women in their lives; just the two men together. Dad was the boss. He was in his eighties and he'd been widowed for years. Every Wednesday I'd go and see how they were going and check on their medications. And every Wednesday the old guy would bake me a cake. When the son got bowel cancer his weight dropped down to about seven stone, he was still trying to work the property. The old man knew that his son was going to die. And he did. He died about six months later. He'd run out of time. If there's one thing missing in today's society, it's time. The irony of it is, people have more time-saving devices than ever before and more immediate ways of communication, yet they don't take the time to sit down and talk to each other. So there were no plans made for the son's palliative care or even what the old guy would do after his son had died. Time's so precious. It's like when you stand on a riverbank and watch the water going past. Once it's gone by, it never comes back. My tenet of nursing has always been, 'When you give of your time, you give of yourself, because you're making that person your focus.' For me it's all about respect and compassion.

Anyhow, while we were there my own father was diagnosed with a brain tumour. They flew him up in an air ambulance so I could nurse him in our log cabin. He had a sixteen-week prognosis and he only lasted nine weeks and four days. While Dad was alive, the physician in charge of the oncology unit would come out and visit him and he'd bring liquid morphine. Unbeknown to me — but known to many at the hospital — this man was a narcotics addict.

Anyhow, after my father died, we had a lot of leftover medications at home. So I put them in an ice-cream container and I said to my husband, 'Take these into the hospital and they'll dispose of it.'

Before my husband got the chance to do that, he got a phone call from the physician. 'Look,' the physician said, 'when you come to town, I'll give you the death certificate. Oh, and just leave the unused medications with me and I'll dispose of them.'

My husband thought, Fair enough, and when he went into town he left the medications in the office. Later on the ampules were found, empty, in an unused renal unit in the hospital. I then started getting these odd phone calls, asking me about how much morphine I'd used when Dad was alive and what I'd done with what was left over. Being a nurse, every time my father had his medication, I'd document it in a journal so that when the home-care lady came, she'd know where Dad was up to with his pain treatment. Anyway, things got a bit nasty and they tried to pin an abuse of morphine on me. They had no factual evidence whatsoever, and because any perceived hint of impropriety would've impinged on my licence, I started digging around the place. At one stage I just happened to be talking to some of the older hospital staff. 'Oh,' they said, 'didn't you know that he's addicted?'

I said, 'No I did not.'

Those days I was active in the Labor Party, so I rang up the chairman of the hospital board and I said, 'I want to have a meeting with you and all the board members and the director of nursing.' When we had the meeting, I tackled them head-on.

I said, 'Why are you permitting this man to feed his addiction? You've had him here with a respiratory arrest, yet you've done nothing about it.'

I even wrote to the Minister for Health and still nothing happened. All I got was a semi-apology from the nurse in charge of the oncology unit, implying how they'd tried to make me a scapegoat in an attempt to protect the man. I left the hospital soon after that. I thought, I've had enough of this lot, trying to protect an addicted doctor at my expense. Anyway, he died in the end. He was a fairly heavy drinker, and one night after he'd had a bellyful he was run over by a train.

For the Love of Mum

In the late '80s we moved to the Upper Hunter region of New South Wales. My husband got a position there within a newly created regional health area and I as a community nurse. Twenty months later there was a change of government and they merged five health regions into one, and the region we were both in disappeared. With our jobs gone, it was, 'What're we going to do now?'

In the end my husband got a job at the University of Southern Queensland. We lived at the bottom of the Toowoomba Range and I worked in community health. A lot of travel was involved throughout the Western Downs. A GP or whoever would ring in and I'd drive out and see if the people required home help to manage themselves or a sick or frail aged relative. Along the way I'd visit a lot of homesteads and small cottages where these old, single women were living. On the mantelpiece there'd invariably be a picture of a handsome young man in a military uniform. When I'd ask who it was, they'd say, 'He was my fiancé. He went away to the war and he never came back.' And so, because a whole generation of those young men had never returned from the war, there was no one left for them to fall in love with. So they'd remained on the farm to help their parents, because unless you were a schoolteacher or a nurse, that's what girls did back in those days.

Another time I was asked to visit a man and see what his needs were with regard to the management of his bedridden semi-comatose wife. She'd had a massive stroke, and, instead of going into a nursing home, he'd insisted that she go home and he'd care for her. I'd been warned that he was demanding and quite odd. When I arrived at the property there were signs everywhere: *Beware Dogs ... Visitors will be shot on sight*, and all that. So, just to let them know I'd arrived, I leant on the car horn. That worked because I could see someone peeping out from behind the curtains and watching me as I climbed over the fence and made my way to the house. When I got to the door I knocked. *Knock knock.* When the door opened I was met by this little man. He looked like a jockey. He was very agitated — glancing around — quite paranoid. Initially I thought he had a stick in his hand but I soon found out that it was a big rifle of some sort. It could've been a shotgun. In those days nurses had a bit of a mantle around them so it was obvious I was a nurse. I said, 'Hello. I've come to assess the needs of your wife.'

'Oh,' he said, 'you've come to see Mum.' He always called his wife 'Mum'.

When I went inside, his wife was lying on a double bed. She was in a semi-vegetative state, with a feeding tube down her nose and into her stomach. She was a mountain of a woman, and with the diet this man was giving her, she certainly wasn't going to lose any weight. She was well looked after though. Her clothes were clean, as was her bedding. But what the husband had done was, on the ceiling he'd mounted a steel rail and a sort of gantry, and hanging off that was a canvas sling. So whenever he changed the bed sheets or washed her or he wanted to turn her over, he'd put the canvas sling underneath her and he'd pull her up, out of the bed, and she'd just hang there, suspended, while he went about his business. And the little man's behaviour towards this woman he called 'Mum' was very odd. While I'd be talking to them, he'd be jumping up on the bed and cuddling her just like a little child would to their own mother. It was quite tragic really. He loved her dearly, but to my mind, he was a desperate man, attempting to cling onto the past.

Then, when his wife died, he really lost the plot. Just after her funeral I went out to see him and he was getting to the stage where I didn't feel confident in being there. His paranoia had increased and he was convinced that the local shire council and neighbours were all out to get him, and the shotgun was always there, sitting in the corner. A week or so later he rang me. It was 5 o'clock in the afternoon. I was just knocking off and he was extremely breathless. He said, 'I need some oxygen. I want you to bring some out.'

I said, 'I can't come out now, but I'll be there first thing in the morning.'

That night he had a massive haemorrhage and died. He had cancer of the lung and no one knew. That's why he was so thin. But the dynamics of human relationships are so complex. What kept him alive was the power of his love for the woman he called Mum. It was all about Mum.

An Ethical Issue

When my husband's contract finished, we moved up to the eastern coast of Queensland where I worked in mental health. We barely had a psychiatrist there. By 'barely' I mean they had trouble getting a psychiatrist to work full time in the unit. Instead, we'd often get retired psychiatrists from overseas who'd only stay for three months. Then sometimes someone would come up from the city for a week, just for locum work, while they did a quick diving course. It was costing Queensland Health a fortune.

So the nurses basically ran the unit, with input from whoever the psychiatrist and visiting resident medical officer was. I was a project officer and I'd do all the mental health assessments of the people who presented at the unit. Say if someone had been found down the street disoriented, talking to a tree or whatever, and the police brought them in, I'd interview them and make an assessment as to their condition. I'd then discuss it with the psychiatrist as to what the problem was and if admission was needed. To make sure there was no underlying cause, the resident medical officer would then do a complete physical examination and a blood screening to make sure nothing untoward was happening. Over my time there I assessed around three hundred and thirty people, and in the end, I got a letter of commendation saying that every assessment I'd made had been correct. I was quite chuffed by that.

My husband and I loved living up on the coast. It had a fabulous climate and we had a beautiful block for my horses. It was a happy space with lots of blue skies and warm winds. At the end of each day we'd go for a swim and we'd be so relaxed that we'd just crash for the night. It was beautiful.

Though the toughest thing that happened there began when a patient disclosed to me that she'd been sexually targeted by one of the male nurses. I said, 'You need to put it in writing and I'll get you a referral to talk to the social worker.' So I documented it all in the patient's file and referred her to the social worker. I also discussed the woman's pending statement with the social worker. But nothing happened, and I later found out that she hadn't written the letter. So when a second woman made a complaint that the man had lured her to a hotel, I said to her, 'You really must write a letter and address it to the medical superintendent so that action must be taken.'

So she wrote a letter. But again nothing happened. Her letter went missing. Then someone finally complained to the Queensland Nursing Council. They have similar investigative powers as the police. And they got the guy. He'd been paying for the hotel rooms with his credit card and the date and times coincided with him not being on our work roster. Cases like that are an ethical issue. This male nurse was in a position of trust and power and he'd target these vulnerable mentally ill women, many of whom had come out of violent relationships. We don't know how many times it happened, but the board decided it was sufficient enough to revoke his licence for life. He was also ordered to pay a huge fine. Then he disappeared into the mines over in Western Australia.

Riot

From there we came down to live just south-east of Brisbane. I'd had enough of mental health so I started going back out to remote communities. One in particular was constantly troubled. On the news just recently there's been reports of further unrest, where the school principal was attacked, the teaching staff left the community and the school was closed down. I've been there three times now and I was there for one of their riots. It happened back in the early 2000s after the terrible incident on Palm Island where an Indigenous man, Mulrunji, died due to the injuries he'd received while in police custody.

The atmosphere from that event had permeated throughout this community, and there was a local guy who had outstanding fines. While the police were combing the houses in search of this fine-evader, they found him hiding in one of the roofs. They arrested him and took him down to the police station. When the family went to visit him they saw some blood on him and said he'd been assaulted. The thing was, because the police had failed to switch the cell CCTV on, there was no recorded proof of any assault. Make of that what you will, but that's what instigated the riot.

I'd only just arrived on an eight-week contract and they put me in a little fibro place, right down the end of the community, across from the police station. The house was elevated, with steps going up the front. The windows had no safety grilles on them, and there was a carport underneath. When I arrived I'd noticed three pallets of those large gas cylinders — all full — in the carport, and I'd thought, Thank God I'm not a smoker.

Anyway, this night I was reading a book and I had the TV on, just as background noise. Then I heard all this shouting. At first I thought it was the TV. But it wasn't, and when I looked out the window, there were all these bare-chested men coming down the road toward the police station. There would've been hundreds of them and they had Molotov cocktails, they had rocks, they had spears, they had baseball bats and all sorts of home-made weapons. Lots and lots of weapons. When they arrived at the police station, they started stoning the front doors. They then set the police boat on fire and started smashing the windows on the troopies. The police had locked themselves inside. They were downright scared and they had a good right to be. I could see it all unfolding from my place, and at one stage, I swear I saw a policeman, down on his knees, with his big Glock, firing over the heads of the people who were trying to smash the front door down.

My place had a twelve-foot cyclone wire fence around it, but there was no padlock on the gate. Next thing, a mob came into my yard. There was a sort of rock garden out the front and they were grabbing the rocks to throw at the police. By now I've got the light off and I'm hiding in the bedroom. But I'm still peeping out the window. I can see what they're doing and I could see what was going on over at the police station. Next thing I hear some of them coming up my front stairs. The stairs were aluminium, and you know when you run up those types of stairs they make a pinging sound. *Ping, ping, ping,* up the stairs. Then *bang, bang, crash, crash,* they're trying to get in my front door, and they're shouting about how they're going to get me and what they're going to do with me.

At that point I snuck out of the bedroom and jammed the lounge in front of the door. I then grabbed the phone and I rang the police station. They didn't answer. They were too busy. By this stage I was frightened but quite in control. Like I was icy cold, but I was in control and feeling nothing. Then I heard them below, under the house, turning the gas cylinders on and trying to light the gas with their cigarette lighters. If the cylinders would've gone up, we all would've been blown to smithereens. So I rang my husband. I said, 'Things aren't looking good here. Could you please report the riot to triple-0 in Brisbane because there's no one answering the phones here.' Then I said, 'I love you. I've gotta go.' And I hung up.

So there I was. I had the lounge blocking the front door. They're still outside, shouting and going on, and they're still in the carport, trying to light the gas cylinders. All I had to protect myself was a broom. For some reason I thought, If they come inside, I'll bash them with a broom. Then unexpectedly, a car pulled up and out stepped a woman. She stood in front of the screaming mob and put her hand up to stop them. In that instant they wheeled around in unison like a flock of birds and ran away.

At the same time another group was heading over to the director of nursing's house. He and his wife lived in an elevated house like mine. His wife was a nurse, too. Up the stairs they go and they do the same thing. Even though he had security doors, they're bashing on his doors, trying to get into his house and they're shouting how they're going to kill them both. Then I thought I heard the sound of a gun going off and they took off. It was as if someone had pushed an off button. There was dead silence. I sat in my house, staring at a wall in the darkness, until an Aboriginal woman came up to see me.

'Are you all right?' she asked.

I said, 'Sort of.'

By the next day they'd brought in all these extra police and things had started to settle back down. All was quiet, so I said to the director of nursing, 'Aren't we going to sit down and have a chat and a debrief?'

He said, 'I really don't think it's necessary.'

I said, 'I think it is. I've got quite a few things I'd like to say.'

So the district manager, director of nursing and nurses got together and we were told, 'Look, there's to be no talk about guns, because there were no guns, right?' Amid that the director of nursing laughed and said, 'Not even my lead shanghai?' So like hell there weren't. But they were all on about none of us mentioning anything about guns.

I said, 'Well, okay, but I also want to talk about my being potentially attacked and possibly raped and my lack of security and all the full gas cylinders under my house.'

They said, 'Well, we didn't put the cylinders there.'

I said, 'Well, they're Queensland Health property and so the locals certainly wouldn't have put them there.'

So there you go. That was it. But of course, things like that rarely get reported. And that's in a community where there's a large number of white police, nurses, schoolteachers and administrators.

Anyhow, the upshot of it all was that they got the young fine-offender out of town and they took him somewhere where he would've gone to jail for a few months to work off his fines.

And so everything settled down and they all got together and they had a barbecue and pretended that everything was wonderful and they all loved each other again. But mark my words: the undercurrent will always be there. Like so many of those communities, this particular one has always had a history of violence and it always will until something's done about it, and I wouldn't have a clue as to what that something is. All I can say is, over my time, I've worked in so many communities where literally millions of dollars are handed out and squandered, and nothing changes because of financial illiteracy or major fraud by some community members. I don't care how politically incorrect it is, but what's destroying the Aboriginal people is that, with them being the oldest hunters and gatherers we're aware of, you cannot maintain a fractured culture in a cash-based society. It just doesn't work. To my mind it's not the money that's needed, it's education at both a white and black level, and that'll take forever.

Featherfoot and the Curlew

To date I've worked in fifty different remote communities. I've been to Thursday Island, Elcho Island, Mornington Island and Kowanyama in Queensland. I've worked in a lot of single-nurse posts in the Northern Territory and over in Western Australia where I was out in the Great Sandy Desert with the Mardu people. White people only became aware of the Mardu in the 1980s, so they still pretty much live in their traditional ways. I loved it out there. I first fell in love with that red dust when I left Melbourne as a seventeen-year-old and went to western Queensland. And once you're bitten by it, you're done. One of my greatest joys was to stand out on a dune in the Great Sandy Desert and listen to a silence that almost shrieks at you. In the scheme of things, it makes you realise just how insignificant you are.

When I go to these places, I run the clinic pretty much like a general practice: nine to five with twenty-four-hour on-call for emergencies. Though out there I'd usually close between 12 and 2 p.m. because that's when the sun's at its zenith and the Aboriginal people have their siesta. They're early risers, and they go to bed as soon as it's dark because there may be a featherfoot about. They have a great fear of the featherfoot. In other parts they're also known as a kurdaitcha man or a tall man. It's a spiritual man who wears shoes made from birds' feathers so that he doesn't leave tracks, and he goes around dispensing punishment, such as pointing the bone, which can lead to death.

At one time I was out at Epenarra. Epenarra's about a thousand k's south-east of Darwin. I was there close on eighteen months. It was a single-nurse post, with a community of around three hundred and fifty. You work like a dog, day and night, seven days a week. One time I invited the older ladies over to my place for a cuppa and some SAOs. They were sitting down, munching away, when one of them asked for more tea. So I got her mug and I went over and filled it up. When I handed it back, she said, 'Featherfoot's bin 'ere.' She said, 'Look,' and there on the bench, where the phone was, was the feather of a bush turkey.

I didn't know how it got there, so I said, 'No, there's been no featherfoot here.'

But they weren't convinced. They got up and left. And that was fair enough. I mean, Christians believe that you can change bread and wine into someone's body and blood, so why would I argue against someone else's cultural beliefs?

Anyhow, after that they'd say, 'Featherfoot's bin to your house so we can't come there any more at night.'

I said, 'Okay then, I'll put a sign up — *No featherfoots allowed* — and then he can't get into my house. Maybe we could write it in language.'

'Not needed,' they replied. 'Featherfoot reads English.'

There was nothing a featherfoot couldn't do. To their mind he could even change shape and form and slip under my door and enter my house.

'No he can't,' I said.

'Yes he can,' they said. 'He can do anything he likes, because he's a featherfoot.' So I let it be.

The babies were always ill out there and I'd get the women driving up to my house in the middle of the night and hitting the horn until I opened the door. 'Baby sick. Baby sick,' they'd shout.

I'd reply, 'Bring Baby up to the clinic where there's good light. I'll see to it there.'

'Nah, nah,' they'd say. 'I can't. You gotta come to my place.'

I'd say, 'Why?' and they'd reply, 'If I take Baby out in the night, featherfoot will get it.'

Anyhow, this community was on the edge of Epenarra Station. The station people ran beef. Of course the white fellers got the good cuts, and what was left over, like the gristle, fat and bone, they'd sell to the Aborigines. But because most of the Aborigines couldn't afford refrigerators, they had to walk the kilometre or so up to the store, morning and afternoon, to buy their perishables. Along the way they had to pass a big water tank and one day somebody said they saw a featherfoot lurking around the tank. Apparently this one was naked, which made him far worse than the rest, and so they wouldn't walk past the water tank because a featherfoot had been seen there. So they stopped going to the store; they didn't eat and the storekeeper wasn't making any money. In the end he had to pick the women up, morning and afternoon, and drive them to his store and back. To make matters worse the rumour then spread that three featherfoot had been seen driving a black Toyota. When I asked if their white one had gone in for a service, I was fixed with a frosty stare.

Epenarra only had a dirt airstrip. If it was wet, and we needed to do an emergency evacuation, we'd have to drive sixty-four k's over to the nearest all-weather strip. This time, early summer storms had come. I had six babies down with gastro and I couldn't drive them to the all-weather strip because the roads were closed. One night, after we'd lost power in a storm, I had the sick babies, along with their mothers, out on the verandah. Every fifteen minutes I'd get up to do their 'obs' and give them fluids down a tube. But as soon as I'd turn the torch on, the old girls would whack me and say, 'Don't do that. Featherfoot will see you.'

I said, 'It'd have to be a bloody brave featherfoot to come anywhere near me, I assure you.'

But that's how terrified they were of the featherfoot. Of course, as I am with most things of a spiritual nature, I was extremely sceptical. But their belief was so strong that it ruled their lives. Then, when I was about to go home on Christmas leave one time, they said, 'You betta be careful. Featherfoot's goin' home with you.'

I said, 'No he won't. I'll be in my car and I've got the dog.'

And they just laugh. 'Stupid white woman knows nothin' about the power of the featherfoot.'

So I headed off on Christmas leave. I think I drove the two and a half thousand k's from Epenarra to Brisbane in two and a half days. My dog and I swagged it in a park along the way. Anyhow, I get home. It's mid-afternoon. My husband's still at work, and there on my front door step was a large white and grey feather. Make of that what you will.

Here's another amazing story. When my mother died I wrote about her death and I linked it with the Aboriginal legend about the curlew. In Aboriginal culture the curlew is known as the death bird. They're beautiful birds with thin yellowy-brown legs and a long dark beak, and they're speckledy coloured; very similar to emu chicks in some ways.

Anyhow, when my mother was sick, every night when the ABC news was on TV, this female curlew would appear in our horse paddock and it'd cry like nothing I'd ever heard; real eerie. It was such a regular visitor that we named her Bima after the Aboriginal legend. Then on the night my mother died, she didn't come. Nor did she come the night after that, nor the next. She'd disappeared.

Then on the anniversary of Mum's death I was washing the dishes. The ABC news was on the telly and my son came in and said, 'Mum, Bima's back.' I checked the time. It was nineteen minutes past seven – the exact same time Mum had died. So I went outside and looked out over to the horse paddock. I couldn't see Bima there, but I could still hear her eerie cry. So I followed her sound around to the other side of the house and there she was, this curlew — Bima. She was out in the garden, just outside

Mum's bedroom door, and she was screeching and dragging her wing on the ground like she'd been severely wounded. Well, I just sat down and I cried and cried.

When I went back out to the community and told the old women what'd happened, they said, 'Ah, she came with a message.'

I said, 'What's the message?'

They said, 'She come to say your mum's okay. That she's happy with the old people.'

As a remote nurse, the most incredible things happen to you and you meet the most incredible people.

Michael's Story
Brave

I grew up in Wiluna, Western Australia, which is at the bottom of
the Canning Stock Route. Dad was the station manager out that
way, at a place called Carnegie. There was no School of the Air
so I did my schooling by correspondence that came out by mail
from Perth. It was a great life. I loved it. But when I was nine,
I got incarcerated in a boarding school in Perth. They were the
worst days of my life. There I was, a little bushie who hadn't seen
any other children apart from my sister and the black kids, and
all of a sudden I was stuck with three hundred mostly city types.
And I didn't fit in, not one little bit, so, just before my thirteenth
birthday, I told my parents I wasn't going back. End of story. And
so I quit school and got a job in the Perth saleyards, yarding up.

A couple of years later the old man got a job managing
Myroodah Station, which is in the Kimberley, out from Derby, so
we all went up there. Myroodah was a sheep place, but it wasn't
sheep country so we went over to cattle. Anyhow, I worked my
way up to head stockman there, then I got the head stockman's
job out of Broome, on Roebuck Plains. That was great until the
big multinationals bought the place and we all became just a
number in their system. So I got out of there and I worked on
a couple of other stations for a while until I got diagnosed with
cancer in the spine. I don't know why it happened; it just did.

That's when I decided there's got to be life after stations, so
when an old mate who owned Sandfire Roadhouse offered me
a job, I took it, and I've been here ever since. Sandfire's on the
Great Northern Highway between Port Hedland and Broome. I

started out doing maintenance around the roadhouse and I also took on the tow truck, going out to vehicle accidents. The thing was, more often than not, I'd end up carting injured people back to Sandfire and putting them on the Flying Doctor plane. Then when I went to an accident where a good mate's brother got killed, I thought, Nah, this's not good enough. I need an ambulance. So I pestered St John, and when they saw that their vehicles were forever doing three-hundred-k trips up and down the highway to retrieve patients, they went with my idea. When I got the ambulance I gave the tow truck up. I couldn't do both. It's up the back now. These days there's a big liability concern, so we'll only go twenty k's to tow someone back into Sandfire, then we'll call up Hedland or Broome and get their tow trucks to come out.

After I got the ambulance and I did the training, I started looking after a hundred-and-fifty-k stretch north and south of Sandfire. The first job I ever did was a fatal, and there were patients as well. At the time I had a broken ankle, but that wasn't going to stop me. I still had a good leg on the other side and I reckoned that those people needed more help than I did, so off I went. Anyhow, by the time I arrived there were enough volunteers to help load the injured into the ambulance. That accident happened sixty k's north of Sandfire, early in the morning. The dad was driving a station wagon and they had the back seat folded down. The wife was asleep in the back, along with a five-month-old girl. The mum got thrown out and she was killed. With cases like that being considered crime scenes, you just cover the body and let the police attend to it. Same with the vehicle; because it's a crime scene you can't move the car. If it's in the middle of the road you just direct traffic around it. What also helps is if you can get some of the other travellers to go up and down the highway to warn any oncomers.

Anyhow, like I said, the mother died. Luckily the five-month-old ended up in a clump of spinifex and had no injuries aside from the prickles. The dad was dazed and in shock. He claimed that the sun blinded him, but given the time of the day, he'd obviously gone to sleep and the police ended up charging him with dangerous driving and causing the death of his wife.

There was also a little eight-year-old girl in the front seat. She was sitting on the lap of her sixteen-stone aunty. The seatbelt was around them both, but from the force of it all, the little girl just about broke every bone from her shoulder right down to her pelvis. Plus, when the car rolled, her arm went out the window and got rearranged. And since then, I've attended thousands of patients and I've never struck anybody as brave as that little girl. There was the aunty, with a bit of whiplash, and she's screaming out in agony, and that little girl, as calm as anything, she looked me right in the eye and she said, 'My mum's dead, isn't she?'

I never lie, especially to little kids, so I said, 'Yes.'

She was just awesome, and when we got up the road, she wanted me to put the siren on. When I told her that we didn't do that out in the bush, she said, 'But I've got to tell the kids at school that we had the siren on.'

So I put the siren on for a bit, then I told her that I had to turn it off or else the battery would go flat. And she went along with that.

But gee she was brave. Even the nurses at the hospital said the same thing. And it wasn't the shock. She was well aware of what had happened to her and to her mum. I'll never forget her. I'd like to see her again one day. She'd be in her early twenties now. Anyway, the good part of that one was that she survived. So that was my very first job in the ambulance. There's been hundreds since, though none with me having a broken ankle and none with such a brave little girl.

Crazy

There's a lot of crazy drivers out there. I had a cardiac patient in the ambulance once. It was coming on dark. There were kangaroos and cattle about so I'd slowed down to a hundred and forty. I had my warning lights on and this clown overtook me in a Commodore, towing a boat. He had two kids with him and no one was wearing a seatbelt. Now, if one thing really gets to me, it's seeing unrestrained children. Kids don't make their choices. Adults make the choices, and I'd rather the police pick them up than me having to scrape them up. And also, that bloke was compromising me, because if he'd had an accident, I'd have to stop and help him, even though I had a cardiac patient in the back. Anyway, I got on the satellite phone and I rang the Port Hedland police and they nabbed him doing a hundred and sixty in the dark. So that sorted him out.

Another time a family pulled into Sandfire. It was a long weekend. They were in a station wagon. The back seat was down and there were five kids in there mucking about so I bailed the dad up. 'You've got to put the seat up and restrain those kids.'

'Oh,' he said, 'but they'll get grumpy if I do that.'

I said, 'Mate, you've already got me grumpy.'

Then he made a big mistake. As he drove off he gave me the finger. So I rang the Broome police and they nabbed him out on the highway. Being a long weekend he got double demerit points and copped two and a half thousand dollars in fines. When the police slapped that on him, he started to give them a mouthful. So they breathalysed him and he must've had a teaspoon too much beer the night before, because they done him for that as well. Then the mum started at the coppers: 'Why don't you go 'n catch murderers or something.' One of the coppers replied, 'We're talking to a potential one right now, lady, and that's you.' Even then she wouldn't shut up so she copped a two and a half thousand dollar fine as well.

Then, when they came back through Sandfire, I was out the front of the roadhouse and all those kids were in booster seats. The dad knew I'd rang the coppers and when he gave me a look I thought, You just try it mate, because as far as I'm concerned, those kids of yours are alive because of what I did.

Another accident I went to, there was the mum and dad and a little girl of about five. They were in a brand-new four-wheel-drive Land Cruiser and they'd hit a cow. The little girl was lying on the back seat — no booster seat or nothing — and she went through the windscreen. Now, you know how cats always land on their feet after they've fallen? Well, kids will rotate and land facedown. That's what this little kid did and when she hit the bitumen at a hundred and twenty k's, it took her face clean off. It was dreadful. There was nothing left. Even her eyes were gone, and there was the dad, who appeared to be freaking out that his new car had been destroyed.

The mum was in total shock so I gave her an adrenalin injection. But this little kid; you know, I looked at this little kid and I thought, I might just let you go, mate. But I couldn't. I just couldn't, and I knew if she did live she'd not only have to have skin grafts until she stopped growing, but she'd also be blind and mute for the rest of her days. And there's the dad, who seemed to be freaking out about the car. I said to him, 'Mate, if I had a box of matches I'd throw one in the fuel tank and finish that bloody car of yours off.' And he had the hide to report me because I'd threatened to burn his car.

Anyway, the coppers said, 'Mick wouldn't say anything like that.' Then they threw the book at him. He was charged with multiple offences, including endangering the kid's life.

They were also going to charge the mother because, even as a passenger, she was just as responsible. Like I said, it's not the kids that make the choices, it's the adults. Anyway, for some reason she was let off. But that poor kid. I shouldn't say it but it would've been better if she'd gone. I couldn't even get an oxygen mask on her. I just fed an oxygen line down her throat and sticky-taped it onto her shoulder. She was five years old and it was the worst accident I've ever been to and I hope the dad ended up in jail.

But it's not only the vehicle accidents. There's also the snake bites. The most common snake around here is the gwardar. They're a cousin of the brown. A big one might get up to four foot, and a bite from one of those is enough to make you pretty crook. But if it's managed properly and you get the patient to hospital, they're usually fine. One night a young bloke got bitten and when we called the flying doctor, we had to guide the plane into our little airstrip with car headlights. That was pretty hairy but he turned out okay. Like I said, it's all to do with getting them to hospital in time.

Then there was a girl from Anna Plains Station. She was a plant operator, driving bulldozers and graders. Anyhow, all the workers decided to come down to Sandfire and have a session on the grog, and during proceedings she somehow got bitten on the ankle by a snake. She was very drunk but the thing was, she refused to let me take her to hospital. She decided to tough it out, which really concerned me, and I told her so; though luckily, by the next day, she was okay. Anyway, with that one, I reckon the snake would've died of alcohol poisoning. So that's the snakes.

Then sometimes at Eighty Mile Beach people get walloped by stingrays. The stingrays bury themselves in the shallows, waiting for something to eat, and if you tread on them, you could be in for it. They're not big rays and it's not life-threatening but they can do a fair bit of damage. They've got bony blades on their tail and if they whip around and do repeated strikes on your shin, where there's not much flesh, they can easily chip the bone.

Cardiac arrests and strokes are also quite common, especially with the grey nomads. My thinking is, it's because all their lives he's gone off to work and she's stayed at home, looking after the house and kids, so they've never really interacted. Then after they retire and go travelling together, they'll start arguing and one of them — normally the woman — will end up having a stroke or a cardiac arrest. See, what they need to do is, when they retire, they should stay at home for six months and learn to live with each other. After that, yes, then go for a few short trips in the caravan. Slowly get used to travelling together, because later on, they've got to live in that little confined space 24/7. I tell you, a couple once came into the roadhouse for a cup of tea and the wife turned around to the husband and said, 'Do you have sugar or not?' and I'm thinking, Well, there you go. That's my point.

And before they go travelling they should go and see their GP and get repeat scripts and a reminder pill box so they'll religiously take their medication. But no, they'll forget for a few days, then they'll take it in one big hit, and if it's for blood pressure, it's really going to whack them. Then a lot of them, if they're going, say, from Port Hedland to Darwin and they get ill along the way, they won't go into Broome to go to hospital because it's not on their itinerary. They're always on a mission. They must be in Darwin at a certain time, so they'll press on and they'll end up in a place like Sandfire, then they're my problem. I mean, that's no way to have a holiday. One of my cousins and his wife do a lot of travelling and they take it nice and easy. No rush. They just pull up when it's time to pull up. It might only be under a shady tree, but they don't care and they've never had an accident.

Then every now and then you get a baby come along. A while back a young couple were on their honeymoon. She was driving their brand-new four-wheel-drive Nissan. It rolled seven times and along the way it hit a tree with such force that the bolts holding the seat were sheared clean off. When I found her, she was stuck in the footwell with the seat jammed on top of her. I could see that she'd bashed her head, but I couldn't get the door open. Luckily a couple of station blokes came along and we anchored the Nissan with their Toyota and we pulled the door off. That's when I noticed she was something like eight and a half months pregnant. She was compos but she was in a lot of pain. The thing was, with being pregnant, I couldn't give her morphine, so she had to tough it out. Anyway, I got her back to Sandfire and we put her on the Flying Doctor plane and she had the baby while they were taking her from the airport into Port Hedland.

The other thing was, her husband was in shock, and that's a killer too. Absolutely. What's more, given the time frame and the distance to hospital, if you think the most seriously injured patient isn't going to make it there alive, but the other one stands a chance, you attend the least injured person first. And that's something particularly hard to talk about. One time I had to let a child go and that was tough, very tough. But you can't let it weigh you down or else you'll just give up and walk away from the whole thing. You can only do your best in the circumstances, and on that particular occasion I ended up saving the mother's life and having to let the little one go. It was a big decision, I know, but it was just the way it was, because otherwise I could've easily lost both of them.

But it's not always bad. A young woman came into Sandfire once with stomach pains. She would've been in her mid-twenties. She was travelling by herself. She said she'd already presented at Newman Hospital with stomach cramps and they'd given her some Panadol and sent her on her way. I thought, Well, if she's already presented once, there's something else going on. She was very slim and she had no bump and when I asked her if she was pregnant she said, 'Oh no, no.'

But you've always got to think outside the square. So I'm taking her to Port Hedland and I'm quizzing her about this and that. Then the penny finally dropped. I said, 'I reckon you're gonna have a baby before we make it to hospital.' And her eyes went like saucers.

Anyway, I was right. Not long after, I had to pull up and I delivered the baby on the side of the road. She turned out to be thirteen weeks premature and the delivery took less than five minutes, which was good for her, and for me too. So we cleaned up and we continued on our way. Usually we do a halfway roadside meet, but by the time I met up with the Hedland ambulance, she was comfortable and she was settled and she knew me. So me and the girl and the baby, we dollied on with the Hedland ambulance behind us, just in case. The baby was a little girl. She named her Mikayla after me.

Whatever It Takes

Before mobile coverage it was pretty much word of mouth. Someone would see an accident and they'd hot-foot it down and let me know. The thing is, they're usually in such a panic that it's difficult to get the correct information out of them. For us locals, with Broome being north of Sandfire, it's 'up the highway' and with Hedland being south, it's 'down the highway'. But they'll turn up in such a stew that they'll swear black and blue that the accident was 'down towards Broome'. What also adds to the confusion is when people don't check the distance. When you ask where they saw the accident, they'll say, 'Oh, just up the road a bit,' and you'll end up driving for a hundred k's before you get there. I mean, there's distance markers every ten k, telling you how far it is to wherever, but they're in such a state that they never think to look at them.

A while back, there was an accident up the road and a bloke got into such a panic that he rolled his car bringing the message down to Sandfire, so then I ended up with two rollovers.

Other times they don't stop and check what's happened. There was an accident one night just outside the roadhouse. A woman came running over and started bashing on my door. 'There's been a rollover out front. There's bodies everywhere.'

I said, 'God, here we go.'

When I went out, two drunks in a Toyota had ploughed into seven cows. The drunks were okay but I had to spend the rest of the night dragging dead cows off the road. So you never know what you're going to end up with.

I've still got a few missing teeth from a boofhead who smacked me when he was on crystal meth. About five years ago I went to this rollover. It was two Pommy blokes in one of those backpacker vans. No seatbelts and all that sort of stuff. They must've had a heap of drugs with them because when I pulled up, Boofhead's mate took off into the bush to hide them. In doing so he'd left Boofhead out on the road. And this feller was real trouble. He looked like one of those soccer hooligans that cause all the trouble at the Pommy soccer matches, even down to the Union Jack he had tattooed on his head.

Anyhow, he'd gone through the front windscreen and he had an ear hanging off and one hand was half ripped off. I mean, I was there to help him, and even then, he was so pumped up on crystal meth that all he wanted to do was to have a go at me. He was a really big bloke too, about six foot. Like I'm not very big so when he shaped up, I said, 'Feel free, mate, but, if you do, for all I care you can go and sit down under a tree and bleed to death.'

Then the prick smacked me in the mouth. So, very much against St John's protocol, I whacked him back. And not even that stopped him.

When the two coppers turned up, they helped settle things down a bit, and when Boofhead's mate walked back out of the bush, the coppers did him for possession. But this Boofhead feller was so violent that I couldn't get a dressing on either his head or his hand. And because the coppers couldn't split up, it looked like I'd be stuck with him in the ambulance. So when a car pulled up and a bloke got out and said, 'I'm a doctor. Can I help?' I said, 'By gee, you can.'

When we eventually get Boofhead into the ambulance, he's still thrashing around so much that the next thing I did, that you're also not supposed to do, was to restrain him on the stretcher with those cable-ties that truckies use to tie their loads down. See, you're only supposed to restrain a patient with the belts on the ambulance stretcher. But the thing is, they can easily work their way out of them. So I cable-tied him to the stretcher, and the doctor was all for it. Given the circumstances, he thought it was a good idea. After that, Boofhead started spitting at me. 'Blow this,' I said and I chucked a pillow over his head. That slowed him down. You don't smother them. It just shuts the world off. Anyhow, by the time we did our halfway-meet with the Broome ambulance he'd snoozed off. So before I handed him over I took the cable-ties off.

The next day Broome Hospital rang me to ask if he'd tried to commit suicide.

I said, 'Why?'

They said, 'It looks like he's tried to slit his wrists.'

That was from the cable-ties being yanked up so tight. I said, 'Gee, sorry. I can't really explain that one.'

I tell you, from all his thrashing around, it took half a day to clean up all the blood that was splattered around the ambulance. Anyhow, that was one of my more difficult jobs, and I've still got a few gaps in my mouth to prove it.

But you could go a couple of weeks with nothing, then you might get two in the one day. Back a while now I did nineteen hundred k's in the one day. The only time I turned off the engine was to refuel the ambulance. First there was an accident, then a snake bite, then a second accident. So I was pretty worn out by the end of the shift.

But I was getting so desperate with it all that I started the 'Blessing of the Roads', which is a RoadWise initiative. I'm far from religious, but I thought, Whatever it takes, I'll give it a go. So now, just before each Easter, I get a minister out to bless the road and the travellers. And like I said, I'm not religious, but it's made an amazing difference. The year before I started the Blessing of the Roads, I went to forty-seven rollovers, three of which were fatal, and since we've started the blessing there's only been twenty rollovers. And it isn't that people are getting smarter either, because I can assure you they're not. So something's made a difference, ay?

Then when the ambulance wore out, they wouldn't replace it. They said, 'Well, you're a good old mate. We know you'll keep on doing it in your own car.'

So the roadhouse bought me a Falcon station wagon. It wasn't marked or anything, but I could fold the seats down and put a stretcher in the back. Then, you know how you get a bit forgetful as you get older? Well, when they came to take the old ambulance back, somehow a lot of their gear didn't go back with it. Funny that, isn't it? Plus I've been donated stuff. I've got two defibrillators, and though I don't have a good relationship with the clowns down in Perth, the Broome and Hedland ambulance people help me out with equipment, plus the Flying Doctor's always helpful.

But I'm out of action at the moment. I've just hit seventy and all the stuff I got away with in my youth has finally caught up with me. One knee's been busted three times from rodeos and just recently I fell over in the shower and dislocated the other one. To make things worse, when I came down, I collected the shower screen and broke my back and severed some of the nerves. I ended up with no feeling in my waterworks and so they've put in a catheter and a bag on my leg. I was on a walking stick for a while. Then, just as I was getting better, I tripped over an electrical cord and broke my back again. So now they're thinking of doing a big seventy-year maintenance job on me to fix up all my problems. Though just between you and me, I reckon I'm past my warranty date. What's more, I hear there's very few spare parts for a 1946 male, so I'm getting visions of a wheelchair. And I'm quite fine with that. I can deal with a wheelchair, but it's going to limit my ability to get out and look after people.

Richard's Story
'Singing'

I was reading a story in one of your books about how a particular group of Aborigines 'sung' a fella to death. Just to recap: the story was told by a pilot who flew a doctor from Alice Springs out to Yuendumu Aboriginal Community, to conduct a medical clinic. When they got there the Aboriginal men were over in one group, the women and children were in another group, and they were all wailing in a real eerie, haunting way. Now I don't know if you've ever heard the sound they make when they 'sing' like that but it can be very unsettling, I can assure you.

The nursing sisters from Yuendumu explained how the Aborigines were punishing the fella for pinching the Tjuringa stones, Tjuringa stones being the sacred stones that the Aboriginal people etch their stories into. It could be about some big meeting or a corroboree or a gathering of some sort. Anything. And they treasure these Tjuringa stones so much that the Elders hide them away for safekeeping, like in a cave or somewhere. Anyhow, they'd caught this young Aboriginal fella red-handed and they decided to sing a death curse on him. You could liken it to the stories you've no doubt heard of pointing the bone. But this was far more intense and serious.

Now the thief was still alive at that stage. The nurses had him safe in the clinic. So when the doctor had finished the medical visit, they got the fella into a vehicle, and, with the Aboriginals still singing him, they drove him to the plane and took off back to Alice Springs. The doctor's plan was to put the fella under anaesthetic, and while he was out, the doctor was going to make a superficial cut across his stomach. Then, when the fella woke up, the doctor would tell him that he'd been operated on and all the 'bad stuff' had been taken out of his system, so now he'd be okay. Apparently that sort of thing had worked for the doctor before.

Now, as you said in the story, when the young fella had walked onto the aircraft at Yuendumu he was fine. He was scared, naturally, but medically he was okay. Yet by the time they'd landed in Alice Springs the young fella had died. There was nothing the doctor could do to save him. He told the pilot that he'd been trying to get an adrenalin shot into the fella's veins, but because his veins had collapsed from the shock of being sung, it was like trying to put a needle into a piece of string. Amazing, isn't it, how he'd walked onto the aircraft, unaided, and he was dead within an hour and a half. He'd been sung to death.

If you believe it's all psychological, that's up to you. Though I'm not so sure. The point I'd like to make in my story is that the Aboriginal people use different sorts of singing for different occasions. It's similar to how we have different songs for funerals and prayer, as well as different songs for weddings and birthdays and so on. They have the same. In that particular case the young fella was sung as a punishment, whereas in my case I believe I was, in part, sung back to health by three old Aboriginal Elders: Ivy, Katie and Daisy. I won't say their 'singing' was the be-all and end-all of my surviving my accident; medical support certainly went a long way in doing that. But when you've been given a twenty per cent chance of survival, their singing may well have helped.

It all started back in the mid-'80s when I was working on Stirling Station. Stirling Station's two hundred and fifty kilometres north of Alice Springs and the homestead's five kilometres in, off the Stuart Highway. Ti Tree was the nearest pub and we were fifty kilometres north of Ti Tree. Eight kilometres from the station homestead was the Aboriginal community of Wilora. Wilora Community consisted of around a hundred people and it had a small Reception to Year 12 school. Stirling also had a small community store which was where the Wilora people came to do their shopping. That was open three days a week; then every so often we'd kill a beast for the Wilora Community. That helped stop them from killing the station's cattle, and it all worked well. They were fairly honest people.

The owners of Stirling used to employ three Aboriginals full time. Then in the busy season, say for mustering and branding and building cattle yards and fences, we'd take on some casuals as well. Anyhow, we used to get mail twice a week, and in the evenings I'd sit down and help these Aboriginal workers with their mail. They could read and write to a degree, but some of the government forms were quite detailed, so they struggled to fill them out correctly. It was through my helping them that I got to know the two teachers who were out at Wilora School. Sometimes on a Friday afternoon or if I wasn't busy on the station, I'd go out and work with the older school students, teaching them basic carpentry and welding and things like that, and quite often it'd come up, 'Richard, you should become a teacher.'

By that stage I'd been up in the Territory for nine years, so I thought, Okay, perhaps it is time to make a change. So I came back down to Adelaide and I went to college. After I graduated I put in for the Territory and I got a teaching position just down the road from Stirling Station, at Ti Tree School. I just couldn't believe my luck.

Ti Tree School had just over a hundred students and only five of them were European. Hardly any students lived in town. The vast majority came from off the various communities within thirty kilometres of Ti Tree. It was during my time there that I got to know some of the Aboriginal Elders very well. For example, the groundsman at the school, Archie, he was an Elder, and the women who worked in the laundry and the kitchen, they were Elders too.

I had a class of Year 6–7s, and, being the older ones, every now and then Archie and some of the other Elders, like Clem and Douglas, would come in and call some of my students out to teach them stories or to learn their culture: they'd teach hunting and tracking skills and about the different bush tucker and how to prepare it for meals. I was very supportive of that, so at the end of first term, I sat down with them and said, 'Look, I appreciate your wanting to teach the culture to the students. So how about we make every Friday a Cultural Studies day and you can have them all day?'

'Okay,' they said, and it worked out well; so well in fact that by the end of second term I was allowed to go to some of their cultural days, which was a real privilege.

I then became an Open College adult educator, which was basically a course coordinator. I took in four Aboriginal communities over an area of two hundred square kilometres, out from Ti Tree. I'd mainly deal with the men while my Aboriginal assistant, Janie, would work more with the women. First we'd go out and speak to the various communities and ask what courses they wanted. Then, if the women wanted to do something like dressmaking, we'd contact some instructors and ask if they were prepared to run the course. I'd then price all the materials they'd need and we'd write a course outline and funding submissions to ATSIC — the Aboriginal and Torres Strait Islander Commission — or DEET — the Department of Employment, Education and Training. If the money came through we'd organise for the instructors to go out to the community and run the course, and Janie and I would keep an eye on things.

Janie and I worked well together. In fact, it was Janie who first introduced me to the three women who were to later sing me: Ivy, Katie and Daisy. Ivy, Katie and Daisy were three widows who lived together in a house out in Wilora Community. As was their culture, because they were Elders, I was allowed to speak to them, but I could only talk to the younger women just as long as Ivy, Katie and Daisy were there with me. Over time I got to know them well and I very much enjoyed their company.

I remember at one stage, we put in for someone to teach the ladies dressmaking and silkscreen printing. The instructor who came down said that their Centralia artwork was so good and different that it may go well in Darwin. So we organised a trip up to Darwin to sell some of the clothing they'd designed out at the Mindil Beach Market.

It was while we were setting up for the markets that I saw Ivy, Katie and Daisy just standing there, staring out to sea.

'What are you looking at?' I asked.

They said, 'Richard, where's the other side of the water?'

I said, 'Well, we're at the Top End of Australia so there's no real other side.'

Now these women had only ever seen rivers, creeks and waterholes. They'd never seen a beach and they'd never been to the coast, and so they just couldn't understand what was over the other side, holding all the water in.

They said, 'What do you mean by "no other side"?'

I said, 'Well, it's the sea. We're surrounded by it.'

That sort of stumped them. Then Katie asked me, 'Well, can you drink this water?'

I said, 'No, it's salty.'

Then old Ivy said, 'Well, can I boil it in the billy and make a cuppa tea?'

I said, 'No, because, being water from the sea, it's too salty.'

Then Ivy looked out over the great expanse and she said, 'Crikey, all this water and it's no good for nuthin'.'

So that was Ivy, Katie and Daisy. They were just wonderful, wonderful women.

And through my work I also got to know the male Elders in the communities very well, too; so well in fact that one of them gave me a skin name, and that was a huge privilege. The story with the skin name started back when I was a teacher at Ti Tree

School. As I said, Archie, the groundsman, was an Aboriginal Elder and when he retired he stayed on living in town. Then after I got the adult educator's job I was telling Archie that I was now going out to the communities, and he asked if he could come along with me, to catch up with some of his mates and the other Elders.

I said, 'Yeah, no worries.' And that was a great experience, because as we'd be driving around, Archie would be telling me about the communities and some of their stories and culture. When we'd arrive, while I was talking with the students, he'd go off and talk to his mates. And sometimes he'd wave me over and he'd introduce me to the Elders. So over a period of four or five months I got to know everyone.

Then one morning I was sitting in the little office in Ti Tree and Archie walked in. I said, 'Morning, Archie.'

He looked at me and he said, 'Morning, Jamba Jimba.'

I said, 'Who are you talking to?'

He said, 'Me, Clem 'n Douglas, we Elders bin talkin' 'bout you for a while now 'n we give you that name.'

I thought it was like a nickname, so I just said, 'Yeah, good. Thanks, mate.'

Then later that morning I was writing a submission for a course, and so that I could spell everything correctly, I was looking through a book of locations and names and there was Jamba Jimba, as a proper Walpiri skin name. So they'd somehow decided that I was to be called Jamba Jimba.

Anyhow, when I saw Archie later that day, I asked him, 'Do you give all the white fellows in town skin names?'

He thought about it for a while, then he said, 'No, just the ones who won't piss off. 'N seein' how we're stuck with you, we gotta make you feel loved.'

Another white bloke, Trev, had been there for a number of years, so I said, 'Then what's Trev's name?'

Archie said, 'We not give 'im a name.' And he put his big hand on my shoulder and he said, 'We only give someone a name if we want 'em here.'

And that was about seven months before the accident, and because I'd been given the skin name of Jamba Jimba that somehow made me a relation to old Ivy. I'm not sure how it all works, but I presume it's like how people's surnames make them cousins and aunties and uncles. Anyhow, from then on, while Katie and Daisy remained my friends, Ivy became 'Aunty Ivy'.

Now to the accident. When I went out to one of the communities, I met four young fellas. They'd been in Alice Springs for the past three years, going to high school. When I asked how they were coping with being back in the community, they said they were bored. 'There's nuthin' to do.'

This was during the build-up to the mustering season. There was a lot of seasonal work coming up so I said, 'Would you like to do some work on the stations?'

'Yeah, that'd be good.'

I said, 'Have you ever worked on stations?'

'Nup.'

'Ever worked with cattle?'

'Nup.'

'Ever ridden horses?'

'Nup.'

Anyway, there was a guy I knew who used to teach stockmen's skills. So I rang Alice Springs and said, 'Quick, get him out here. I've got some young men that he could teach stockmen's skills to and they'll get work out of it.'

'No,' they said, 'he's flat out for the next few months.'

I said, 'Well, I worked on stations for nine years before I became a teacher; can I run the course?'

'Yes,' they said.

So I rang one of the station managers I knew, and after I explained what I was planning to do, he said, 'If you can teach them the ropes, they can work here, no worries.'

I said, 'Okay then. Can I borrow five horses?'

That was all okay, and when he sent the horses down, he said, 'Richard, there's one horse there that we're having a bit of trouble with; can you educate her?' So I gave the tamer horses to the young fellas and I took on this horse and it just didn't feel quite right.

The next day I was explaining to the principal of Ti Tree School about what I was doing and that I needed to give these horses some work.

He said, 'Can I have a ride on Saturday?'

I said, 'No worries. I'll be giving this particular horse a bit of extra work anyway, to try and calm her down a bit.'

When the principal and I went out on the Saturday, my horse still didn't feel right. Anyway, we got back to Ti Tree and the principal and I went our separate ways. I then run into Jim, the manager from Ti Tree Station. Jim knew a lot about horses. We used to be partners in camp drafting events. I said, 'Jim, there's something wrong with this jolly horse.'

He said, 'How about you take her for a lap around the oval and I'll have a look at her?'

Anyhow, I'd just broken into a canter when she went down on her knees, and I came a cropper. Down I went and I hit my head. Not hard enough to crack it, but it knocked me out and apparently I was bleeding internally. A closed head injury they call it. Jim realised straight away that I was in big trouble so he jumped in the car and headed back to the clinic to get the nursing sister. She grabbed her gear, and her and the Aboriginal health worker raced out in their vehicle. There was a Flying Doctor radio in their car, and as soon as the nurse took one look at me, she made an emergency call to the RFDS. The nurse then went back to the clinic to sort things out in preparation for the arrival of the Flying Doctor while the Aboriginal health worker kept the respirator mask on my face.

When the Flying Doctor arrived I was flown straight down to Adelaide where I was placed on life support in Royal Adelaide Hospital for nine days, with less than a twenty per cent chance of survival — or so the doctors told me — and then I was in a coma for a further three months.

In all I had to stay in Adelaide for near on a year while I recovered from the accident. If you can imagine, there I was at the age of thirty-one having to learn how to talk, eat, drink, read, write, the whole lot, all over again. But during a two-week break between being in Royal Adelaide and going into the rehabilitation centre, I grabbed the chance to whizz back to Ti Tree to get some of the things I'd left behind.

When I arrived, there was Archie walking down the street. So I went over and said, 'G'day, Archie.' I said, 'It's really good to be back.'

But when I went to shake his hand, he wouldn't even look at me. He just sighed and shook his head. I said, 'I'm only here for a few days because I have to go back to Adelaide.' He seemed a bit happier at that. Then when I added, 'But hopefully I'll be back early next year; back to work,' he slapped his leg and said, 'Oh *yukata*,' which means 'shit'.

I said, 'What's wrong?'

He then looked at me and he said, 'They gonna call me a silly old man 'n not listen to me no more.'

As it turned out, after I'd had the accident, the people out in the communities kept asking Archie when I was coming back. I said, 'Gee, that's nice of them to have been so concerned about me.'

'No it's not,' said Archie.

I said, 'Why?'

Archie pointed to the airstrip and he said, 'I seen 'em put you on the doctor plane 'n you was proper crook.' He said, 'So I go 'n ask 'em at the clinic, "What's happened to Richard?" 'n they tell me you was no good.'

I then explained to Archie how I was lucky to be alive, because if it wasn't for the nurses at the clinic, and if it wasn't for the Flying Doctor Service, and if it wasn't for the doctors in Adelaide, I'd be *kumanji*, which means dead.

I found out later that Archie had gone to the clinic a number of times asking about me, and on each occasion the nursing sister had told him that I was in the Adelaide hospital. When she used the medical term to explain that I was in a coma, Archie didn't understand what she meant, so she just said, 'Richard's still asleep.'

After about ten days of this Archie said, 'That's ten days, sister. He's not sleepin'. He's *kumanji*.'

Archie had then got together with Clem and Douglas and they called a big meeting to announce that I was *kumanji*. So that was that; Archie had told everyone I was dead. Now, all of a sudden, I'm back and I'm alive and I'm standing right in front of him. So my coming back really threw a spanner in the works. No one would know how to cope with it because once someone's dead, they never come back to life. Never. Once you're dead, you're dead.

After I'd seen Archie, I thought I'd better go out to Wilora Community. That's where Aunty Ivy, Katie and Daisy were. So I went to Stirling Station. As it happened it was shopping day, and because you can't interrupt the women while they're shopping, I waited outside. When Katie and Daisy walked out I said, 'Hello Katie. Hello Daisy.'

But they didn't say anything. They just stood there, agog. Then Katie handed her shopping over to Daisy and took my hand. I was surprised. Aboriginal people just don't do that. Then Daisy put down all the shopping and she shook my hand. And she'd never done that before. Then, because they all lived together, I said, 'Is Aunty Ivy in the shop?'

'No, she's at home. You gotta come home. She'll want'a see yer.'

So I drove back out to Wilora Community with Katie and Daisy. When we arrived, Aunty Ivy was sitting in the front yard of their house, boiling the billy on a campfire. As they got out of the car, Katie yelled out, 'Ivy, look who's here.'

Aunty Ivy looked up. When she saw me, her old face wrinkled into a smile. 'You want'a cuppa?' she said.

'Yes please.'

As I said, when I was the adult educator, I worked with an Aboriginal lady, Janie. Janie was the one who'd introduced me to Aunty Ivy, Katie and Daisy. Anyhow, Aunty Ivy was looking down at the billy and she said, 'Janie tell us you was in hospital 'n you was proper crook.'

I said, 'Did you think I was *kumanji*, like Archie told you?'

She looked at me. 'Nah,' she said, 'Katie, Daisy 'n me, we sing for you Richard; we sing for you to make you better.' So they'd sung whatever songs were necessary to help my spirit survive. So that's one story about singing.

Then, after I'd recovered, I returned to Ti Tree. I was up there for about nine months, but after the accident, I couldn't cope with all the changes, so the doctors sent me back down to Adelaide for more rehabilitation. I'd been home for about seven years when, right out of the blue, I started to wonder how things were going back up in Ti Tree, and in particular about Janie. As I said, I knew Janie very well because she'd been my assistant when we lived in Ti Tree.

Anyhow, I couldn't quite fathom what was going on with me. I thought I'd left it all behind. Then a few days later — on the Saturday — I was having breakfast and a cold shiver came over me, just like that; goose pimples and the hair on my arms stood up. It wasn't a cold morning so I thought, Okay, these things happen. But about an hour later, I began shivering again. I thought, God I wish I was back in Ti Tree. It's warmer up there. Then that night, I was hit by the shivers again. I thought, This isn't right. I must be getting crook. On the Sunday I got hit by the shivers a few more times. I kept thinking, This's just not right. There's something wrong. With all this going on, for some strange reason, I got it in my head that I just had to speak to Janie. On the Monday morning I thought, Well, the teachers at Ti Tree would be having a cuppa before the students get there. I'll ring the school and say hello to Janie, just see how things are going. So I rang the school. Someone answered. I said, 'Can I speak to the principal please?' The principal came to the phone. I introduced myself, explained my connection, and I said, 'Any chance of speaking to Janie?'

'No mate,' he said. 'She's moved out to Ali Curung.' Ali Curung's further north. 'Oh, okay,' I said and I hung up. But that afternoon and all through the night I was hit by the shivers.

Early Tuesday morning I rang Ali Curung School. The principal answered. I said, 'I used to work with Janie at Ti Tree. I've heard she's moved to Ali Curung. Is there any chance of talking to her?'

He didn't say anything. Dead silence. I thought, Gee, something's up. Then he said, 'I don't believe this. Janie's been talking about you for days, saying how she has to speak to you. Hang on, I'll go and get her.'

The instant Janie came to the phone, she said, 'We didn't know where you was living no more. So Katie and Daisy and I, we bin singing your name 'cause we have to tell you, your Aunty Ivy, she's *kumanji*.'

As it turned out, Aunty Ivy had been very ill when I first started thinking about Janie and Ti Tree. Then when she died, Janie, Katie and Daisy started singing my name and that's when I'd started getting the shivers.

Rosemary's Story
Mobuditi

I've recently read your book *Great Australian Outback Police Stories*, and thank you. Cops have great stories, and Dad had some beauts. Dad was a special constable in New South Wales. During the Cowra breakout in 1944 he was given the job of going out and warning the local farmers that the Japanese had escaped. Problem being, it was just after it'd been broadcast over the radio that people should arm themselves against any strangers they might see. Dad said that those were the longest walks he ever did, going from farmhouse to farmhouse, scared stiff how one of them might take a pot shot at him, and being farmers, they were unlikely to miss.

Actually, one of Dad's city experiences intersects with one of my nursing stories. From the 1930s through to the '50s, Tilly Devine was a noted organised crime boss and brothel owner. Anyhow, Dad was a young cop on the beat in Woolloomooloo when he was confronted by a razor gang. When Dad took on a boxing stance to defend himself, Tilly appeared and whaled in. 'Blue,' she yelled, 'you don't fight people like this with the Marquess of Queensberry rules!' And she started kicking and scratching and bashing them with her deliberately heavy handbag until she'd beaten them off. So Dad was always grateful to Tilly for saving his life.

Almost forty years later, when I was nursing, Tilly was admitted to the Prince of Wales Hospital in Randwick. By then her second husband, Eric Parsons, had died of cancer and she was old, bankrupt, sick and worn down. At that time there were no repatriation beds available around the eastern suburbs area, where she lived, and it looked like she'd have to go home alone. After I'd done a bit of digging around, I said to her, 'I believe you were married to a Mister Parsons who was a member of the British Navy during World War One?'

'Yes,' she said. 'I was.'

I said, 'Well, that makes you eligible for a repatriation hospital bed at Concord.'

When she asked why I was doing this for her, I told her Dad's story, and she nodded with a wry smile. Anyhow, we did get her into Concord but unfortunately she died soon after. So that's just one of Dad's stories, and the crossover we had.

My own stories, from over forty-eight years of nursing, probably don't rate in comparison. There are some though. Mum was a nurse. She did her training in Sydney, at St Vincent's, before she went bush, and after she married Dad they lived in Sydney. Then, when the Japanese submarines bombed Bondi during World War Two, she packed us kids up and took off bush again, this time working as a child health nurse in south-western New South Wales. And so that we'd all be together, Dad soon got a move out that way, to a little place between Young and Cowra, called Bribbaree.

So the notion of working in the bush was always with me. I did my nursing training at the Prince of Wales, which was where I met Tilly Devine. But an incident that really shocked me was when a little black kid who'd been in Bourke Hospital arrived at the Prince of Wales twenty per cent dehydrated. He eventually improved, but to me, his condition was either due to the people out there not knowing what they were doing or it was a blatant case of racism. And that's what really confirmed my resolve to go out in the more remote areas and help people. With wanting to be as well prepared as possible, I went to London and did cardiothoracic at Brompton Hospital before I returned to Sydney to do my midwifery. It wasn't possible to do an actual degree in nursing back then so I did a degree at the University of New South Wales, majoring in education and anthropology. During that time I had a chat with Fred Hollows, the noted ophthalmologist who was doing a lot of eyesight restoration work out in the remote areas. Fred's recommendation was that I go to Melville Island during my university holidays and work in Milikapiti Aboriginal Community, just to see how I'd go.

Melville's one of the Tiwi Islands, in the eastern Timor Sea. I arrived there at the end of 1975, just after Cyclone Tracy had hit nearby Darwin. Because all the aerials had been knocked out, if I wanted to talk to a doctor in Darwin, I had to radio Katherine first and they'd put me through. At that time the Northern Territory Health Department was coming out of the stone ages, and I mean that. In the communities they were allowing a DDT-based cream to be used on the Aborigines to kill their nits. So I got on the radio and said, 'For God's sake, this stuff's banned on cattle so I'm certainly not going to use it on people.' What I didn't realise was that when you broadcast something over the radio, everybody can hear it. They even picked it up in Papunya, which was over a thousand miles away. So that was the beginning of the end for the cream and I packed my lot up and sent it back.

I was at Milikapiti for three months. They were troubled times. To start with, the other nurse who was supposed to be there had taken off to Darwin and hadn't told the health department she'd gone. That left just me and the Aboriginal health workers. To make matters worse there was a murder. A male Aboriginal shot another male Aboriginal, and though I attempted to save his life, he died. As a result of the shooting, the local white fellers, who were already going through the craziness that people go through in the wet season, started packing their guns. To add to the catastrophe, the police from Darwin arrived and started marching around in their smart khaki uniforms, with their guns and so forth, and were treating the Aboriginal people so appallingly that it was causing great concern. So much so that one of the Aborigines, fearing that his old rifle would be confiscated, attempted to hide his in the clinic. When I saw the gun I said, 'I am not treating anybody while this gun's here, particularly in the current circumstances.'

When no one was game enough to own up, I covered the gun with a raincoat and took it to the manager of the settlement. When the cops checked the rifle out, they found it was a leftover from the First World War. Naturally it wasn't licensed and so there was more intimidation. But strangely enough, the NT Health Department didn't have a guns policy, so I demanded they create one, and that they do it pretty quick.

Amid all this there was a dispute over the dead man's body being taken to Darwin for a postmortem, and of course due to Cyclone Tracy, Darwin was a complete mess. Again I had to step in and help with the negotiations. Then once that was sorted, there was the debate about how the body should be transported to the plane. Initially the police wanted to take it out in one of their vans. I strongly disagreed with that and offered to drive the body out to the airstrip in the clinic vehicle, and when the body came back, I'd bring it back into the town. With the mother of the deceased wanting a traditional funeral, there was a further delay until a certain type of ochre had arrived from central Australia. That done, everybody got painted up and started going through a series of distressing corroborees. No white fellers were invited. Still, I went along anyway and afterwards the mother said how pleased she was that I'd come, because I'd played such an important part in it all.

I found the funeral process tremendously interesting, particularly in regard to their customs in dealing with the death of the man. Among the Tiwi, to avoid attracting the spirit of the dead, the immediate family has to change their names. The spirit is called *mobuditi*, and of course kids being kids, they picked the names of their favourite pop stars and sports people.

I recall one kid calling himself Fogerty, after John Fogerty, the lead singer from the band Creedence Clearwater Revival.

So in terms of a quick dive into the intense environment of remote cultural conflict and Aboriginal custom, my time at Milikapiti proved extremely valuable to my future work.

Of Country and Family

After I'd finished my degree I had another chat with Fred Hollows. At that time, Fred was in Sydney, doing interviews for the Alice Springs Health Service, and when I'd told him about my Milikapiti experiences, he said, 'Yep, it sounds like you might be good for Papunya.'

Papunya's an Aboriginal community a hundred and fifty miles north-west of Alice Springs. So off I went to Papunya. It was 1978. Back then Papunya was also a troubled community, though more due to the number of different tribes having been forced off their traditional lands and placed in together. Add to that the sly grog trade and you've got a potent mix. By then the Papunya Art Movement was underway and part of our nursing agreement was that if rain came while the artists were working outside, we had to help rescue the paintings.

The people's living conditions were quite basic. On the outstations they either lived in wiltjas or in structures made of corrugated iron. The corrugated-iron ones were mostly a half-hoop-like structure, while some of the others were just more like a shelter, with corrugated-iron sheets being placed sideways for walls. As for the traditional wiltjas, their design was quite brilliant. They had a bower frame and were insulated with bush and grass, with cloth covering the opening. The opening could be changed at any time, so if there was a hot wind coming from one direction, they could close that aspect of the wiltja and open the cooler side.

In the town itself, there was one little wrecked fibro house at the entrance which the more racist whites would point out to visitors and blame its condition on the Aboriginal people. The white fellers lived in wooden houses while most of the Aborigines were in two-roomed unlined shacks, built on concrete slabs, with an unlined corrugated-iron roof. As I recall, those houses didn't have power or water. Their water came from communal taps, and they had communal laundry tubs and communal toilets. When we eventually got a washing machine at the clinic we allowed the people to do their washing there. The flow of the community water was problematic. When their water dried up, I'd fill a jerry can from our rainwater tank and give it to them. More often than not that usually happened on a forty-degree day, which caused me to be forever going to the manager's office and confronting them over the matter.

As for the people's health, to be blunt, it was dreadful. When I first got there, there were two men from NT Health who were forever blaming the women for the kids getting sick. That was a real tough rap seeing how these were traditional people, with some of them having only recently been dragged out of the desert by white fellers. A lot of them didn't speak English, and being of different tribal groups, there was a huge status difference. The more traditional Pintupi wore a basic loin cloth–type thing and the men had a grass band around their heads. Another group were the Luritjas. The word *Luritja* is an islander word meaning 'stranger', and sadly, within the community, they were treated as strangers and were discriminated against by the other groups.

After self-governance came to the Territory in 1978, they started sending people out to get the parents of the Stolen Children to sign an official consent form to legalise the removal of those children. One man, Yala Yala, was about six-foot-two and he was married to a very tiny woman. Yala Yala's white-feller name is Gibbs and his skin name is Tjungarrayi. He and his wife were the parents of a little girl who, under the Commonwealth Government's Child Welfare program, had previously been taken into care in Darwin. By then the daughter would've been about eleven.

With Yala Yala being unable to understand the legalese English used in the document, a linguist who was working at Papunya explained that he had two options: either to sign the form or not sign the form. But in one of the most ethically heartbreaking moments I've ever witnessed, Yala Yala signed the form. After he did, he said to the government people, 'I understand that our daughter's grown up only knowing English. I understand it'd be very difficult for her to come back here to live. But you must tell her that this is her country and that we are her people and she will always be part of us and she will always be most welcome.'

I later saw John Howard on the television with one of Yala Yala's paintings hanging up behind his desk. When he said he had no reason to apologise for the Aboriginal children being taken, I wrote to him and said, *The painting that's hanging behind your desk was done by Yala Yala Gibbs and I know for a fact that his daughter was 'officially-legally' stolen in 1978. And that act, John, was done under your Commonwealth law while you were in Parliament.* To add insult to injury, I was talking at an Aboriginal Women's Conference in Adelaide in 1979 at the time the South Australian government was destroying the records of the Stolen Children. The women got so distressed that they were trying to work out how to break in and steal the remaining records in an attempt to track down their children.

Anyhow, enough of that. Apart from learning and experiencing a wealth of the Aboriginal people's culture, one of the most wonderful things that happened to me at Papunya was when a young health worker, Tanya, came into a normal labour. She arrived at the clinic with her mother, who we'll call Nakamarra. Nakamarra was a pretty woman who had a slight mental illness — a condition she'd had for some time. But Nakamarra was insistent how the labour be conducted. She wanted a low-light environment, so I lowered the lights. She wouldn't allow any analgesia to be administered. Of course I'm panicking because

I'm used to bright lights, oxygen masks and everything. Then Nakamarra taught me a special massage technique that went from the back, over the loins, to the thighs, and Tanya had as close to a pain-free labour as I've ever seen. The baby boy was delivered with ease and his temperature was being maintained by lying between Tanya's legs, and there he lay, with the cord still pulsing beautifully. He then stretched his arms and he smiled. It was the most beautiful birth I'd ever seen.

Another extraordinary delivery happened when the women wanted a traditional birth. In case there was trouble they'd moved into a small corrugated-iron humpy near the clinic where I'd be near at hand. Anyhow, I was called over. When I went inside, the baby had just been born and it was doing the same thing: waking with a smile. I remember looking around that little humpy and there was the baby, there was the baby's mum, there was the baby's grandmother, there was the baby's great-grandmother and there was the baby's sister and they were all beaming with joy.

Other than the joys, there were the occasional tragic situations when traditional punishment was meted out. One time some young men went into Alice Springs to get some grog. Anyhow, they got drunk, and on their way back they rolled the car and one of them died. Trying to be sneaky, the others left the body out there and they snuck back into town and crept off to their various homes. Now, as far as custom went, leaving the body out there was the very worst thing they could've done, and so all hell broke loose. The community council met: 'This has to be dealt with.' And so they lined these young men up and they started by spearing them in the appropriate fashion, which is an inch either side of the upper-outer aspect of the mid-thigh.

That finished the traditional punishment. But then some of the others attacked the young men with their bush knives and we ended up with two severed femoral arteries at the clinic, which I dealt with. I was then roused on because the community wasn't happy about them being fixed up in the clinic. They thought they should've taken their punishment. Of course, then the discussion was, is the use of a knife traditional punishment? To my mind I had to do something because if the men would've died from knife wounds, the perpetrators would've been charged with murder and could've ended up in jail for the rest of their lives.

The same thing happened after a young man was speared in payback for hitting his mother. He came to the clinic and so I cleaned the wound up, put a dressing on it and gave him some painkillers. The community leaders then arrived: 'Don't do it again. This's our law. It's our means of punishment.' But again, being a nurse, if someone's in need of help, it's my duty to treat them.

Another young man rolled his car and broke his neck. The accident occurred out on the plains. So I drove out there, along the corrugated dirt and across a couple of creeks. He'd died by the time I arrived and when I finally got him back to Papunya I expected everyone to be upset by his death. But no; they were happy. 'He was sung for hittin' his mother,' they said, 'and so he deserved what he got.' So what their causation is, is very different from white-feller way.

Another time a local was operating as a featherfoot — a man of the law. On this occasion a nurse saw this man hiding out the back of her flat. She didn't see that he was wearing feather feet, so she didn't know he was there on a matter of law. The nurse knew the man, so she walked out the back and said, 'G'day,' and called him by his traditional name. And that caused the spirit from the featherfoot-construct to go back into the spirit world and the man died on the spot — right there; dead.

Another custom I'd only read about in anthropological literature was that every fifty years or so the Aboriginal men hold a big corroboree. This corroboree brings in men from Fitzroy Crossing, all the way through Warlpiri country, to

Papunya, down through Pitjantjatjara country and across into Western Australia. Anyway, I'd been asked by the people in the community to inform the storekeeper that he'd need more food because the corroboree was soon to begin. When I told him, he wouldn't believe me. I said, 'Okay, so where's all the men then?' When he looked, there were no men left in Papunya. They'd already gone.

As I was heading back to the clinic, in the far distance I saw a huge cloud of dust coming toward Papunya. Out from the dust appeared all these tray-back long-wheel-based Toyotas, loaded with men, standing shoulder to shoulder. Some were even up on the cabins. These vehicles came through the rough grass, and into town. At that moment the female Aboriginal health workers hit the floor. They daren't look because this was men's business, not women's business. Then straight through the town these vehicles went and off to where the corroboree was being held. And these vehicles, jam-packed with men, just kept coming and coming. Without a word of lie, there would've been thousands of people.

Part of a normal corroboree would be man-making — initiation stuff — and occasionally I'd be driven out to treat someone who'd received an accidental injury or was ill. I wasn't allowed to bring anyone back into the clinic. I could only treat them out there, and while I was there, I had to keep my eyes down. I'd just see my patient, do my thing and leave. But these much larger corroborees would've been more about dancing, and telling stories about where they come from and their responsibility to the world around them. They'd also learn about their Dreaming and their songlines. I was told that one songline follows the mountains all the way through to Port Keats — Wadeye. Another goes south to Uluru and beyond. I was told that even the emus and dingos follow these songlines.

Another belief involves transubstantiation, which is where they can basically change substance. I used to go to a rocky outcrop about a hundred and fifty clicks west, into the desert. One particular rock was the cap of the waterhole. When it was rolled away, all the little finches and other birds would arrive out of nowhere. It was just beautiful, and it was pointed out to me how, within that rocky outcrop, certain rocks not only belonged to certain people but they were also part of their spirit.

And with healing, they believe that a high temperature is caused by a spirit entity, and that entity can be removed by massage. I was in Alice Springs one time when an Arrernte woman asked if I'd go to a Pitjantjatjara council meeting and get the Nguraki — a traditional wise-man or doctor — to come and do a healing session on her sick twelve-week-old. At first I thought, Gee, that's a pretty heavy-duty request to ask me, a white woman that they wouldn't even know, to go into a Pitjantjatjara council meeting. When I rocked up they said, 'Why should we do this?' So I used a bit of cunning and said, 'Well, you are sitting on Arrernte country and an Arrernte woman really needs to have her sick baby seen by a Pitjantjatjara Nguraki, because she thinks they're really strong.'

So this lovely Nguraki agreed to come and do a healing session on this sick baby. While he was massaging the baby, something shiny flew out of his hand, and in that instant, the child's temperature dropped and it became well. So there's just so much we don't understand, and there's just so, so much we could learn from these people.

In saying that, we must also try and understand how alien places like Alice Springs are to a lot of these tribal people. I once took some women into the Alice for their antenatal check. It was the beginning of November and when we walked into the hospital, they saw all the white fellers standing around, hissing and shouting and going on. The women started tugging at me. 'Quick, we need to get out'a here. Somethin's wrong. This's really powerful stuff. These white fellers, they've been sung.'

'It's okay,' I said. 'They're listening to the Melbourne Cup.'

Some of them had heard about the Melbourne Cup and so they settled down a bit and we proceeded to obstetric outpatients. But the thing is, if we destroy those sort of spiritual beliefs and customs, we'll really screw up their concept of who and what they are.

Their link to country and family is also integral to their being. Another time a Papunya woman had been admitted to Alice Springs Hospital with a stab wound to her chest and so she had a chest drain sutured in. With having been separated from her country and her family and now finding herself in this alien environment, totally at the hands of white fellers, she was terrified.

A few days after she'd been taken to Alice Springs, her family came into the Papunya clinic. 'Somethin's wrong,' they said. 'We need to know how she is.' So I radioed Alice Springs Hospital and asked them how she was and they said, 'She's fine. She's doing really well. Her chest is clearing beautifully.' I then went back to her family and told them that she was fine. Next day, the same thing: 'Somethin's wrong. We need to know how she is.' And so I again radioed the hospital and again I got the same answer: 'She's fine. She's doing really well. Her chest is clearing beautifully.' And all this radioing to Alice Springs went on every day for over a week and the hospital kept saying that the woman was fine.

Then one day her family arrived at the clinic. They were smiling and going on. 'You're not goin' to believe this,' they said, and they brought the woman in.

This woman had done something almost inconceivable. She was one of the ones who'd been brought into Papunya in the early '60s, so she knew her country and she knew its ways. But she got so terrified in Alice Springs that she'd ripped the chest drain out, stitches and all. With sheer good luck her lung didn't collapse. But she'd made a dressing from what was around her and had patched the wound the best she could. She then escaped from the hospital, then through Alice Springs. She knew the white fellers would be looking for her out along the roads so she got herself up into the MacDonnell Ranges, and she started walking.

There'd been recent rains and so she was able to drink from the rock pools and she ate bush tucker. The distance from Alice Springs to Papunya would be, as the crow flies, about two hundred and fifty k's. And for a whole week, this wounded woman walked and she walked and she walked, weaving her way north-west, through all that gorge country, until she came through the grass and into Papunya.

And those bastards hadn't even told me that she'd left the hospital. Worse still, I was stupid enough to believe them when they said she was fine. But now, there she was, with her family beaming and dancing around her with delight.

Sarah's Story
Wonder

I was born in Palmerston North, New Zealand. Then, when I was about one, my parents moved over to Melbourne. So I would've been about six when we went to Hong Kong to live on Lantau Island. My dad's quite alternative, so Lantau would've been his idea. He's a musician and he wrote jingles for advertisements and music for TV shows over in Hong Kong. But I think he preferred that we were in a house, in a little village, with hills all around us, instead of high-rise buildings. Then not long after we arrived, my parents split up, and I haven't heard from my mother since. So it was left to Dad to bring me and my six-month-old brother up. We did have live-in help, or domestic helpers as they were known. A lot of people over there had them.

I went to a school in our little village. I'd walk up a path, up into the hills. The school was just one big room with around twenty-five students, in all grades. There were only a couple of us foreigners, so it was a Chinese-based curriculum. We'd start the day by watching the Hong Kong news in Chinese and most of the daily instruction was in Chinese.

Then we came back to Australia in 1997, the same year China took Hong Kong back from the British. The changeover wasn't why we returned; it was more that Dad wanted me to go to an Australian high school, and anyway by then the company he was working for had gone bust and things had slowed down for him. When we first came back we lived on the Gold Coast. I was well ahead of the other kids academically so I breezed through the end of primary school. But when I got into high school I started to go downhill. I don't know if it was the change in cultures or what, but I ended up in the wrong crowd and by fifteen I was pregnant with Tiarna. After that I pretty much dropped out of school and I was a single mum from just after she was born. I didn't have any help from Tiarna's biological father, but his family was very supportive of me, as was my dad, and my brother was pretty okay about being a ten-year-old uncle. When Tiarna was about one and a half I did try to go back to high school, but by then I had different goals, and with having a baby to care for, I didn't have much spare time, so it didn't work. It wasn't until she'd grown up a bit more that I began a bridging course through Griffith University to do nursing.

My attraction to nursing was thanks to the TV show *All Saints*. I loved that show. Other than that, I wanted to become a midwife because when Tiarna was born, some of the midwives at the hospital gave me a hard time about being a single teenage mum. Not all of them of course, but there were comments made along the lines of, 'Do you just go around sleeping with everybody?' Things like that. So I felt quite judged and I was inspired by that to become a midwife who was non-judgemental.

Once I'd completed my bridging course I enrolled in a Bachelor of Nursing. A year and a half into the course my dad decided to go travelling with my brother, which meant I was on the Gold Coast by myself. That's when I moved to Ipswich to be closer to Tiarna's biological father's family. Tiarna's parental godmother is like a real mum to me. We have a great relationship, which was helpful, because not long after we moved to Ipswich, Tiarna started school and I was still able to continue my studies.

By then I'd met my current husband, Adam. He'd gone to the same Ipswich school as Tiarna's biological dad. Adam knew the family. They liked him and we ended up getting together. And as they say, the rest is history in that regard. Funny how it works, isn't it?

When I finished my studies, I got a graduate position at Queen

Elizabeth II Hospital in Brisbane, in emergency. I'd drive up from Ipswich each day, which wasn't much fun. But I'd already done one of my nursing pracs at QEII, in emergency, and I knew it was what I wanted to do. Perhaps it's because I'm the kind of person who gets bored easily, and with working in emergency, everything's unpredictable.

At that stage I had no desire at all to be a remote nurse. But once I'd completed my midwifery, I started thinking about becoming a flight nurse. The only trouble being, I was quite anxious about flying because I had visions of the plane dropping out of the sky. I then found out that NSW Air Ambulance had a fly-along system where registered nurses like myself could go out on a flight to see how things went. So I took professional development leave and I went down to Sydney for two days to do a fly-along with them.

When I arrived on the first day and they said, 'Nothing's on,' I sat around thinking, Just my luck. I've come all this way and nothing's going to happen. Then we got a call to go to Lord Howe Island.

Lord Howe's a three-hour flight from Sydney. It's the most beautiful place. All the flight nurses were telling me that it's everybody's dream to go out there, and so now, there I was, I'd turned up on my first day and got to fly to Lord Howe. It was for a woman with a gastrointestinal bleed and we just flew out there, picked her up and brought her back to Sydney. That was my first day, and I absolutely loved it. So when I came back to Queensland I started applying for flight nursing jobs all over the place. Adam was fine with that. He just goes along with things, and being a plumber, he can get work just about anywhere. What's more, he loves his fishing, so when a job came up at Bundy — Bundaberg — which is near the sea, he said, 'Yeah, go for it.'

After we moved to Bundy, I went to Brisbane to do my orientation, and the pilot described my first flight as being the most turbulent he'd ever experienced. It was so bad that I ended up whacking my head on the roof. That's when my anxiety came back. But after the pilot and the nurse who was orienting me started laughing about it, I felt more at ease.

My first solo day was also very interesting. First we got called out to Cunnamulla to pick up a Frenchman who'd had an accident on his motorbike and needed to be flown to Toowoomba for surgery on his knee. He was a student who was living in Sydney and his brother had come over from France for a visit and they'd decided to go travelling on their motorbikes. Anyhow, they were riding in the dark, about twenty kilometres out of Cunnamulla, when he hit a kangaroo. As it turned out, the visiting brother — who wasn't hurt — was a medical student and so after he rang for help he was able to administer first aid until the ambulance arrived and then we flew the injured man to Toowoomba.

To end the day, we were tasked to fly a paediatric team — a doctor and a nurse — from Brisbane out to Woorabinda Aboriginal Community, to pick up a sick baby. Woorabinda's west of Rocky — Rockhampton — and it was the first time I'd been to an Aboriginal community. By the time we arrived it was getting on night, it was very hot and groups of Aboriginal kids were wandering down the middle of the street. It was a sort of 'bare' place, is how I'd describe it, and I wasn't used to going into such a small hospital. We were there for quite a while because the paediatric team had to assess the baby, then stabilise it and connect it up to their monitoring system. As a flight nurse, I was only there to assist them in the setting-up and transfer. The mum also came with us. By that stage the pilot was running out of flight hours, so instead of taking us all back to Brisbane, we flew to Bundy and a night crew took over from there. So that was a long and interesting day.

Another eye-opener was when we transferred a prisoner from Hervey Bay. I'd never had anything to do with criminals. But before we transfer any prisoner we do a risk assessment that takes into account the person's history of aggression and violence, and if alcohol and/or drugs are involved. If they get a score of five we generally take a doctor with us, and sometimes, in the worst cases, a prison guard. I didn't ask what this man had done, and even though he was handcuffed and he was in shackles, that was quite an anxious flight.

There was another case, more recently, where I was on night shift and we were tasked to transfer a prisoner from Hervey Bay to Nambour Hospital. He also had gastrointestinal bleeding and so he'd been intubated in the intensive care unit at Hervey Bay. With this prisoner being assessed as a very high risk we took a doctor from Brisbane with us, just in case we had to sedate him if he became aggressive on the aircraft. It took the doctor and me about an hour and a half to transfer all of the compatible monitoring onto the patient and then we transferred him over to our stretcher. He was in his fifties, and even though he was sedated and intubated, they wanted two prison guards to come with us. So I had a feeling he'd done something quite bad.

Thankfully the transfer was uneventful. But in the ambulance on the way into Nambour Hospital I was told that the man was a convicted serial rapist. Anyhow, after we got to Nambour Hospital it took another hour or so to transfer him again and do the handover. After all that was done I found myself sitting in the ambulance bay of Nambour Hospital at 6 o'clock in the morning, with a pile of equipment and the stretcher base, waiting for a maxi-taxi to take me back to the airport, so I could then load it all onto the aircraft back to Bundy. Despite my fatigue, I love my job, but it does sometimes makes you wonder, doesn't it, as to all the trouble we go to in transferring people no matter what their background is.

Shirley's Story
No Longer Exists

I was born in the Riverina area of New South Wales, in the old hospital at Ardlethan. That hospital no longer exists. It closed down in about 1956. They've just got a small bush nurse's clinic there now, which I'll get to later. My parents had a wheat and sheep property near Ardlethan, at a place called Kildary. Kildary's about ten miles out of Beckom. Some of your readers may know of Beckom from your books *Swampy* and *Beckom Pop. 64*, though there's certainly a lot less than sixty-four people in the town now.

The bush was a fantastic environment to grow up in. For my schooling, I started off at Beckom Public School. Then, when the Mirrool school bus started to come closer to our farm, we all went to Mirrool. There were four of us children in the family. I'm the second eldest. I have an older brother, Bruce; a younger sister, Marianne; and the youngest is Max. There was also a little girl that came between Marianne and Max but she died at birth. Anyhow, the little school at Mirrool no longer exists now, either.

For high school I went to Ariah Park, which is only a stone's throw from Mirrool. Ariah Park went up to intermediate level — Year 10. Then, if you wanted to further your education, you went to either a boarding school or some larger town where you had to board anyway. But I always wanted to be a nurse. When I was a kid, Mum was often sick and so Dad would take us into the Temora Base Hospital to see her and I just loved the smell of the place, absolutely; that and the fact that a hospital was a place that could make people better.

I left school in Year 10. But at sixteen I was too young to go straight into nursing so I did a year of bits and pieces. I even worked as a telephonist in the Beckom Post Office. That no longer exists, either. Pam Thomas was the postmaster back then. Those were the days of the old plug-in telephone exchanges, where you put your call through to an operator at the post office and they connected you on to whoever. In the bush, a lot of the calls went out on a shared telephone line or party line and if someone else along the line picked up the phone, they could listen in on your conversation. And we heard some beauties.

In those days nursing was more like an apprenticeship really, where a lot of your learning was done on the job. Of course you still had to pass your exams to become an RN — registered nurse. I did my training at Temora Hospital and we also did study blocks over at the JJ Brennan School of Nursing, in Cootamundra. That doesn't exists any more, either. But in its day, a lot of girls throughout the area did their study blocks there. We all stayed in the nurses' home at the hospital and we had some fantastic times. Every so often we'd lie out on the roof and tease the girls who'd gone out with boyfriends. Then sometimes, when one of the boys rang the nurses' home to see if they could talk to one of the girls, we'd answer the phone with, 'Cootamundra Police Station here,' which would really put them off guard.

But we worked very hard during our training and quite often, in our second and third years, we'd be the only ones there for the emergencies. I have great memories of those days, some sad, some happy. One of the sadder ones was when a girlfriend I'd trained with went out with a bunch of other girls and the girl who was driving had been taking drugs and she crashed the car and my friend was killed. That sort of stuff, but that's just life isn't it? Still, the good times far outweighed the sad. Another time, I was left on the ward by myself and this guy stopped breathing and I was able to resuscitate him. I felt pretty good about that because I was pretty much a novice at that stage. Oh, and I remember walking into a room and the sister and a few of the other students were gathered around, looking down at this guy, and I said, 'So what's wrong with him then?' and the sister said, 'Well, dear, he's dead.' That was the first dead person I'd seen.

Then there was my first injection. A lady was unconscious and the senior nurse said, 'You may as well do this one, Shirley.' So there I am, needle poised, aiming it at the lady's backside, and I'd lose my nerve. I did that three times before I got the needle in. I mean, being unconscious, she wasn't going to feel anything anyway, was she?

But I enjoyed that sort of learning environment where all the other nurses would encourage you. They'd say, 'Just walk in there like you've done it a thousand times.' So that's what you'd do; you'd walk right in there displaying all the bravado in the world. Also, I think by training in a small hospital, we got a wider nursing experience than the trainees did in bigger places where they had more medical support. We were more hands-on. We were it — the workforce — and so we just had to get in and do it.

After Temora, I worked at Ardlethan. By then the old hospital had closed and I was in the little bush nurse's clinic. It was actually quite a nice setup. The clinic room had a couple of wind-up wind-down beds. Adjoining the clinic was a nurse's flat, where I slept during the week, then someone would relieve me on the weekends so I could visit my parents. There was also a little kitchenette and a laundry. I was the only one at the clinic. There was no doctor. It was just a casualty place really. I was allowed to keep someone for up to ten hours. After that, if they were still sick, I'd send them off to Temora Hospital in the ambulance. And when I needed a second signatory for the drugs register, I'd ring the policeman and he'd come up and sign them off with me. But most times it was just people with their kids who had temperatures. Though one guy did have a heart attack in his car, right outside the front door. The problem being, because I was on my own, I couldn't get him out of his car. So he died. That was pretty tough, but there's a lot of stories like that in nursing.

From Ardlethan I went over to the Barellan Hospital. Barellan's about thirty miles west of Ardlethan. That's where Evonne Goolagong, the famous tennis player, grew up. My granny lived there. She was sick and so I also kept an eye on her. See, because nurses are in demand they can move around with ease. There used to be a 'blue book' and a 'brown book'. You carted the blue book around with you and wrote in all the places where you'd worked. The brown book belonged to the hospitals and it was sent from hospital to hospital, wherever you worked. It was really a behind-the-scenes reference system that let the hospitals know whether you were worth employing or not. But I only worked in Barellan for a short while as I'd already been accepted to do midwifery at Crown Street Women's Hospital in Sydney, and that's where I went next. Crown Street doesn't exist these days, either.

The 'grand idea' was to do general nursing, then midwifery, then Tresillian, which is working with children. But in between all of that, I got married, had a baby girl, Leonie, and then got divorced. I lived up in Newcastle for a while, then I came back out to the Riverina, as a single mum, to work in Griffith Base Hospital, Griffith being close to Mum and Dad. I was on permanent night duty in the male ward. I did permanent nights because the girls I shared a house with were able to look after Leonie at night. Leonie was about two by then, and during the day I'd have someone babysit for a few hours while I got some sleep.

Griffith had a large population of Italian migrants, many of whom couldn't speak English. In fact, a lot of their school-going children would act as their parents' interpreters. Italians are very emotional and demonstrative. On night duty, the nurse who was in intensive care and the nurse from the male ward had to share the casualty service, if the need arose. This night someone rang the emergency bell so the nurse from intensive care and I went rushing out and there's this family of Italians. One of them was leaning against the wall moaning and carrying on like he was on death's door. We were about to chuck him on the trolley and rush him inside when his relatives started leaping up and down: 'No, not him. No, not him. Back of car. Back of car.'

We then left this moaning man against the wall and took a look in the back seat of the car, and there's a bloke having a heart attack. That's when we realised that the moaning bloke was doing his own form of pre-grieving. So we got the heart-attack guy on the trolley, wheeled him inside and called the doctor. All turned out well. He was fine. It was just an initial case of mistaken identity.

Another story happened with my best friend and housemate, Michelle. Michelle came from Hillston. I'll never forget her Hillston home telephone number: Black Stump Two. Anyhow, Michelle entered the Queen of Hearts competition. It's sort of like the Miss Australia thing where you raise money for charities. This one was for heart disease and I somehow became Michelle's one-person committee. It was then somehow decided that I was to paint my face blue and dress up as a sick heart. Being a sick heart, it was also somehow decided that I was to be sat in a wheelbarrow then wheeled — with very little care, I may add — in and out of all the shops up and down the main street, collecting money as we went. One of the hospital wardsmen was to don a pink dress and take on a nurse's role, and Michelle was to walk along puffing a cigarette. It was an experience I'll never forget because the next day I was covered in bruises from being bounced up and down in the wheelbarrow. So much for charity.

While we're on about smoking: one day this old gentleman arrived at the hospital. I forget what his complaint was. Anyhow, the doctor came in to have a look at him. He checked the old gentleman's blood pressure, got out his stethoscope and had a listen to his heart and lungs. Got him to stick his tongue out. Got him to cough. Looked into his eyes.

'What's the prognosis, Doc?' the old gentleman asked.

'Give up the cigarettes,' the doctor replied, 'or they'll be the end of you.'

'But Doc,' said the old gentleman, 'I'm a hundred and two and I've been smoking since I was nine.'

Cracked Up

After Griffith I went to Canberra. My daughter, Leonie and I lived out at Queanbeyan and I travelled in and out each day. Leonie was about four and had just started school and I was still a single mum, until I met Paul and we later married. Paul was a landscape gardener. The company he worked for did a lot of landscaping around the city. I worked in the endocrinology cardiology unit at the newish Woden Valley Hospital. The endocrinologists were after stable, staff and because I'd had a fair amount of experience, I became one of those stable staff.

That job set me up for the rest of my career really. It fascinates me how the body functions. In fact, I enjoy the medicine side of things far more than surgery. With surgery I took the view that relatively well people came in to be chopped up, get better and go home again. Whereas in medicine there's loads of variables, lots of complications and things that change and rearrange. With people in those circumstances — say someone with diabetes or someone with a heart attack — it's really all about helping them help themselves to have a more comfortable life.

For example, a lot of young people used to come in with type 1 diabetes and they'd have all sorts of horrendous stories. One young woman, Lynn, had such a unique type of diabetes that she'd virtually lived at the hospital for two years. There was a certain enzyme in her body that neutralised any of the insulin we'd give her. Lynn and I got to know each other well. One day we were chatting away when a patient rang the call-bell so I said, 'Lynn, you can go and answer that.'

She said, 'No I can't.'

'Yes you can,' I said. 'You've been here longer than I have.'

So off she went. Next thing she's back: 'Shirley, it's a man and he wants a bottle to pee in.'

I said, 'Well, get him one. You don't have to hold it for him or anything.'

So she did and when she returned she said, 'I haven't been here longer than you.'

I said, 'Yes you have. If you work it out, I'm here eight hours a day, five days a week, and you're here twenty-four hours a day, seven days a week, so work it back from when you first came to hospital.'

And when we worked it out she'd been there thousands of hours longer than I had.

In Lynn's case we ended up trialling a new permanent slow-drip insulin treatment on her. She was one of the pioneers of that treatment in Australia and she was later able to go home. So Lynn became a part of history.

Anyhow, I went on to become second-in-charge of the endocrinology cardiology unit, and when a friend went home to England, I became the nursing unit manager. By that stage Mum and Dad had retired to Wagga Wagga, and so after Dad died and Mum started to struggle, we decided to move to Wagga. Paul wanted to open a wholesale nursery business, there was a good school there for Leonie and I could get work in the hospital. So that's where we went. But after having worked permanent nights back in my Griffith days, I swore I'd never do it again. To my way of thinking, permanent night duty can get pretty debilitating, so in Wagga, I just did rotational stuff.

Those were the days when MRSA — methicillin-resistant Staphylococcus aureus — was a huge thing. MRSA's sometimes known as golden staph and it was rampant in the hospitals. Basically it's a bacteria that's resistant to most antibiotics. Those days, if someone got the infection, we had to isolate them. In Wagga we had a whole wing set aside for MRSA people.

It was crazy stuff. People used to do terrible things, like wash themselves with petrol, in the false belief they could get rid of it, when in fact all they needed to do was wash with soap and water. A lot of paranoia surrounded it. One day I walked into the room that was next to the MRSA isolation wing and there's this man cringing back in one of the beds, with his eyes bulging out of his head.

I said, 'What on earth's the matter?'

He pointed to the floor. 'It's coming to get me. It's coming to get me.'

'What's coming to get you?'

He said, 'MRSA,' and when I looked to where he was pointing, there's this huge cockroach walking across the floor.

'It's coming to get me,' he said.

I soon fixed that. I stomped on it. *Squash.* 'There you go,' I said. 'No more worries.'

Then there's what's called the pressure rounds. That's where you turn the people who are permanently in bed over on their side and give them a back massage and stuff like that. We had this large lady who filled up most of her bed. In cases like that, two of you attend the patient. So, to roll them over, one pushes the patient while the other one pulls. Anyway, this lady had a glass eye and each night she'd take it out and put it in a little dish on her bedside table. This time she must've knocked the table and her glass eye had fallen out of its dish and had fallen into her bed. So there we were, my colleague was pulling, I was pushing. And as this lady rolled over on her side, I saw this woman's glass eye stuck smack-bang in the middle of her backside. All I could think of was Humphrey Bogart's line: 'Here's looking at you, kid'. Anyway, I plucked the eye out from the lady's bottom, held it up, and said to my colleague, 'Look what I've just found,' and we both cracked up, if that's the right term to use in a case like that. Oh dear, the things you see.

But I really missed the type of work I did back in Canberra. In fact, a lot of the time in Wagga, they'd give me the people with diabetes to look after. So I went to work in Community Health as a diabetes educator. Then when I saw a job as unit manager of the Diabetes Centre in Launceston, I applied for it. For that I did a telephone interview, which I thought went well, but when I didn't hear anything I thought, Oh well, somebody else's got it. Too bad, Shirley, get on with life. But about a year later I got a call from one of the assistant directors of nursing from Launceston: 'Are you still interested in that job?'

I said, 'Look, can you give me a few days to think about it and I'll ring you back?'

I then rang a friend in Tasmania who told me that there'd been heaps of political stuff going on after the Diabetes Centre had been opened. But due to a lot of local support it was going to stay open. By then my marriage to Paul had fallen apart. I was in my early forties. I was by myself. My mother had remarried and was in Adelaide. Leonie was in her early twenties. She'd had Jade by then and they'd moved over to Bunbury, in Western Australia. There was nothing left for me in Wagga so I thought, Gee, if it involves endocrinology, it's all I've ever dreamed of. So I rang back: 'Yes, I'm still interested. I'd be happy to move down there.'

So off I went to Tassie. But they just kept moving us around. From Launceston Hospital we moved to a newly refurbished office in Mulgrave Street. As soon as the internet got put on there, everybody else wanted it, so they moved us out and put us in the old x-ray department. Once we settled in there, someone else wanted it, so we were moved into one of the old hospital wards that'd been refurbished.

Now don't get me wrong. Tasmania's absolutely beautiful. I loved it, and I made some wonderful friends. But from a family perspective, I was either travelling to Adelaide to spend time with my sick mother or I was travelling to Western Australia to spend time with Leonie. And with travelling from Tassie to both those places I had no time to go anywhere else. So I figured, if I moved to WA, I'd be closer to Leonie and it'd be easier to get to see Mum in Adelaide.

The first job I got was in the southern Wheatbelt region, at Narrogin, as a diabetes coordinator. Then I went down to Albany to work in Primary Health as their regional consultant for chronic disease. One of the things I really liked doing was the project work. After one paper I wrote, we got a grant from the Australian Better Health Initiative to do a chronic disease program. Through that we connected with the Southern Inland Health Initiative. That was a project involving millions of dollars where we looked at how we could better change the system for people with chronic conditions. I've always felt that an efficient health system needs an electronic medical records system. And we were determined for it to happen. I used tell people, 'When I'm old and crotchety and retired, I bet that's when they'll do it.' And they're doing it now, and I'm not really that old.

I also got involved in what's known as telehealth. That's a system where all the little one-nurse places can set up a consultation, via video link, with a city doctor or specialist. It's the way of the future. For example, my new partner, David, and I now live up on the far north-west coast of WA, at Derby, and the other day David had a teleconsultation with the pain clinic in Perth. Now, if he'd had to travel to Perth for that appointment, first he'd have to fly there and back, and we've only got three flights a week to Perth. So he'd be away from home for a few days, which means he'd have to take time off work, which may mean a loss of wages. Then there's all the accommodation and other expenses involved while he's down in Perth. And really, the specialist may only want to see him for ten minutes. So if you can do all that via video link, it's better for everyone concerned. And it's not a second-best service. Telehealth's as good a service as any.

Anyhow, I've been nursing for forty-eight years and I've achieved far more than I thought that little girl from Kildary ever would. So I reckon it's now time to stick my feet up, relax, and have a good look around the place. To that end we're heading off to New Zealand in February. In June we're hoping to do the Canning Stock Route; September we're going over east for a sixtieth birthday, and we'll come back to Derby via Broken Hill and Alice Springs. Yes, so time to relax.

Tayla's Story
Isolated

I always wanted to be a nurse. I grew up in Western Sydney and with my mum working in aged care, when I was fifteen and still at high school, I became a part-time assistant-in-nursing at a nursing home. After I left school, I took a year off to save money and travel. Then when I was nineteen I began my three-year full-time Bachelor of Nursing at the Australian Catholic University, in North Sydney. The uni course was mostly theory and we'd only do three-week practical blocks each semester. To my mind that's a bit of an imbalance. Starting off this year as I did, a fully fledged RN out in the central-north of New South Wales, at Walgett, I was pleased that I'd had that basic hands-on experience of working in the nursing home.

I'd say that my wanting to go remote came about in my last year at uni. By that stage I was sick of the hustle and bustle of the city, and the thought of working in the outback seemed exciting and challenging. To that end I nominated my top four work preferences to be in remote facilities. From that, Walgett accepted me into their remote rotation program — RRP. The RRP is where they send newly graduated RNs like myself out to places like this for three-month stints, to cover for the regular nurses when they go on leave. So I came out here for my first three months, and when they asked me to extend for six months I said, 'Yes,' and now they've asked me to stay on for the full twelve months, which I've gladly accepted.

I guess, like in a lot of remote areas, it's difficult to get staff. Even while I've been here, I've seen a large number of agency nurses come and go. Maybe it's because Walgett's a long way from the city and there's less government funding; I don't know. But to prepare me for the experience I spent two weeks in Dubbo doing training. So I thought I was well prepared. But nothing prepared me for the drive out to Walgett in mid-February, through such a dry, flat landscape. By the time I got here the temperature had nearly reached fifty degrees centigrade. At the best of times I'm uncomfortable with the heat, so when I was lugging all my stuff from the car to the nurses' quarters, I was thinking, Tayla, what on earth have you done.

Compounding that was the shock of just how small Walgett was in comparison to western Sydney. It's by far the most isolated place I've ever been to. Some parts are quite run-down, and with desert-type trees scattered around the place, it's certainly not what I'd envisioned. Walgett's got around two thousand five hundred people. The ratio between Indigenous and non-Indigenous would probably be fifty-fifty, with a majority of Indigenous people living in the town and most of the Europeans living out on farming properties.

There's up to eight of us in the nurses' quarters. We have our own rooms and bathrooms and we share the kitchen and lounge room, and with our quarters being on the hospital grounds, we can just get up and walk to work. The hospital's got a sixteen-bed acute section, which also includes four observation areas; then we have a two-bed resus – resuscitation unit – for emergency and an eight-bed aged-care unit. We also have x-ray facilities and a radiographer, which for a remote area is quite advanced. Unfortunately a lot of the Indigenous people are prone to chronic kidney disease and diabetes. I'd say it's to do with diet and largely genetic. To that end we have a dialysis unit where the patients come in three days a week. In all there's probably a total of about twenty nurses, ranging between RNs, EENs and AINs. We don't have any Aboriginal nurses, which is a shame. But we do have multiple Aboriginal liaison officers, so with about eighty per cent of our hospital presentations being Indigenous, they're always made available for those patients and play a huge role in the care we provide.

We do have a GP clinic attached to the hospital. Our doctor works there six days a week and he's also on call to the hospital. He'd be in his forties. His wife's also a doctor and she works over in the GP clinic as well. It's a long day for him. Before he starts at the clinic, he'll do a round of the hospital patients. Then, if we need him during the day, we can call him over at the clinic. In the afternoon, he comes over and does another hospital patient round before he goes home, and he'll be on call for the remainder of the day and night. Each month he does three weeks of being on call and clinic work, then he gets a week or so off and we get a locum to come in.

As for experiences, my first baptism into remote nursing was one particularly crazy shift. It was a Good Friday and within fifteen minutes we had three patients come into emergency. Two had been in a motor vehicle accident and the other had a severe blood infection. We only have two nurses and one doctor on per shift, so when something like that happens, because we've still got to look after the ward patients plus those in our aged-care section, it can get super chaotic.

The problem with the severe blood infection was that he didn't present to the doctors when he first got the infection and it got septic and spread through his blood system. The two who'd been in the accident were also in quite bad shape. After our initial observations, we had to x-ray them. The trouble was, we've only got the one x-ray bed. So we had these patients; we've put hard collars on them and we've got to do spinal precautions. That's where the doctor checks to see if they're able to move all their limbs. He'll then assess the spine to see if he can pinpoint any tenderness. Then we do a log-roll to transfer the patient to the bed. For that you ideally need five people: someone at the head, supporting the neck, and two people on each side, and as a team, you roll the patient without allowing them to do any movement themselves. In that case, with just us two nurses and a doctor, it was all hands on deck and we had our security man helping us as well as the radiographer.

That night was a sink-or-swim moment. We barely got a bathroom break. But that's what you do; you just focus your energies on the patient, which, nine times out of ten, is stabilising them enough before you can get them to a larger hospital where there's more facilities. So once we'd stabilised and triaged all three patients, they were airlifted to Dubbo Hospital. In that case I was lucky to have been working with a very experienced emergency nurse. Even still, that night, when I got back to my room, I couldn't sleep. As a young nurse, new to the game, I was tossing and turning, worrying if I could've done anything better or different. But when I went in the next day, I was reassured that I'd done a good job. And that's one of the reasons I've accepted to stay out here for a while longer. They're a great group of nurses. They're so supportive and we've got such a strong relationship that we're able to debrief and discuss things openly. Anyway, that was definitely a very interesting night.

Another thing I've had to overcome is being faced with cardiac issues. For some reason, things like that quite scare me. I think it's because with heart attacks, it's vitally important how you treat the person. The thing is, people out here don't usually call an ambulance, especially when they're very sick. They just turn up at the hospital and so there's no forewarning. One night, the other nurse and I were doing some paperwork when somebody started bashing on the door. It was a man, and as soon as he walked in we could see he was a classic presentation of a cardiac event. He was sweaty and clammy, yet cool to touch, and he had chest pain. So we started implementing treatment straight away and when we popped him on the monitor, his ECG showed that he was having a heart attack.

The doctor was there within five minutes and that's where the critical care advisory camera is so cool. It's a camera that's set into the ceiling of our resus bay and when we put a patient on the bed, under the camera, the doctors and the specialists over in Dubbo or Orange ICU are able to view and discuss the patient's condition with our doctor. With that patient, we were advised to Metalyse him. That involves an injection into the vein that thins the blood and dissolves the blood clot that's causing the heart attack. There's huge risks involved in administering Metalyse to a patient in a large hospital, let alone in a small hospital like Walgett. But in this case it worked almost instantly and the man started to feel better. By that stage a plane was on its way to pick him up and he was flown to Orange Hospital where he recovered. I felt very relieved about that because if that patient would've waited another half an hour before coming into the hospital, he could've needed full resuscitation, which is scary.

Obviously not everything's a massive emergency. As with everywhere, there's the usual drug and alcohol issues and the like, but most of the people just need a little reassurance. A lot of kids come in. Paediatrics isn't in my scope of practice, and as a young woman who's never had children, that's been a little daunting. I also think, unfortunately, with our history together, there's still a lot of tension between Indigenous people and white Australians. So there's a big gap of trust, and in a place like Walgett where everyone's seemingly related or connected somehow, if you make a mistake or you're not honest with someone, word quickly gets around. So I've put a lot of effort into trying to build trust with members of the community and I'm now at the stage where the parents seem fine bringing their kids into the hospital to see me and then to accept the advice I give them. And that's very important, especially in a place like this where some of the girls start having children at the age of fourteen or fifteen.

So nursing in Walgett is massively different from a city hospital, where the newly graduated nurses have lots of doctors and back-up and far, far more facilities. Out here, the doctors trust our assessment of a patient. And that's something I'm getting more confident in doing — trusting myself — which is going to come in very handy in my future as a nurse.

So yes, as for my future, I'm not a hundred per cent sure. I am interested in doing a post-grad in emergency nursing, and to do that I'll have to go to a big city hospital. On the other hand, I'm enjoying my time here so much that I wouldn't rule out working remote in the future.

The biggest problem for me is that with being only twenty-three and single, things in Walgett are quite limited as far as entertainment goes. And also, I'm seven hundred k's away from my family. We're very close, and with this being the first time I've lived away from home, if I have a rough shift or I'm feeling a bit sick or emotional, I do miss them.

Yvette's Story
Longing to Be

I was born in the same hospital where my mum trained as a nurse back in the old all-white-starched-uniform days — Yallourn Hospital, Victoria. Dad was from Tasmania. His family owned the fish-and-chip shop and milk bar in Dunalley, right on the beach. After my parents met, he moved over to the mainland and began working in the mining industry as an interstate truck driver.

I'm the second eldest of six. My schooling was complicated because we virtually lived in Dad's semitrailer, while he was travelling all over Australia. We did home-schooling most of that time. It was a hard life, but fun, and we gained great life skills along the way. We got to meet a lot of different people and experience things that other kids never did. When it was cold we slept in the cabin of the truck, behind the driver. On nice nights, we'd sleep in hammocks under the truck or up on the trailer, in the load itself. So when we did eventually settle down and I attended the one school, it was a bit difficult. But I adapted. Then oddly enough, in a case of history repeating itself, years later, as a family — along with our pet bird — we spent two years travelling around Australia in a bus and I home-schooled the children along the way.

Anyhow, I was seventeen when I met my hubby. We just clicked and that was it. I was in the last months of high school and I was also working part-time at McDonald's and doing volunteer training in the newborn section at a child-care centre. I really liked that, but oh, forever niggling away inside me was the idea of rural and remote nursing. That may well have come from my gypsy-style childhood because I've always had this deep longing to be out in the middle of nowhere; out in my beautiful country. To me it just seems to soothe my soul and gives me a renewed strength.

Anyhow, after the children got a little older, I completed my assistant in nursing in aged care and following that I did my enrolled nursing certificate. I then worked in a busy north Brisbane emergency department, and I just loved it. It's fast-paced and you see life at its barest. What's more, I knew that I'd need emergency if I was going to do rural and remote work. So it was a very busy time. I was working and I was studying for my Bachelor of Nursing, and because my husband was away a lot with his job, I also had the three children to look after. I actually felt a bit selfish about that, because while the girls were older, my son, Jamie, had to go into school child-care three days a week, which he really didn't like, and nor did I.

But I stuck with it and I eventually graduated. Then, with the longing to go rural and remote still being strong, I did an emergency care certificate in remote nursing and my maternity through CRANA — Council of Remote Area Nurses of Australia. By that stage my two girls were in their late teens and Jamie had just finished high school and was working part-time. So I had a chat to an agency. The next day they called back: 'We've got a three-month contract for you over in the Kimberley region. You can start in a week.'

I was so thrilled that without even thinking, I said, 'Yes, I'll take it.' But when I got off the phone, it hit me. I was like, Oh my God, what've I done? I haven't even discussed it with my husband.

So I rang him up at work. 'How long's the contract for?' he asked.

I said, 'Three months.'

He said, 'What?!'

I said, 'I know. What've I done?'

'Well,' he said, 'it's what you've always wanted to do, so give it a go.'

When I got off the phone I still must've been in shock because Jamie said, 'Mum, what's up? Has someone died or something?'

'Oh Jamie,' I said, 'I've just accepted a three-month nursing contract.'

'Great. Where is it?' he asked. So I got out a map and when he saw that the Kimberley was over on the far north-west coast of Western Australia, he went, 'Oh Mum,' and he just sat there for a minute. Then he said, 'You know what?' He said, 'If you're feeling scared about it I could come with you for the first month.'

So I rang the agency back and asked them if it was okay to take my sixteen-year-old son along with me and they said, 'Yeah, that'd be fine.'

Next thing we're on a sixteen-hour flight from Brisbane to Melbourne to Perth then to Broome. When we got on the bus in Broome, for the final leg out to the community, the driver said, 'You'd better sit down the front 'cause the locals are having a fight down the back of the bus and it could get nasty.'

And they were. And it did.

Anyway, we didn't get into the community until one in the morning, and when we got off the bus and into the steamy heat, we waited in the pitch dark, with our suitcases tight beside us. Then a car came along. It flashed its lights and a guy said, 'I'm from the hospital. Chuck your bags in the back. I'll take you to your accommodation.'

I said, 'I hope it's near the hospital.'

He said, 'Yeah, it's just across the road.'

It was about 2.30 by the time we got settled and I had to start my first shift at a quarter to seven. But I was so anxious, I couldn't sleep. Then when I got up and went to leave the house, a mob of locals were congregated in the park across the road. I'd never been to a place with such a large Indigenous population before, and with our experience on the bus still fresh in my mind, I tried to leave the house three times, but I just couldn't. Anyway, Jamie said, 'Come on, Mum, I'll walk you over.' So he walked me over to the hospital, and that was it. I loved every minute of that contract. I only did emergency, but oh, we saw some pretty horrendous stuff. Most of it was fuelled by alcohol: there were stabbings, hangings and an unbelievable amount of attempted suicides, particularly by young people, which was extremely saddening. And if a local was unwell they'd leave it until the very last moment to come in — which was what happened to a seventeen-year-old girl who had a severe urinary infection. Still, we did our best. We tubed her and all that and we got her down to Broome. But she never made it.

While I was there I was also on ambulance duties with a driver. One night I had this lady yelling over the phone, 'Sister, sister, come quick! I got liver pains. Tummy pains.' So I asked if she'd taken Panadol and so forth. 'Yes, sister. Come quick! Too much pain.'

Off we go in the ambulance. Seeing it was dark and some of the locals didn't have electricity in their houses, I took my torch. When we found the place, there were so many family members all living together that I went through the house calling out, 'Where's the sick person?' Then I heard a lady yelling out the back. When I rushed out, there she was. She was in pain all right. But not from tummy or liver problems. She was having a baby. I was horrified. I hadn't done a delivery alone before. It wasn't my line of work. She was probably twenty, and thank God, it just popped out: a healthy babe, no problems.

Then there were the vehicle rollovers and the accidents where people had collided with those big Brahman bulls. And gosh, it is just unbelievable the damage they can do to a vehicle and to the people in it. To make things worse, a lot of the locals didn't wear seatbelts, so people got tossed out everywhere.

Another time this man walked in with a bag of blood-covered clothes. Two of us were on night shift. 'What's happened?' we asked. 'Where's the injured person?'

'Out on the mudflats,' he said.

I don't know if you know or not but everywhere along the Kimberley coast there's crocodile warning signs. So we get out there and there's this woman lying down on the mudflats. It's pitch dark. We shone the touch around — no crocodiles. None that we could see, anyway. So it was out with the gurney and down we go. The woman was extremely intoxicated but we managed to get her onto the gurney and drag it back, up through the mud while mindful that a crocodile might come out of the dark and attack us. We then got her into the ambulance and took her to the hospital. It turned out that she'd been attacked with a machete. She had huge gash wounds in her head, so we shaved her fuzzy hair, cleaned the wounds the best we could, then stapled them up. And she survived. It was quite surprising really. By the following week she was up and walking around the community, still with her head shaved and the staples in.

So that Kimberley experience was a very interesting and a great educational one, and the staff were fantastic. They were just so accommodating. They took Jamie and me out fishing. One barramundi we caught was, without a lie, as big as myself. I mean, I am only five-foot-one, but still. And seeing how we didn't have our own transport they took us up the Gibb River Road. Another agency nurse lent us her vehicle so we could go to Broome. I mean, like really, who does that?

Fabulous

After my stint in the Kimberleys I rang the agency again. 'What've you got?'

They said, 'How about four weeks on an island in the Northern Territory, just off Arnhem Land. You catch a flight from Brisbane to Darwin then a light plane out from there.'

'Fabulous,' I said. 'I'll take it.'

And I absolutely loved it. It was a very traditional island community. The main town had just a couple of extremely expensive little shops. You could order food to come over on the barge, though I didn't because I was only going to be there a short time. My accommodation was wonderful. It was a two-bedroom weatherboard house, with a bath. It had a nice cool front verandah and a fully fenced small backyard.

As for staff, we had a nursing manager, two other nurses and three Indigenous healthcare workers. You weren't allowed to visit any of the communities without a healthcare worker. As clinic visits went, I'd be flown out to the very remote island communities twice a week, I'd drive out to do outstation clinics twice a week, and I'd spend a day in the main community.

When I first arrived I thought, Oh my God, here I am, once again outside my comfort zone. Like I'd never driven a four-wheel drive on sand before, and when I did, I got bogged twice, and we once got lost. The story there was that our driver had been up dancing all night, during one of their many sorry business times — funerals — and he needed to sleep. There were two of us nurses so we said, 'Okay, you just get some sleep. Where do we go?'

'Go straight,' then he fell asleep in the back of the vehicle.

So we're going along exactly like he said — straight. A couple of hours later we said, 'This can't be right.' So we woke him up, and when he had a look, he goes, 'We're lost.' So he took over the driving and we had to retrace our tracks all the way back to the community.

On those drive-out clinics we'd take lots of water and a packed lunch, plus all the medical gear we needed for the day. We'd head off around 8.30 a.m. and get back at 4.45 p.m. The communities knew when it was clinic day, so when we arrived, we'd back the four-wheel drive up into whatever shade there was, pull out a mat, pop it under a tree, and away we'd go. We mainly did primary healthcare, like checking blood pressures et cetera, and because most of them were diabetic, we'd do their blood sugars. People say it's all to do with diet, but I don't know. I mean, most of them were still living quite traditionally. They caught their own fish and hunted kangaroo and turtle, then they'd order in flour to make damper.

Most lived in corrugated-iron humpies, and to catch the breeze off the water, they'd sleep on a front verandah section. There was no running water. Amenities were shared. In the centre of a community they'd have a Telstra phone box, with a massive tower, then there'd be a couple of basins and taps and a couple of long-drop toilets.

To get to the island communities, we'd fly out in a tiny four-seater. For safety reasons we had to weigh ourselves and our gear before we took off, so we'd only pack the bare essentials. I'd always take some eucalyptus cream for the elderly, to help their old bones. They'd come over to the clinic: 'Sister, you got some rubbin' cream?' We'd also leave a couple of bottles of liquid Panadol with a nominated community person, just in case it was needed; like they might phone through and say, 'Hot child, sister.' And you'd try to assess the situation over the telephone: 'Okay, how old?' And they'd sort of say an age and you'd try to assess the child's age more closely by asking, 'Are they walking yet?' or 'Do they go to the little school?' From that you'd judge the dosage of liquid Panadol.

With flying being so expensive, apart from our set flying clinics, a plane was only used in an absolute emergency, and even then the pilots wouldn't fly in the dark. The only time I went out without one of the healthcare workers was for an emergency pick-up. A seven-year-old girl had fallen on some rocks and had received a real whack to her head. So we flew out to her homeland community and I did the emergency care required, bandaged her up, then we brought her back and cleaned her wounds and sutured her head and gave her antibiotics. She then stayed overnight with a family member. In the morning she was all good so she was flown back to her community.

Another night a lady rang me: 'Sister, hot baby. Newborn. Only home a couple'a weeks.'

Alarm bells started ringing as soon as I heard 'newborn'. 'Okay then,' I said, 'we'll give the baby some Panadol and see how it goes.' Because all the medications are colour-coded and bagged and tagged in big letters, in both our language and theirs, I went through the procedure. 'Can you find the bottle in the pink bag?'

'Yes, sister.'

'What does it say?'

'It's a little tiny bottle; a baby one.'

By then it was about 3 o'clock in the morning. So, going on age, I suggested a standard dose of Panadol. Then I said, 'I'm going to hang up the phone now. Go and give the baby the Panadol, then call me back in one hour.' The hour gave me the time to arrange a flight to get the mum and baby to a hospital. When she rang back and the baby was still hot I said, 'When the sun comes up I'm going to get the doctor plane to come for you.' So we flew out at daybreak and we brought the mother and baby back and organised the Flying Doctor to take them to Darwin.

Thankfully, on that occasion, the baby was well enough to be returned to the community within one week.

But this island was fabulous. On the whole the people were healthy and because they were in the sea so much, their skin was good and they didn't get as many infected sores. Plus, there was no alcohol or petrol — only diesel — so there wasn't much violence. So when the agency asked if I'd like to extend my contract for another month I said, 'Yes, but I'd like a couple of weeks' break to be with my family.'

That second time, my twenty-three-year-old daughter and my two-and-a-half-year-old granddaughter came with me, and they had a wonderful time. My granddaughter just ran free with the other kids. She's in Kindy now and every time they have show-and-tell she takes along her old photos of her time on the island to show to all the kids.

Heartbreaker

After the island I did more remote work in the Territory. Those were mostly desert communities, with their unique red sandy-dirt landscape, where it was so dry and hot that most days it felt like your eyes were going to be burnt out of your head. But I do love the Territory. It's a place where you feel alone without feeling lonely. The people are different and the sunsets and sunrises are some of the best I've ever seen.

Still, it was a mixed bag. One community was away out on the northern edge of the Tanami Desert, south-west of Katherine. A nursing friend and I went there on a six-week contract. After we arrived in the light plane we had to drag our bags over to our accommodation in what felt like fifty-degree heat. And it was pretty primitive. We lived in a drab grey Besser-brick flat with an old but just functional kitchen. It had electricity, thank goodness, and an air conditioner that rattled like an old steam train. There was a lounge chair and a large television that worked, thank God. The two bedrooms were separated by a curtain, and we got a double bed each. A so-called 'security fence' extended three quarters of the way around our flat. But at least we were close enough to the clinic that when we were on call, we could run over and open up the locks. There were no security alarm buttons to press, which was a bit of a worry. Though if there were problems, probably no one would've come to our rescue anyway. But we adapted.

In a lot of these desert places, the clinics are quite similar. They're also Besser-brick. There's a resuscitation room with a couple of beds, a room to ourselves and a room for the flying doctor who visited fortnightly, if we were lucky. After a morning clinic meeting we'd open the doors at around 8.30 and everyone would come in and wait in line. We'd do their blood pressures et cetera and, if they had sores or coughs or whatever, we'd treat those as well. Because we were working as a sole practitioner, we followed the NT health bible, which was the CARPA Standard Treatment Manual, and we never deviated from that.

There were six of us nurses at this particular clinic, and without a word of a lie, some of our shifts were twenty-three hours long. A lot of the children were unwell and underweight and suffering from respiratory problems. Their skin was quite infected with scabies and in some cases had turned septic. A lot of them had boils. There was just the one shop, which was astronomically expensive, so their diet was terrible. Another problem was overcrowding. With a community of fifteen hundred people living in just four streets, you fear to wonder just who lives with whom and what health issues can arise from such a situation; and so we had a lot of emergencies. When small children and the elderly are ill they go down quickly and so we'd fly them out, usually to Darwin. If Darwin wasn't able to accept them, which was rare, they'd be flown to Alice Springs. And sometimes, because CareFlight and the RFDS were so busy, it'd be a nightmare to organise a plane.

Then there were the camp dogs. Dogs are considered part of the family and so the people lived and slept with them for warmth in winter. In most places the dogs were terribly neglected and, due to the rampant fleas, hardly had any fur. And they were angry. One day my friend and I got bailed up by four dogs. We tried to ward them off by swinging our bags at them, but that didn't work. In the end we were just lucky that a car full of locals arrived and shooed them away. But if I thought the NT desert was hard work, I then took a six-week contract up in the remote Cape York region of Queensland, and I tell you, by the third week I was ready to give up nursing. And that's the truth.

This particular community was an absolute heartbreaker. It consisted of about fifteen hundred people. Apart from horrific health issues, the big problem there was, and still is, like in so many of these communities, for some unfathomable reason, a number of different clans had been put in together. And with none of them having ever got on in the first place, when you mix in alcohol, drugs and petrol, it can only mean trouble. It was supposed to be a dry community, but it wasn't. I lived in a compound, which was okay, but come 7 o'clock at night, the community exploded into a disco-cum-riot. There was fighting, screaming and abuse; people were running down the road threatening each other with long blade knives. And this would go on all night long, night after night. I hardly got a wink of sleep and neither did the other staff. I tell you, I've never seen anything like it in my entire life.

One time I was in the clinic when a young woman started banging on the door: 'Help. Help. Help!'

In this community there was always a security guard with you, thank goodness. Anyhow, we let this young woman in and she was just covered in human bite marks, all over her back, on her chest and all over her legs. Half her hair had been pulled out by the roots. She was covered in dirt. She would've only been about seventeen. I asked her if she'd been raped but she didn't want to say what had happened. Then after I put a blanket around her, she looked up at me and said, 'Can I just lie somewhere safe and rest?'

So I put her in a bed and pulled the curtain around her and she slept for about an hour. When she woke up, I got her a drink. Because human bites get infected so quickly, I rang the RFDS to let them know that I needed to give her a stronger antibiotic. As I was cleaning up her bites, she told me her sad story; one that's too horrible to repeat here. When I asked if she wanted to press charges she said, 'Yes,' and so I called the police. But when they arrived, they didn't seem too fussed about the matter.

I said, 'Well, aren't you going to take photographs of the bites to be used as evidence?'

'No,' they said.

I said, 'Well, are you at least going to take a statement?'

'No,' they said. 'If she wants to, she can come in tomorrow and do it.'

I mean, what can you do in a situation like that? So I just thought, Yeah, okay, whatever. I'll just let it be for now.

Another time we got a call to go and pick up a guy who'd been glassed in the face. As there was just me and another female nurse going out in the ambulance, we asked for police assistance, and their response was, 'We'll wait for you at the end of the street.'

So that's what they did, and as we were driving down the street, people were chasing after us and throwing rocks and things and they were abusing us and calling us 'white cunts'. Then, when we spotted an intoxicated man stumbling down the road with half his face hanging off, I jumped in the back of the ambulance, and as we drove by, I threw open the door and shouted, 'Get in!'

After we got him back to the clinic we took a closer look. He was a mess. He'd been sliced open from his nose right down through his cheek. You could even see through to his teeth. He really needed to be flown out and be seen by a facial specialist, so when he steadfastly refused to go, I said, 'Well, I'm not suturing that mess, no way.' And so one of our other nurses tried to suture him up the best he could. We got an IV line and gave him a strong dose of antibiotics. But when we tried to get him settled, he pulled his IV line out, shrugged us off and stumbled back out into the night.

That happened a week or so before I was due to leave the community, and when I went back to my accommodation, I was devastated. That did it for me. I thought, I'm done.

Then out of the blue a friend rang. She'd been a remote nurse for thirty years and just from my voice she knew something was wrong. When I told her what'd happened she said, 'Yvette, I'll tell you what; when you get home, take your usual two weeks off, then go and do a rural contract to get your bearings back and then you'll be fine. It's just what us nurses do.'

I was like, 'Yeah, okay.'

Anyhow, I made it through my contract — just — and I followed her advice. I took my usual two weeks off, then I did a six-week contract in central Queensland, at a great little rural hospital. Now I feel much better. I'm fine. I feel rejuvenated and I'm back to loving my work. That longing to be out in the middle of nowhere has returned, though I'm definitely not going back to that previous place. I'm off to the island again.